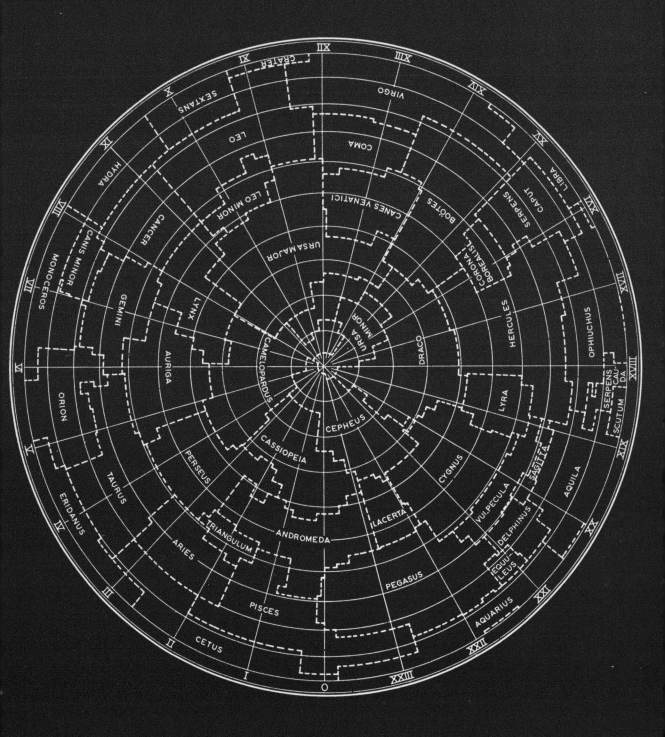

ATLAS OF THE UNIVERSE

BR. ERNST AND TJ. E. DE VRIES

ATLAS
OF THE UNIVERSE

Translated by
D. R. WELSH M.A.

Edited by
H. E. BUTLER M. A. Ph.D.
Royal Observatory, Edinburgh

With a Preface by
H. A. BRÜCK
Regius Professor of Astronomy at the University of Edinburgh
Astronomer Royal for Scotland

NELSON

1961

THOMAS NELSON AND SONS LTD
LONDON AND EDINBURGH

THOMAS NELSON AND SONS
NEW YORK

THOMAS NELSON AND SONS
(CANADA) LTD
TORONTO

THOMAS NELSON AND SONS LTD
JOHANNESBURG
MELBOURNE

SOCIÉTÉ FRANÇAISE D'ÉDITIONS NELSON
PARIS

PREFACE

Astronomy, more perhaps than any other science, is passing at present through a period of rapid and profound progress.

New observatories have been set up in many parts of the world, and elaborate telescopes of radio astronomy operate now side by side with those of optical observers. Rockets, satellites and space-probes have become an everyday occurrence, and before long actual physical contact is to be established where up to now observations from afar had to suffice.

Progress in astronomical instrumentation has gone hand in hand with remarkable advances in our understanding of the fundamental problems of astronomy, questions concerning the nature of the stars, their distribution throughout space, and the structure of the entire universe.

What in the first quarter of the century was still called the stellar universe is now revealed as being no more than a small corner in an enormous agglomeration of stars and diffuse matter. This, our Galaxy, large as it is, has proved to be only one amongst countless similar galaxies which are observed out to the greatest distances which can be reached with our most powerful optical and radio telescopes. The limit of vision of the latter instruments has been shown to be close to that ultimate horizon which is set to all our observations by the expansion of the universe.

On the question of the structure of our home galaxy, it is not so long ago that the dark clouds of cosmic dust in between the stars seemed to make it impossible for us ever to study regions beyond a limited distance. All this has been changed by radio astronomy, and we can now trace spiral-shaped patterns over large parts of the Galaxy.

Progress has perhaps been most far-reaching in the study of the constitutions of the stars and of their changes in the course of time. The age-old question of stellar evolution, once a purely speculative field, has become accessible at last to proper physical investigation; it has moved into the very centre of astrophysical theory and observation, adding a new dimension to our vision of the universe.

Innumerable books have been written in recent years trying to convey to the general public some of these great discoveries. Many of these have, unfortunately, tended to stress the more sensational aspects of the subject—as if the exciting facts needed any such embellishment—and have neglected to explain the solid foundation of hard work on which the whole structure is based. Little distinction is often made between properly established facts and fanciful imaginations, with the result that the value of astronomy as a science has been lowered in the eyes of more serious-minded outsiders.

It is a pleasure to find a book like the present encyclopedia in which facts and ideas are presented simply, concisely and soberly. It has been written by non-specialists for non-specialists, but it has been edited and brought up to date by a well known professional astronomer. Readers will find here answers to a host of questions on the many aspects of present-day as well as classical astronomy. Particularly noteworthy are the diagrams which avoid the over-familiar patterns and give a fresh and original angle on many points. The plates, excellent in themselves, are very well arranged; they alone make the book worth possessing.

To the schoolboy, to the amateur astronomer, to the man in the street, and, last but not least to the lover of the beauty of the world around us here is a book which will give a wealth of information and many hours of pleasure.

H. A. BRÜCK

Edinburgh
1961

CONTENTS

For list of symbols and abbreviations see p. 104

Ancient astronomy

During the past fifty years the science of astronomy has developed to such an extent that, by comparison, all that had been discovered before seems to fade into insignificance. Apart from those in theoretical physics, the most important factors in this progress were: the penetration of the secrets of the atom, observation with ever larger telescopes, observations from rockets and satellites and, of course, the degree of perfection reached in celestial photography. This last has benefited not only science but the layman too, for the material collected can rival in beauty the direct contemplation of the starry splendour of the skies. With the aid of some of these photographs, this Atlas presents the picture of the universe developed by modern astronomy. An attempt has been made to choose illustrations which have some relation to each other. The text explains the significance of the Plates and at the same time gives a continuous description of the universe, from the Earth to the farthest limits attained by modern astronomy. For full explanations and questions of detail, the reader is referred to the headings of the alphabetical section.

Although the main emphasis is laid upon the latest discoveries, it would not be right to pass over the Greek achievements in the field of astronomy. In a large work, later called the *Almagest* after the Arabic translation, Ptolemy put forward a closely reasoned theory to account for the movement of Sun, Moon and planets which was in general agreement with the natural philosophy of Aristotle. This work also contained a catalogue giving the position and brightness of 1,025 stars, and this list retains its importance as material for comparison even in our time. The Earth was thought to be spherical and to stand in the centre of the universe. Around the Earth revolved seven spheres to which the Sun, Moon and planets were attached; the fixed stars were in the eighth sphere. The extraordinary loop-shaped paths of the planets in the sky were explained by Ptolemy in terms of a combination of two circular movements: the planets revolved in circles, called epicycles, the centres of which revolved around the Earth in larger circles, called deferents. Although it was an ingenious mathematical theory, based upon lengthy and accurate observation, Ptolemy's work had to make way for newer theories and better means of observation. Slowly, and in the face of great opposition, the western world during the sixteenth and seventeenth centuries managed to break free from the Aristotelian natural philosophy and the Ptolemaic view of the universe. The sixteenth-century engraving reproduced above is based upon the Ptolemaic system: the curious astronomer tries to look behind the screens to discover the mechanism of the revolving spheres.

1

MODERN ASTRONOMY. Modern astronomy began on the evening of 7th January, 1610. On that evening, with his newly-made telescope, which he had constructed after hearing that one had been made in Flanders, Galileo discovered the ring mountains and craters of the Moon. Two of Galileo's telescopes (inset) are preserved in the Natural History Museum in Florence. The largest has a lens of about 1 inch in diameter. The Doge of Venice was so pleased with the telescope given to him by Galileo that he tripled his yearly allowance. During the next three centuries the telescope continued to be improved. The Hale telescope (on Mount Palomar in California) shown here has a parabolic mirror with a diameter of 200 inches, and intercepts 40,000 times more light than Galileo's telescope. The light reaches the large mirror (at the bottom of the photograph, hidden by the heavy steel construction) through the opening in the dome, and is reflected and converged to a focus in the cylinder at the top of the telescope, where it can be recorded photographically. The cylinder affords space for the observer. Since 1850, with the help of a photographic plate, it has been possible to store up the light that enters a telescope hour after hour. In this way it is possible to photograph celestial bodies which the eye cannot see even through the largest telescopes. With the ever-improving means of studying the heavens, the interest of astronomers has also shifted.

Until about 1850, the focal point of this interest was the solar system. Astronomers investigated the laws governing the movements of the planets, and calculated the influence which the planets exercised upon each other. A new planet was discovered in a place which had been determined by calculation. After 1850, interest was concentrated mainly upon the stars and the nebula-like objects which had long been known to exist but whose true nature was undetermined. Only in the course of the past fifty years has the structure of the universe become clearer. In 1932 astronomy was enriched by a new scientific aid, the radio telescope. Due to the developments associated with wartime radar, this instrument, which records the radio waves emitted by celestial bodies and gas clouds, has led to discoveries of far-reaching importance. The hypothesis of the spiral structure of our own stellar system has been confirmed and the spiral arms have been charted. The photograph shows the 250 ft.-diameter radio telescope—the largest in the world—at Jodrell Bank in England. The radio waves from space are reflected by the mirror and focussed on an antenna. This aerial is held by a 62 ft. mast at the focal point of the 750-ton steel parabolic reflector, which can be rotated so as to cover every part of the sky. An electronic analogue computer controls remotely the elevation and azimuth motors; the latter are in the bogies supporting the 2,000-ton structure on a 350 ft. circular track.

3

THE RISING OF ORION. Before penetrating to the limits of the perceptible universe, it is worth while pausing to look at the sky above us. In the northern hemisphere, on winter evenings, we can best appreciate the beauty of the constellations. The view to the south-east is outstanding. The three stars of Orion's Belt, with the red star Betelgeuse above and to the left and Rigel below and to the right, form a distinctive pattern. Above is the constellation of Taurus with the bright stars in the form of a V set amongst the many fainter stars of the Hyades group, and above them, the small sparkling group of stars, the Pleiades. Even against the glare of city lights, all these can clearly be seen. If we are out in the country, the broad band of the Milky Way can be seen farther to the left, stretching high up in the sky. Primitive man, living close to nature and under skies unspoiled by the smoke of industry, was greatly impressed by the splendour of the starry sky and soon discovered the relationship between the rising, culmination, and setting of certain groups of stars and the seasons which largely determined his activities. He peopled the heavens with legendary characters and passed on by word of mouth stories about them. Sometimes the legends were peculiar to a small group of people and to one particular constellation but in the cases of the more striking constellations, legends were widespread.

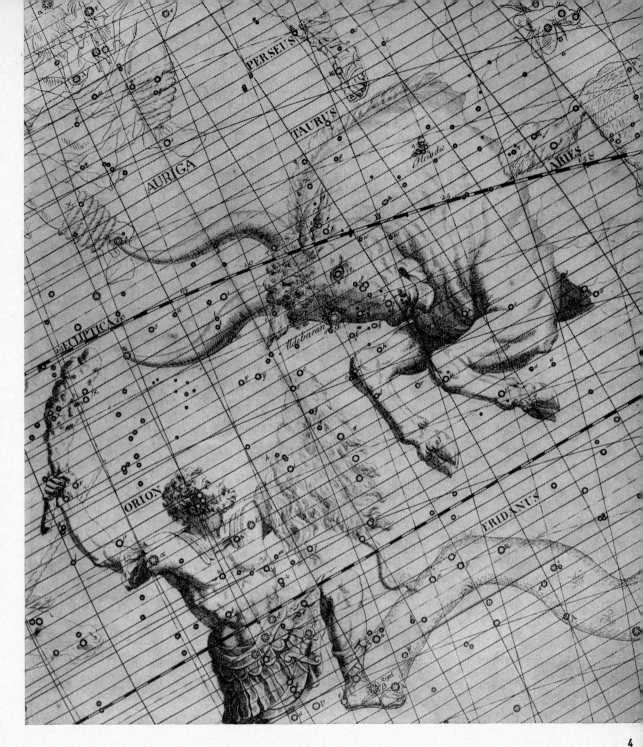

As an example we give here a Basque legend concerning the stars of the Great Bear, or Plough: a farmer had two oxen stolen from him (the two front stars of the Plough are the oxen, the next two are the thieves). He sent his servant (the first star of the handle) and then a second servant (the last star). When they did not return he set out after them with his dog, raging and swearing. As a punishment he was made to follow them for ever across the sky. Whoever doubts the truth of this, the legend goes on, has only to look well at the middle star of the handle. He will see a bright star and next to it a very small star: the farmer and his dog. The Greeks drew on the rich treasury of Eastern tradition, and the present-day nomenclature of the northern hemisphere is still the same as that of the Syrian shepherd or the Egyptian farmer. Orion is mentioned in the Book of Job and by the prophet Amos. Among the Greeks he is the proud hunter who is placed in the sky at the intercession of Diana. Orion repels the Bull with his shield; at his feet sits the timid hare. Sirius, the large dog, and Procyon, the small dog, follow him, while the Pleiades, the seven daughters of Atlas and Pleione, flee before him. Coming much nearer to modern times, we still find them depicted in the same way in charts of the heavens from the sixteenth to the eighteenth century. This picture is composed from Plates taken from Flamsteed's 'Atlas Cœlestis' of 1729.

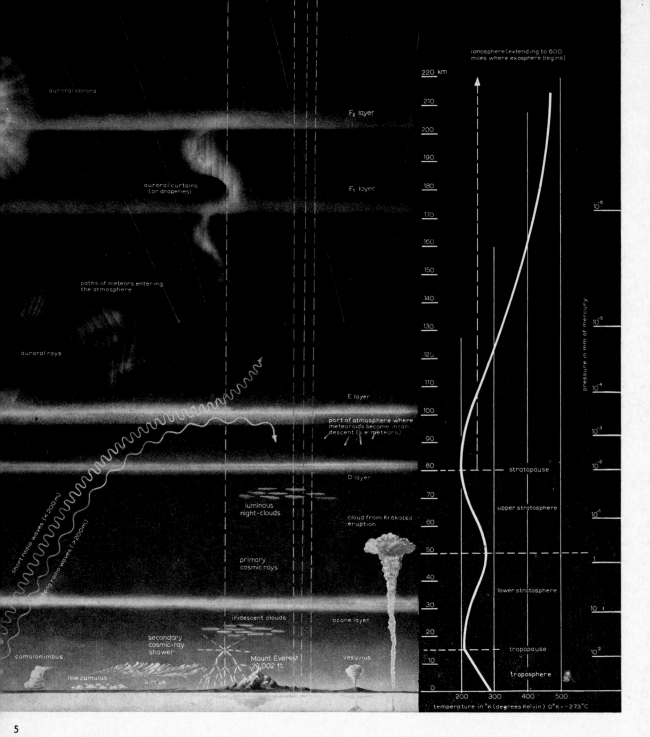

ionosphere (extending to 600
miles where exosphere begins)

220 km

210

200   F₂ layer

190

180   F₁ layer   10⁻⁶

170

160

150

140

130   10⁻⁵

120

110

100   E layer

part of atmosphere where
meteoroids become incan-
descent (i.e. meteors)   stratopause   10⁻²

D layer

luminous
night-clouds   upper stratosphere   10⁻¹

cloud from Krakatoa
eruption

primary
cosmic rays   lower stratosphere   10⁻¹

iridescent clouds   ozone layer   tropopause   10²

Mount Everest
29,002 ft.   Vesuvius   troposphere

200   300   400   500
temperature in °K (degrees Kelvin) 0°K=-273°C

auroral corona

auroral curtains
(or draperies)

paths of meteors entering
the atmosphere

auroral rays

short radio waves (<200m)   long radio waves (>200m)

secondary
cosmic-ray
shower

cumulonimbus

low cumulus   cirrus

pressure in mm of mercury

5

THE PROTECTIVE ATMOSPHERE. In comparison with the barren wilderness of the rest of the universe, our planet is a paradise. The surrounding layer of atmosphere is as thin as a membrane (if the Earth were the size of an apple, the atmosphere would be even thinner than the peel). It protects us in many ways and creates the conditions which make life possible. Until recently, direct observations (with unmanned balloons) did not extend higher than 20 to 25 miles. Indirect observations (radio, visual, etc.) provided the information above. Now, however, research rockets provide direct observations at all greater heights. The lower layer, the troposphere, contains 75% of the mass of the whole atmosphere; all meteorological phenomena are observed in this layer. It extends for 11 miles at the equator and for 5 miles at the poles. It is warmed by the Earth's surface and its temperature decreases with height to —80°C. The next layer, where the vertical air movements are very weak, can be divided into the lower and upper stratospheres. Above 20 miles the strong ultra-violet light of the Sun causes the oxygen to form ozone which itself strongly absorbs ultra-violet light. This causes the temperature in the ozonosphere to rise. This ozone layer protects the living tissues on Earth from the destructive effect of ultra-violet radiation. Ultra-violet light of even shorter wavelength ionizes the other layers, thus creating the ionosphere above the stratosphere.

Sun's rays

Earth's
shadow
cone

atmosphere

satellite's orbit

Moon

possible form
of satellite

meteoroid

satellite's orbit

meteor

POSSIBILITIES OF SPACE TRAVEL. The first man-made satellites are already circling the Earth, and automatic instruments are sending back to Earth data on the strength of the Sun's ultra-violet radiation, on cosmic radiation, and on the frequency of meteorites, so that the necessary protection can be given to the first space travellers. For instance, it has been calculated that a meteorite weighing only one ten thousandth of an ounce can, when travelling at 20 m.p.sec., pierce normal aluminium sheeting; the artificial satellites are telling us how frequently these meteorites will really be encountered in practice. The idea of men travelling about the solar system is no longer pure fantasy. The development of future space ships is being vigorously pursued. One of the most difficult steps is successfully to bring the ship back to the surface of the Earth. Most of the satellites, on returning, have heated up on encountering the atmosphere and quickly broken up or burned out. Obviously, this problem must be completely solved before the first man can be allowed to leave the Earth's surface. In the Plate, a satellite is shown still illuminated by the Sun while twilight is descending on the ground beneath and night is farther to the right. It is from such regions that the satellite can be seen moving across the sky as a point of light, once the sky has become sufficiently dark. Several of them have been, and are, clearly visible with the naked eye.

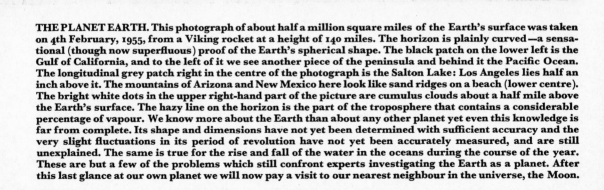

7

THE PLANET EARTH. This photograph of about half a million square miles of the Earth's surface was taken on 4th February, 1955, from a Viking rocket at a height of 140 miles. The horizon is plainly curved—a sensational (though now superfluous) proof of the Earth's spherical shape. The black patch on the lower left is the Gulf of California, and to the left of it we see another piece of the peninsula and behind it the Pacific Ocean. The longitudinal grey patch right in the centre of the photograph is the Salton Lake: Los Angeles lies half an inch above it. The mountains of Arizona and New Mexico here look like sand ridges on a beach (lower centre). The bright white dots in the upper right-hand part of the picture are cumulus clouds about a half mile above the Earth's surface. The hazy line on the horizon is the part of the troposphere that contains a considerable percentage of vapour. We know more about the Earth than about any other planet yet even this knowledge is far from complete. Its shape and dimensions have not yet been determined with sufficient accuracy and the very slight fluctuations in its period of revolution have not yet been accurately measured, and are still unexplained. The same is true for the rise and fall of the water in the oceans during the course of the year. These are but a few of the problems which still confront experts investigating the Earth as a planet. After this last glance at our own planet we will now pay a visit to our nearest neighbour in the universe, the Moon.

THE MOON. The Earth's nearest neighbour is about 240,000 miles away. The Moon has a diameter of less than a quarter of that of the Earth. A passenger plane could cover the distance between the Earth and the Moon in 40 days, a space ship in a few days. At a distance of about 1,200 miles the crew would, with unaided eye, be able to see the 4-day-old Moon much as it is shown on the Plate. The terminator (the boundary line between day and night) now falls over Mare Nectaris and travels slowly to the right: the Sun is rising above Mare Nectaris. The morning terminator travels from left to right until 10 days later we see the full Moon. After this the evening terminator appears. As it in turn crosses the face, the section that one can see becomes smaller. In a fortnight the evening terminator has also reached the right side; and it is then night on the side facing the Earth. After this, the cycle begins anew. Owing to the extremely low altitude of the Sun, the elevations on the surface near the terminator are very plainly visible. In the lower left-hand side of the Plate we can see part of the Mare Fœcunditatis. The great walled plain Petavius with a few high mountain peaks in the centre lies $1/_2''$ from the left and $2^1/_2''$ from the bottom. The illuminated side of the Moon has a temperature of about 130°C.; after the passing of the evening terminator it drops rapidly to −150°C. The Moon has no atmosphere. The journey to the Moon and any stay upon it will thus present many problems.

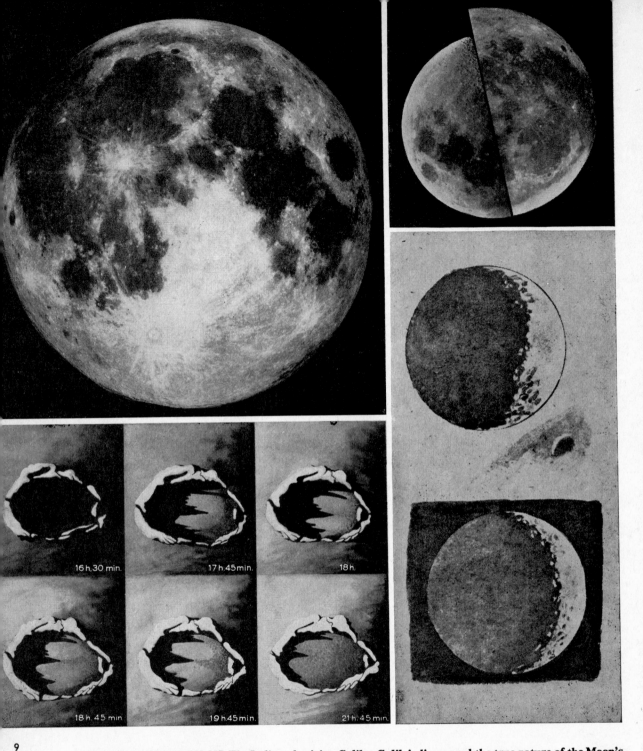

9

THE HARE ON THE MOON. The Italian physicist, Galileo Galilei, discovered the true nature of the Moon's surface. On the lower right we see, one above the other, two of his first sketches. With the naked eye we can clearly see the dark plains, formerly inaccurately called seas (Maria). The arrangement of the Maria (top left) is considered in some countries to resemble a jumping hare; the small oval Mare Crisium, on the right, is the ear; Mare Fœcunditatis, below, forms the head, Mare Tranquillitatis the chest, and the shell-shaped Mare Serenitatis the hindquarters. One forepaw is visible under the head; this is the small Mare Nectaris. Needless to say all resemblances disappear when viewed through a telescope. The great plain above and to the left of the hare is Mare Imbrium. On the left side, below the centre, lies Mare Nubium and next to it the small Mare Humorum. Only this photograph of the full Moon is reproduced as it is seen in the sky; all the others show the Moon as viewed through a telescope (left and right, top and bottom transposed). The Moon's orbit is elliptical. Owing to its varying distance from the Earth, the apparent diameter varies between 29·3 and 33·5 minutes of arc. This is plainly visible on the composite photograph in the upper right-hand corner: the right half is part of a photograph taken when the Moon was closest to the Earth, the left half shows the Moon at its farthest point.

MARE IMBRIUM. The evening terminator has already reached the mountain chains which enclose Mare Imbrium. The isolated mountain tops of Pico (8,000 ft.) and Piton (7,000 ft.) on the left side of the plain (respectively $1^3/_4''$ and $2^3/_4''$ from the lower edge) stand as brightly illuminated points in the evening sunlight and cast long shadows. The mountain range, the Carpathians, begins upper right below the great crater of Copernicus. It joins on to the farthest spurs of the Apennines which begin under the crater Eratosthenes (upper centre) and fill the whole of the left upper edge. On the left edge, in the centre, only a few illuminated summits of the Caucasus can still be seen. Below them are the Alps with the great transverse valley ($1^1/_2''$ from the bottom, $^1/_2''$ from the left-hand edge), 80 miles long and 6 miles wide in the centre. The Alps end a short way past the great Plato crater with its dark inner plain. To the right, underneath, is a wide 'bay' (Sinus Iridum) hemmed in by the Jura mountains. Now, a few measurements: the Alps are as large as Switzerland; the West Riding of Yorkshire would fit into the Plato crater, and the smallest crater visible is as large as Manchester. It is interesting to observe the rising and setting of the Sun above a crater. The photographs of Plato, on the opposite page, were made with a 6-inch mirror telescope on 25th November, 1952. The Sun took from half-past four to a quarter to ten to rise above Plato.

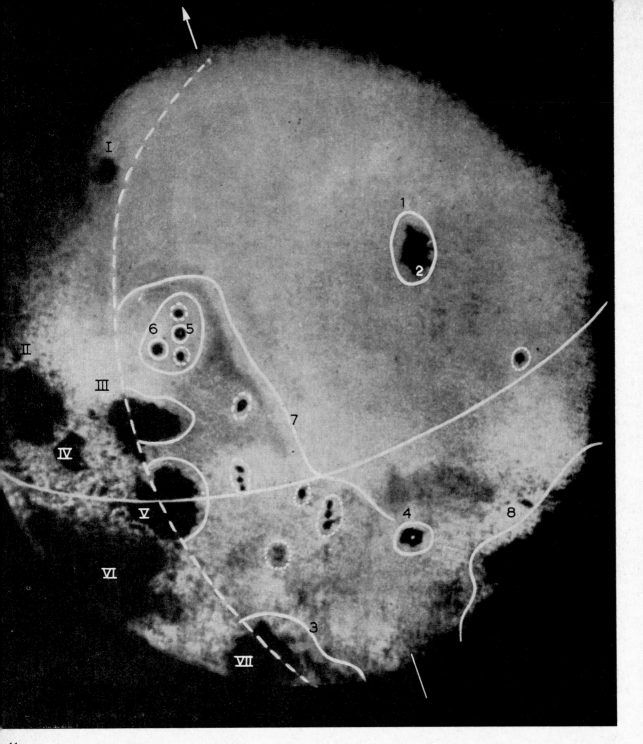

11

THE HIDDEN FACE OF THE MOON. Tidal friction in past ages has caused the revolution period of the Moon around the Earth and its axial rotation period to become equal, so that on Earth we have never seen much more than half the Moon's surface. It was therefore one of the greatest triumphs of modern science and technology when, on 26th October, 1959, the Russians released pictures taken by their rocket vehicle Lunik 3, which had successfully passed behind the Moon and photographed those parts of its surface that are always turned away from the Earth. One of these pictures is shown above. Although the definition was poor by normal standards, the far side of the Moon appeared to contain fewer 'seas' and contrasting areas than the near side. Among the few prominent features revealed were a large crater (1) 200 miles in diameter, named the Moscow Sea, and a range of peaks (2), named the Sovietsky Mountains. On Plate 12 we see the south-eastern part of Mare Imbrium (cf. Pl. 10). In the centre lies the ring mountain Copernicus. It is 56 miles in diameter and has sides 12,000 ft. above the floor. In the centre a few mountain peaks can be seen, the highest of which rises 2,400 ft. above the plain. The somewhat smaller crater Eratosthenes (left) has a central mountain in which yet another craterlet is visible. The string of craters like a pearl necklace between Copernicus and Eratosthenes originated perhaps alongside fissures in the ground.

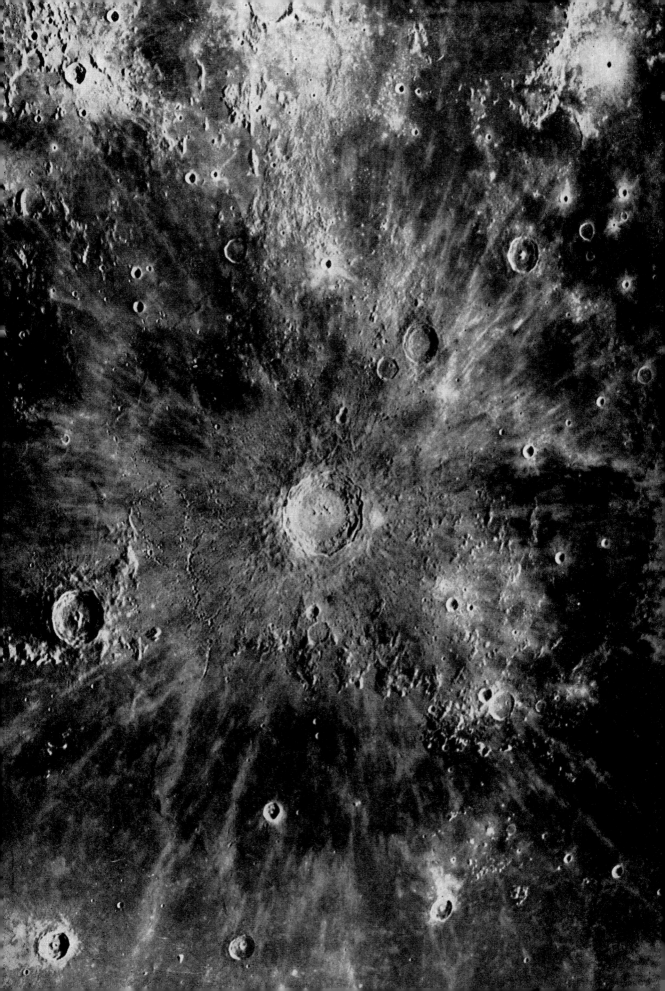

Plate 8

Plate 14

Plate 12

Plate 10

COMBINED PHOTOGRAPHS OF FIRST AND LAST QUARTERS. At full Moon, the fact that the Sun is nearly 'behind' the observer means that the shadows cast on the Moon's surface are invisible. Consequently there is a great loss of contrast and many fine details disappear. All other phases show only part of the Moon's surface. This illustration is composed of one photograph of the first quarter and one of the last quarter joined in the middle as carefully as possible. The effect is somewhat unnatural because one side is illuminated from the right and one from the left, but it gives a detailed survey of the entire surface of the Moon. The frames indicate the areas reproduced on other pages. It is the task of selenography to explain all the peculiarities on the Moon's surface. Two contrasting theories exist to explain the origin of the craters classified, according to diameter, as walled plains (40–150 miles in diameter), ring mountains (15–50 miles) and crater pits (less than 11 miles): either they are of volcanic origin, or they are the results of falling meteorites. Both theories are defended by a variety of arguments. In many places partly superimposed ring mountains of different ages can be distinguished. On the north-east boundary of Mare Nectaris, for example (arrow 1), the sharp edge of the younger ring mountain Theophilus partly covers the edge of the older ring mountain Cyrillus, the edge of which has almost fallen in. Thousands of clefts are clearly visible through a

large telescope. Near arrow 2 can be seen some of the largest clefts on the Moon (excluding the Alpine valley). The straight Wall in Mare Nubium (near arrow 3), a feature 100 miles long and some thousands of feet high, is in reality a subsidence alongside a cleft. The most remarkable features of the Moon's surface are the systems of rays which proceed from some of the younger ring mountains. They are lighter than their surroundings, cast no shadow and penetrate all formations. They are clearest when the Sun is in a vertical position. On Plate 9 one can see them radiating especially from the ring mountain Tycho: the longest stretch for 1,100 miles. Copernicus, too, and Kepler, to the right, have fairly extensive systems of rays. They appear to be caused by material ejected by these craters. Plate 14 shows the enormous walled plain Clavius. It is 145 miles across and if we were to stand in the middle of it, because of the Moon's curvature we should see nothing of the great rampart upon which lie several large craters (upper left, Rutherford; below, Porter). Above right is the ring mountain Blancanus; the illuminated edge rises about 12,000 ft. above the inner plain. This photograph was taken with the Hale telescope. Although the Moon is no longer of primary interest for astronomers, it still confronts them with many problems, but many of these will doubtless be resolved when the first instrument-carrying rockets land on the Moon.

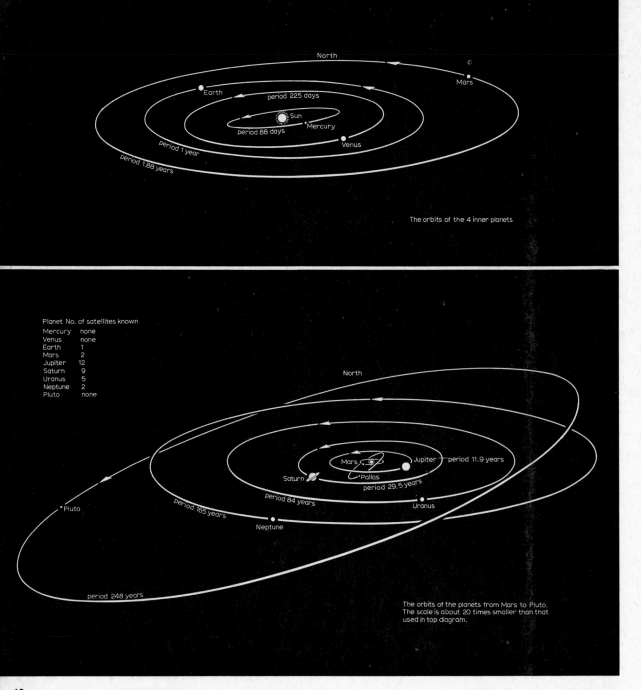

North

Earth

period 225 days

Sun

Mars

period 88 days

Mercury

period 1 year

Venus

period 1.88 years

The orbits of the 4 inner planets

Planet	No. of satellites known
Mercury	none
Venus	none
Earth	1
Mars	2
Jupiter	12
Saturn	9
Uranus	5
Neptune	2
Pluto	none

North

Mars

Jupiter

period 11.9 years

Saturn

Pallas

period 29.5 years

period 84 years

Uranus

Pluto

period 165 years

Neptune

period 248 years

The orbits of the planets from Mars to Pluto.
The scale is about 20 times smaller than that
used in top diagram.

15

THE SOLAR SYSTEM. For centuries the attention of astronomers was devoted almost exclusively to five celestial bodies. Those were called 'planets' (i.e. wanderers) because they moved in relation to the other 'fixed' stars. It was discovered by Kepler that these planets, and the Earth, move around the Sun in approximately elliptical orbits. The orbits of Mercury and Venus lie within that of the Earth. After Earth comes Mars, with a rather eccentric orbit. This orbit is shown in the lower figure on a scale reduced by a factor of 20 as compared with the upper. Jupiter and Saturn were also known to antiquity. The rest were discovered later: Uranus (1781), Neptune (1846) and Pluto (1930), as well as several thousands of minor planets between Mars and Jupiter; the only minor planet whose orbit is shown (lower figure) is Pallas. Comets, the smaller fragments of which occasionally fall on Earth as meteorites or burn up in the atmosphere as 'falling stars', and the very small particles of dust which cause the zodiacal light, complete the list. The periods of revolution of the various planets increase with their distance from the Sun: Mercury revolves round it in under a quarter of a year; Pluto takes 248 years. The average surface temperatures on sides facing the Sun decrease as the distance from the Sun increases: Mercury 340° C., Earth 22°, Jupiter —130°, until we reach Pluto, which is probably about —225° C.

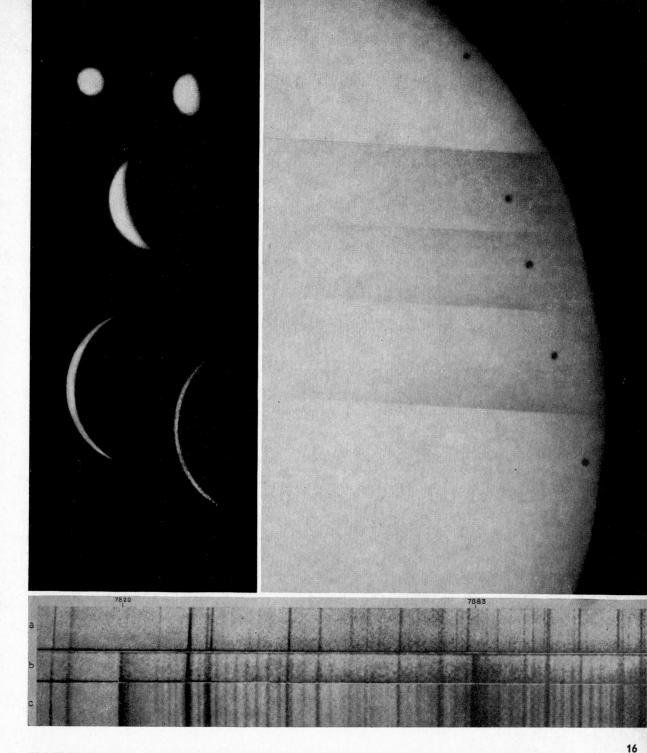

CLOSE TO THE SUN. As Mercury and Venus are closer to the Sun than the Earth is, their periods of revolution are less than a year (88 and 225 days respectively), and they show phases. A half cycle is illustrated on the left. Top: 'full Venus', when the Sun is almost between it and Earth. Venus appears small because it is at its farthest from Earth. It grows bigger as it comes nearer but is now illuminated from the side by the Sun. When it attains its greatest size it is almost between the Sun and Earth. All that is seen then is a thin sickle; it is almost 'new Venus'. About 13 times in a century Mercury transits across the Sun's disk. The illustration on the right is made up of five photographs taken on 14th November, 1953, the top one at 15 h. 49 m., and the bottom one about 2 hours later. Transits of the Sun by Venus are rarer: the last was in 1882, the next two will be on 8th June, 2004, and 6th June, 2012. Mercury is slightly bigger than the Moon and has either no atmosphere or a very tenuous one. Lead would melt on the sun-lit side; the temperature on the other is little above absolute zero. Venus is nearly as large as Earth and has an atmosphere which can be seen as an extension of the narrow sickle. The outer layer of its atmosphere contains carbon dioxide, as shown by its spectrum (c in lower photograph), where two dark carbon dioxide bands can be seen which are absent from the solar spectrum (a).

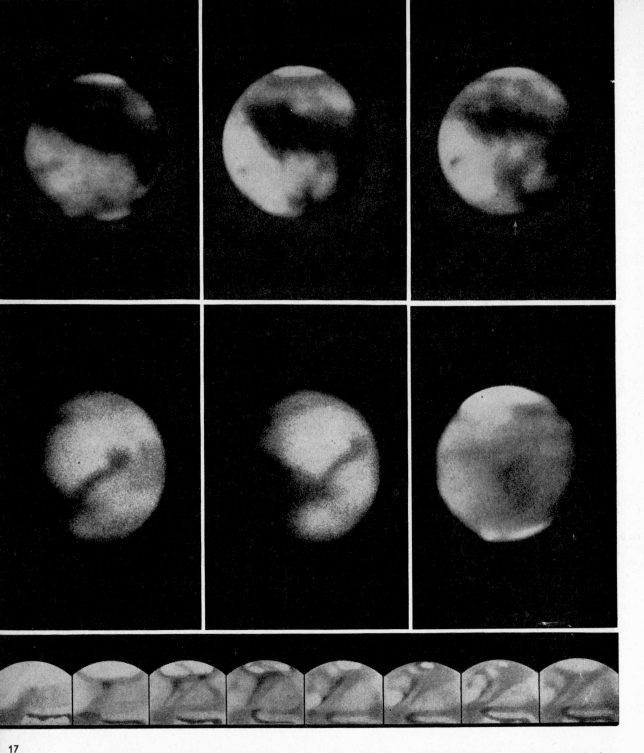

17

THE RIDDLE OF MARS. The first sight of Mars through even a fairly large telescope is disappointing. At its very shortest distance from Earth, all that can be seen is a small orange-red disk on which are some vague markings possibly including a white spot on its edge. The fact that Mars is viewed and photographed through our turbulent atmosphere means that the finer details are normally blurred out of existence. Only occasionally is it possible to see Mars clearly. After protracted periods of observation with a large telescope, charts such as those at the bottom of Plate 18 can be obtained. The reddish-brown deserts which make up $^3/_5$ of the surface area can be made out with certainty, as well as smaller bluish-green areas and bright polar caps. The sizes of the latter vary with the seasons, which are nearly twice as long as those on Earth. The eight drawings (Plate 17 bottom row) by G. de Vaucouleurs start with winter in this hemisphere. The polar cap, which probably consists only of a thin crust of hoar-frost, is about 5,000 miles across. As summer approaches, the ice cap grows smaller and changes occur in the area surrounding it. Sometimes large areas are covered by yellowish or bluish clouds. In 1877 Schiaparelli announced the most amazing astronomical 'discovery' of the century—the famous canals of Mars, broad lines which sometimes seemed to double. Some 400 of these were charted. They are easier to see when the polar caps are melting.

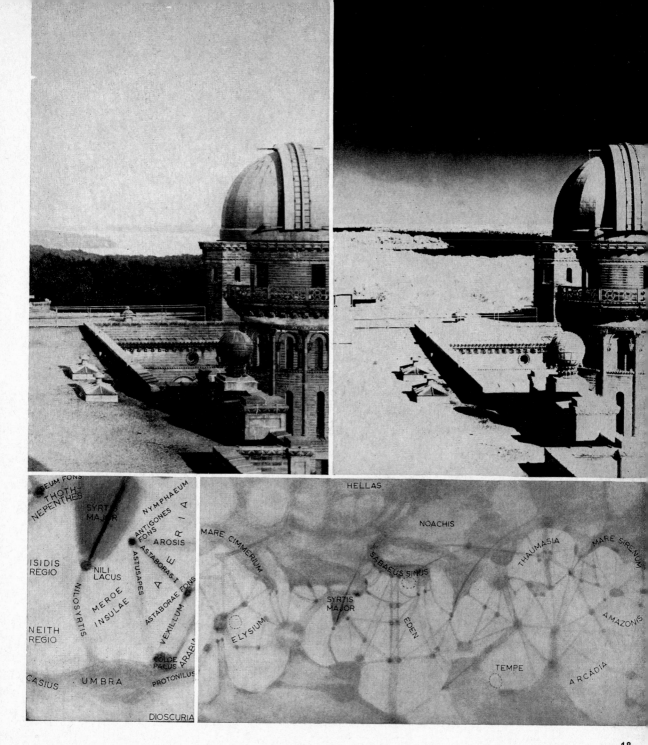

As telescopes improved, however, less and less was seen of the canals. Tests have shown that even ex-
perienced observers may easily see lines where only a number of hazy spots exists. Nevertheless, this does
not mean that all changes observed on Mars must be dismissed automatically as figments of the imagination. The three photographs at the top of Plate 17 are all of the same side of Mars, taken in 1907, 1939 and
1954 respectively. At the bottom we can clearly see the development of a dark region which was given the
name Thoth Nepenthes. Mars has a tenuous atmosphere and if we wish to see it rather than the surface of
the planet we must photograph Mars through a blue or ultra-violet filter (Plate 17, third photograph, middle
row). Ultra-violet light is strongly scattered by the atmosphere while red rays penetrate it. This is demonstrated by the two photographs of the Yerkes Observatory in Plate 18. The first was taken through an ultra-
violet filter, the second through an infra-red filter. With infra-red rays even the horizon is clearly to be seen
through a thick layer of atmosphere but the ultra-violet reveals only near-by features, the blue sky showing
as a bright background. Mars rotates on its axis once in about 24 hours, so that its surface features are
considerably displaced in even a few hours. See the long dark strip of Sabaeus Sinus in the first two photographs of the middle row (facing).

19

JUPITER, GIANT AMONG PLANETS. Jupiter's mass is greater than that of all the other planets put to-gether. This huge planet rotates about its axis in 10 hours, and is consequently much flattened at the poles (centre, right). The light and dark bands on Jupiter are clouds of ammonia and methane crystals. The large (red) spot on the right-hand photograph, taken through a blue filter, is a variable object of unknown nature floating in the atmosphere. In the left-hand photograph (red filter) the spot is scarcely visible. Satellite II, or Ganymede (as large as Mercury!), lies to the right above the planet, on which its shadow can be seen. Radio radiation picked up from Jupiter in 1954, was probably due to thunderstorms in its atmosphere. Its four largest satellites were discovered by Galileo. On the right below we see an extract from Galileo's notes in which he records the position of the satellites. Viewed through even a small telescope the motion of the tiny satellites round the large planet is an absorbing sight. The strip at the top shows the positions of the satellites on four consecutive nights. In code: (II J I IV III), (I IV J II III), (IV J I III)—satellite II was hidden behind Jupiter on this evening—(IV II I III J). An occultation of Jupiter by the Moon is an extremely interesting spectacle. The three lower photographs were taken on 16th January, 1947, at intervals of 4 and 8 minutes. In the first only two satellites of Jupiter are visible, and no part of Jupiter's surface.

A GOOD SITE FOR OBSERVATION. The air surrounding the Earth is a powerful 'colour filter' which absorbs most of the radiation reaching the Earth from outer space. Radio astronomy takes advantage of a 'window' which admits radiation with a wavelength between 30 metres and 1 cm, whereas normal astronomy, using optical instruments, must mainly rely on radiation of wavelengths between 0.00008 and 0.00003 cm. There is extremely valuable information to be derived from radiation of shorter wavelengths. Unfortunately, this radiation does not penetrate the atmosphere. The 10th October, 1946, saw the first successful attempt to photograph the solar spectrum down to a wavelength of 0.00002 cm, from a V2 at an altitude of 50 miles; it revealed the two strongest lines in that part of the spectrum. Since then, observations of the Sun from rockets and satellites have been made in wavelengths as short as 8A in the X-ray region, and observations of the stars have been made down to 0.000012 cm (1200 A). But even observation of radiation admitted by the atmosphere is hampered by irregularly fluctuating conditions in the atmosphere. To reduce the inconvenience from this source to a minimum, modern observatories are often built on elevated sites. The photograph above is of the French Pic du Midi Observatory high in the Pyrenees. Mount Wilson Observatory and Mount Palomar Observatory are also situated on top of their respective mountains.

SATURN: PEARL OF THE SOLAR SYSTEM. The Italian, Galileo, was the first to notice something unusual about the planet Saturn, which he described as consisting of three bodies. With his small and still very imperfect telescope Christian Huygens was able, in 1656, to detect a ring round the planet, while nine years later he also discovered Saturn's largest satellite, Titan. Eight other moons of Saturn were discovered at later dates. The top photograph is the best one of Saturn taken with the Hale telescope. It clearly shows the oblateness of the planet, while the shadows of the ring on the planet and of the planet on the ring are also plainly visible. J. D. Cassini, a famous seventeenth-century Italian astronomer, discovered that the ring consists of several concentric rings. The outermost ring is less bright than the second, from which it is separated by a dark space called Cassini's division. The third ring from the outside (the crape ring) is invisible on the photograph because it is tenuous and does not reflect much sun-light. The rings are believed to consist of small fragments of ice and probably exist because Saturn's tide-raising forces prevented them from forming a stable satellite. The rings are inclined to the planet's orbital plane, so that we alternately see the southern face (first small photograph, taken 1916), then the northern face of the rings (1933, 1934); between times they are seen edgewise, as in the last photograph (1937).

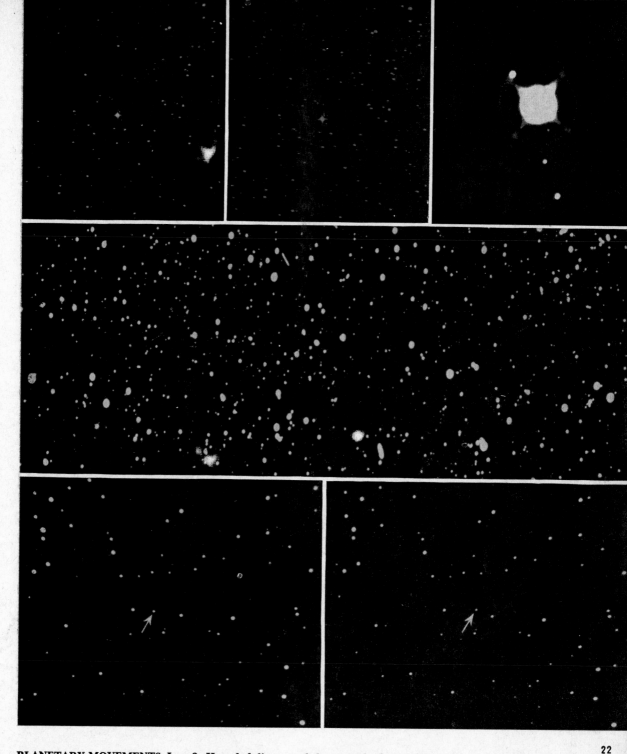

PLANETARY MOVEMENTS. In 1781 Herschel discovered the seventh planet of the solar system, Uranus. It is shown in the top right corner with its 5 moons. The small satellite inside the halo is Miranda, discovered in 1948 by Kuiper. The other two photographs of Uranus in the row were made on successive evenings. It will be seen that the position of Uranus among the stars shifted slightly. From perturbations in the motion of Uranus, Leverrier computed the position of an unknown planet, and Galle found it, Neptune, nearly in that position. Uranus and Neptune are nearly 3 times the size of Earth. The planet Pluto was discovered in 1930. It is almost 40 times farther from us than the Sun is. The bottom two photographs show its position among the stars on 10th and 11th March, 1934. According to a 'law' published by Bode in 1772, which tried to systematize the distances of the planets from the Sun, there was a planet missing between Mars and Jupiter. In 1801 Piazzi at Palermo discovered the minor planet Ceres, with an orbit between those of Mars and Jupiter! Of these asteroids 1,600 are now known, the bulk of them having been found photographically. Plates exposed for a considerable time show stars as small round disks, but the asteroids, which have been moving all the while, appear as small bars. Trails of two asteroids can be seen in the centre photograph; the brighter is Bellona.

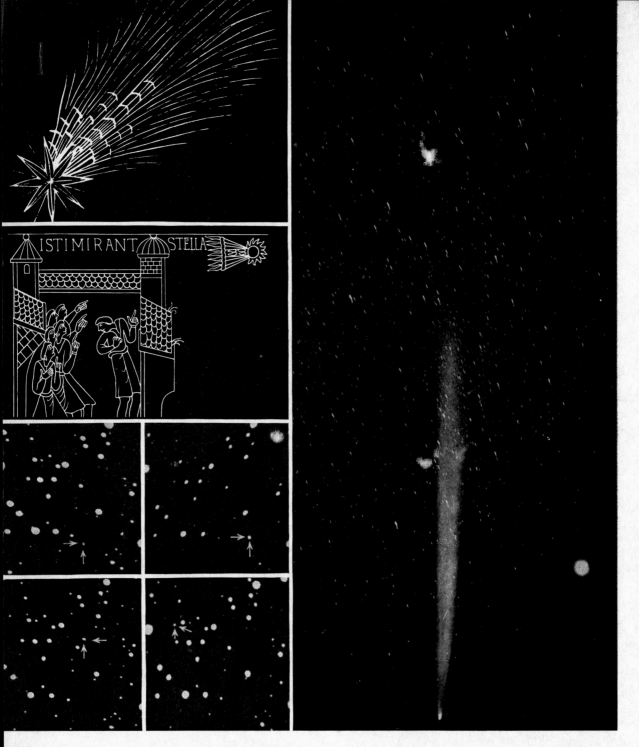

23

COMETS. An American astronomer once defined a comet as 'something that is just different enough from nothing to be something'. As a comet approaches the Sun it may become an impressive sight—one that in bygone ages inspired terror—for that is when the tail develops. When Halley used the available data to calculate the orbits of 24 comets recorded between 1337 and 1698, he observed that 3 had followed almost the same path. He was convinced that these were three returns of a single comet which took 76 years to revolve around the Sun. He did not live to see the return which he forecast. To date it has been possible, from ancient documents, to confirm 28 appearances of Halley's Comet, e.g. the comet of 684 mentioned in the Chronicle of Nuremberg (left, top) and the well-known comet of 1066 depicted in the Bayeux Tapestry (left, centre). A return of the comet was forecast for 1910. The year before that it had been photographed as a very faint spot among the stars (four photographs taken on 16th, 17th, 24th and 26th September). The large photograph was taken on 13th May, 1910. The bright object to the right of the tail is Venus. 1957 brought the unexpected appearance of two fairly bright, new comets—Arend-Roland with its much discussed Sun-ward spike (Pl. 24, above), and Mrkos. The two remarkably detailed photographs (below) of Morehouse's Comet (1908), were taken within a few hours of each other and form a stereoscopic pair.

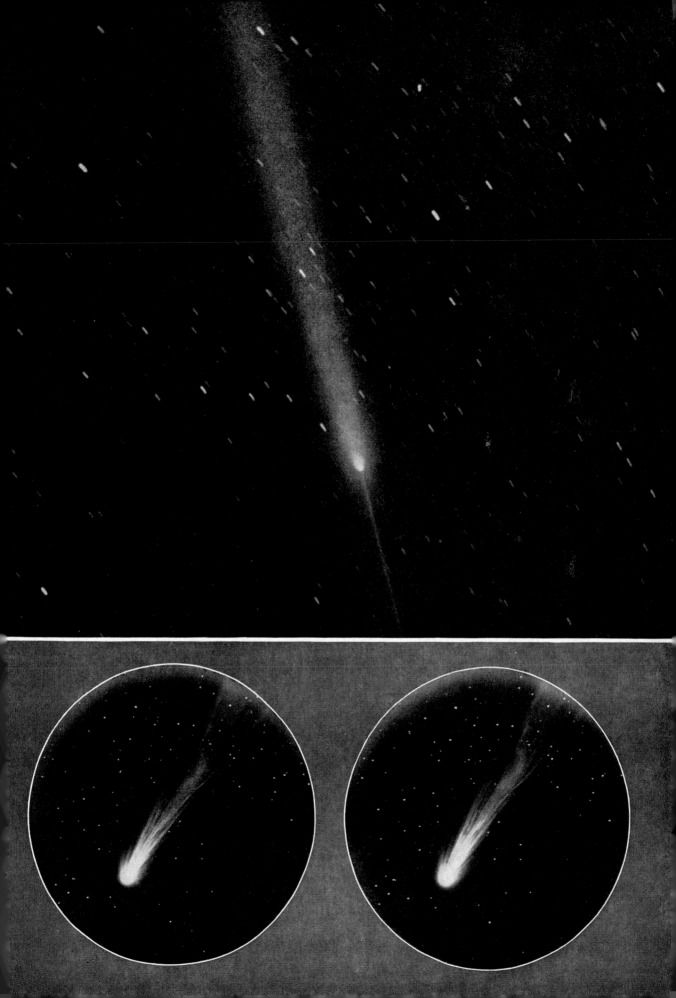

25

THE ARIZONA CRATER. Every day some 25 million dust particles from space enter the Earth's atmosphere, where they burn up. Those of about 1 mm or more in diameter can be seen moving among the stars as fine streaks of light—'falling stars' or meteors. Meteors have been incidentally photographed in some of the Plates in this volume. In Plate 23, for instance, one can be seen through the tail of Halley's Comet; two bright meteors and a weaker one can be seen in the right-hand photograph of Plate 34; while another is visible to the left of the Cirrus nebula in the lower photograph of Plate 48. Larger particles may reach the Earth; they are then known as meteorites. In the plateau region of Arizona there is a crater about 4,000 ft. in diameter and 600 feet deep, the Arizona or Barringer Crater. In 1905 D.M. Barringer showed that the crater had been made by a large meteorite. The meteorite fell in prehistoric times and only the dry climate of Arizona has enabled the crater to preserve its shape so well. In 1956 an expedition systematically examined the area round the crater and found some 12,000 tons of material deposited there by the meteorite. Three years after the true nature of the Arizona Crater had been discovered, a large meteorite fell with such force in Siberia that it was recorded on all the seismographs in Central Europe. Yet it was not until 1927 that scientists discovered what had happened. 200 craters, large and small, were found, while trees for 20 miles around had been blown over

and were lying along lines radiating from the craters. At present about 40 large craters created by the fall of meteorites are known. Great meteorites also fell on Earth in earlier geological eras but traces of these have disappeared as a result of various types of erosion. In the view of some experts, the 'craters' which are such a prominent feature of the lunar landscape were also formed by meteorites. These craters have preserved their shape well because the Moon has no atmosphere or water, and erosion cannot occur there. Chemical analysis has shown that this material from sources beyond the Earth does not contain any elements not found on Earth. Some meteorites consist mainly of iron and nickel, others of stone. Very powerful and expensive cameras have been built to determine the orbits and speeds of meteors. It is hoped in this way to establish with certainty their origin. Also until recently this was one of the few methods of getting information about the density and temperature of the extreme upper layers of the Earth's atmosphere. The need for this is now somewhat less as high altitude rockets and satellites are able to collect the data directly. The lead content of meteorites gives some indication as to their age, and their helium content as to the intensity of cosmic radiation in ages long past.

SOLAR ECLIPSE. When the Sun rose at Chicago on 30th June, 1954, it was already partially eclipsed for part of the world. The various stages of this eclipse were photographed from an elevated site with a camera having a small lens aperture and a very short exposure time. The same plate was exposed at intervals of 15 minutes. The photograph shows the Sun rising gradually in the sky, and also shows how the Moon, moving from west to east across it, increasingly covers and then uncovers it. The third exposure was made during the few minutes of total eclipse so precious to astronomers. Just as the last brilliant point of the Sun disappears behind the pitch-black disk of the Moon, a pearly white light flashes into view round its edge. The somewhat elongated shape of this light—the solar corona—indicates a period of minimum sunspot activity. Small 'flames' can sometimes be seen round the black edge. These are prominences, reaching up from the chromosphere which itself is hidden behind the Moon's disk. The brightest stars and planets become clearly visible during a total eclipse. The observations that can be made on such an occasion are so important that scientific institutes frequently send expeditions to areas where the eclipse is total. Predictions of the times and places of totality can be made with great accuracy. Many expeditions fail because the sky is overcast at the time of the eclipse. In 1954, after long preparations, the Potsdam Obser-

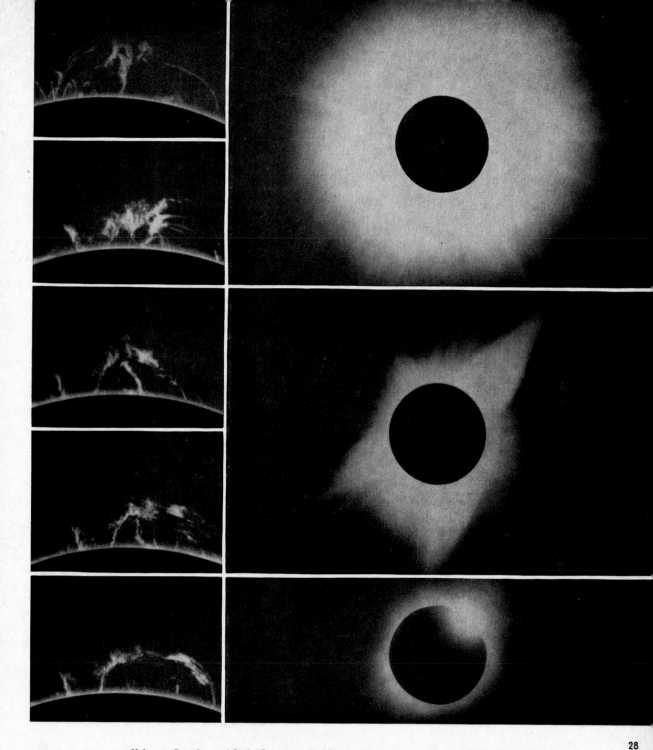

vatory sent an expedition to Sweden, with the finest available aids, in order to obtain definite confirmation of the bending of stellar rays by the Sun, as forecast by Einstein in 1916; but the sky was clouded over! The same group of scientists went to Colombo one year later, with the same instruments. Here, too, observations were prevented by the weather. The corona, the outermost part of the Sun's atmosphere, is distributed evenly round the Sun during a period of maximum sunspot activity (right, top). During a period of minimum activity it is clearly concentrated round the Sun's equator (right, centre). As soon as the light from the Sun's surface flashes into view between two lunar craters, at the end of an eclipse, the light of the corona is almost immediately outshone (right, bottom) and the 'diamond ring' is seen. Since 1930 an invention of the French astronomer, Lyot, has made it possible to photograph the inner corona and likewise prominences with the aid of special filters, at times other than eclipses. Prominences are huge streams of gas issuing from active areas of the Sun in the form of luminous fountains, sometimes reaching heights of more than 500,000 miles. Theoretical research has been greatly assisted by the projection of long series of photographs or prominences in fast motion. In this way a clear picture is gained of their complicated movements. The five photographs on the left are all of the same prominence and were taken in June, 1937.

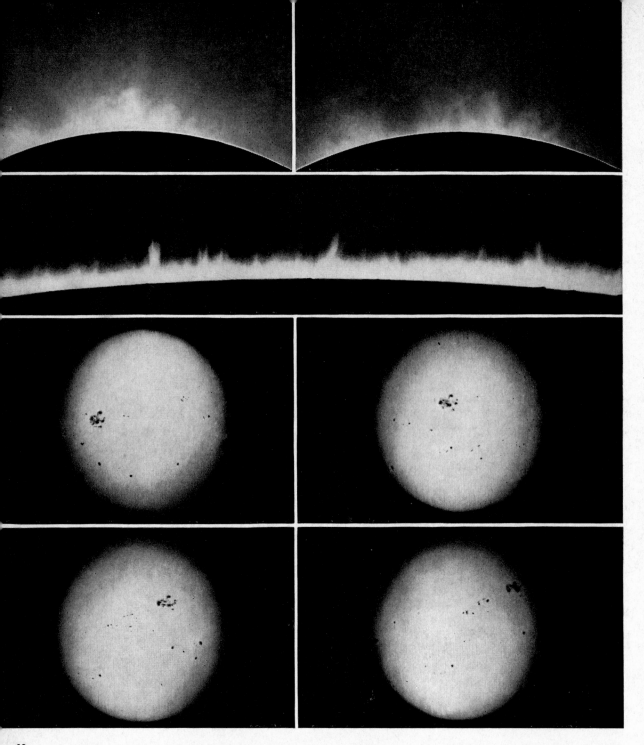

SOLAR ACTIVITY. Sunspots are the most striking proof of movement and activity on the Sun. They were used at an early date to determine the time of rotation of the Sun. The four lower photographs were taken at intervals of several days and clearly show the movement of the group of spots. The day to day study of the growth and disappearance of sunspots is a fascinating pursuit. It was found that the Sun does not rotate as a solid body; one revolution of the huge gaseous sphere takes $24^{1}/_{2}$ days at the equator and over 30 days near the poles. This was later confirmed by spectroscopic research (Doppler effect). The true nature of the spots long remained a complete mystery. At one time they were thought to be solar volcanoes, then open spots in the Sun's atmosphere. In fact, they are areas where the gas is 2,000° colder than in surrounding areas (6,000°K) possibly because powerful magnetic fields oppose heat flow from the interior. The nucleus (umbra), which is jet-black in comparison with its environment, is surrounded by a lighter border, the penumbra. The small spots (Pl. 30, bottom right) are roughly the size of the Earth. In 1843 the German, Schwabe, (who drew the position of sunspots daily for 17 years because he was searching for a new planet within the orbit of Mercury) discovered that the number of sunspots shows a pronounced maximum and minimum every 11 years. The region of the Sun which we normally see is called the photosphere (Pl. 30 top

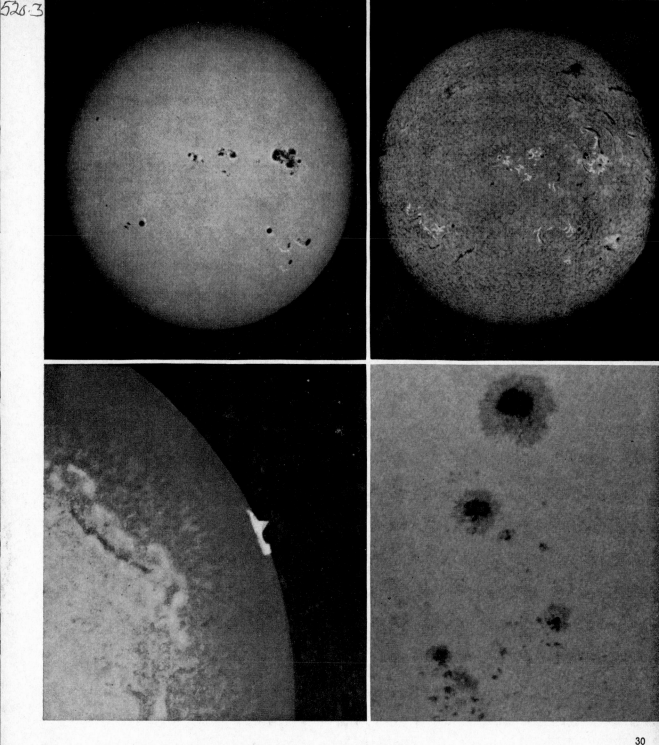

left). In good photographs the photosphere is not completely uniform but appears to be covered with white spots (granules) against a darker background. These are hotter currents of gas which rise locally from deeper levels, cool off within a few minutes and then disappear. The photosphere is surrounded by the chromosphere which normally is not visible. The Fraunhofer lines of the Sun's spectrum originate in the lowest layer of the chromosphere. By photographing the Sun in the light of any of these lines we can make the chromosphere visible. The second photograph (Pl. 30 top right) was taken at the same instant as the first but in light of one such Fraunhofer line (Hα line of hydrogen). Over the sites of sunspots we now see bright groups of faculae, i.e. hotter areas in the chromosphere. The dark streaks are prominences, which are seen projected against the Sun's disk. Solar 'flares' or 'eruptions' often blaze up in the vicinity of rapidly developing sunspots (lower left). These eruptions, which last only for minutes at a stretch, are sometimes associated also with powerful radio-wave radiation. Also their fierce ultra-violet radiation ionizes the upper layers of the Earth's atmosphere, causing sudden failure of short-wave communication. Between one and four days later the gas expelled from the Sun reaches the Earth, where it causes magnetic storms and sometimes particularly bright aurorae, or polar lights.

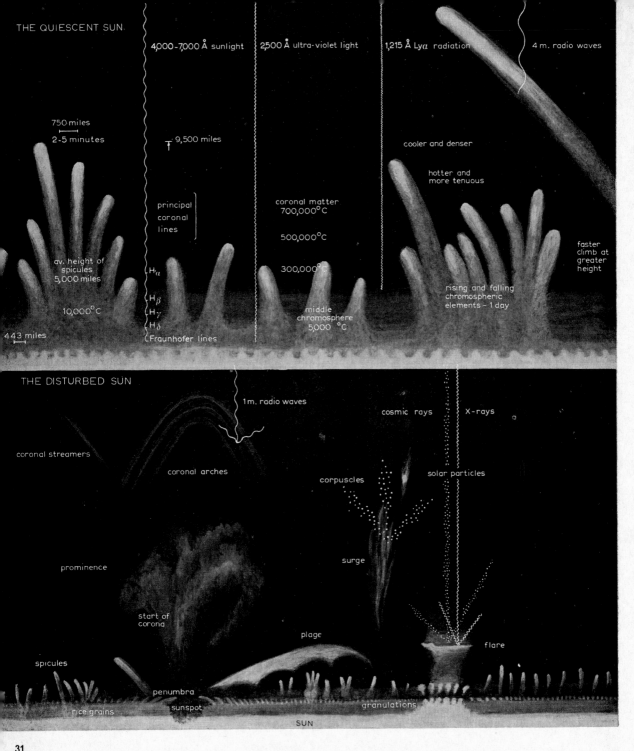

THE QUIESCENT SUN

4,000-7,000 Å sunlight   2,500 Å ultra-violet light   1,215 Å Lyα radiation   4 m. radio waves

750 miles
2-5 minutes

9,500 miles

cooler and denser

hotter and
more tenuous

principal
coronal
lines

coronal matter
700,000°C

av. height of
spicules
5,000 miles

500,000°C

faster
climb at
greater
height

Hα

300,000°C

10,000°C

Hβ
Hγ
Hδ

middle
chromosphere
5,000 °C

rising and falling
chromospheric
elements – 1 day

443 miles

Fraunhofer lines

THE DISTURBED SUN

1 m. radio waves

cosmic rays   X-rays

coronal streamers

coronal arches

corpuscles

solar particles

surge

prominence

start of
corona

plage

flare

spicules

penumbra

rice grains   sunspot

granulations

SUN

31

THE QUIESCENT AND THE DISTURBED SUN. The top illustration represents a section across a quiescent region of the Sun. The white band at the bottom is the photosphere with granulation. The cooler and denser spicules rise from the overlying chromosphere into the hotter and thinner corona. Plate 29 (second row) is a unique photograph of the corona, taken with the coronagraph at Sacramento Peak in the U.S.A. The scale used in the upper diagram (Pl. 31) is reduced by a factor of 5 in the lower, to accommodate the much more extensive phenomena of the disturbed Sun. Of these the most striking are the sunspots, with which plages and prominences are associated, and the solar flares with their accompanying surges. The rest of the Plate is self-explanatory. Plate 32 (the chromosphere is relatively much thinner, and the dispersion of the prism is much exaggerated): if sun-light is analysed with a spectroscope, a band of colour is obtained which is broken by thousands of dark lines —the solar spectrum. The Plate shows in what parts of the Sun this spectrum is formed. If the slit in the spectroscope is aimed at the centre of the solar disk, the lines of the photosphere and the inner chromosphere show on the continuous spectrum of the photosphere as dark absorption lines (I). If, however, the spectrum of the light just outside the Sun's disk is used, the same lines appear as bright emission lines (II). In both cases there are other absorption lines due to gases in the Earth's atmosphere.

40

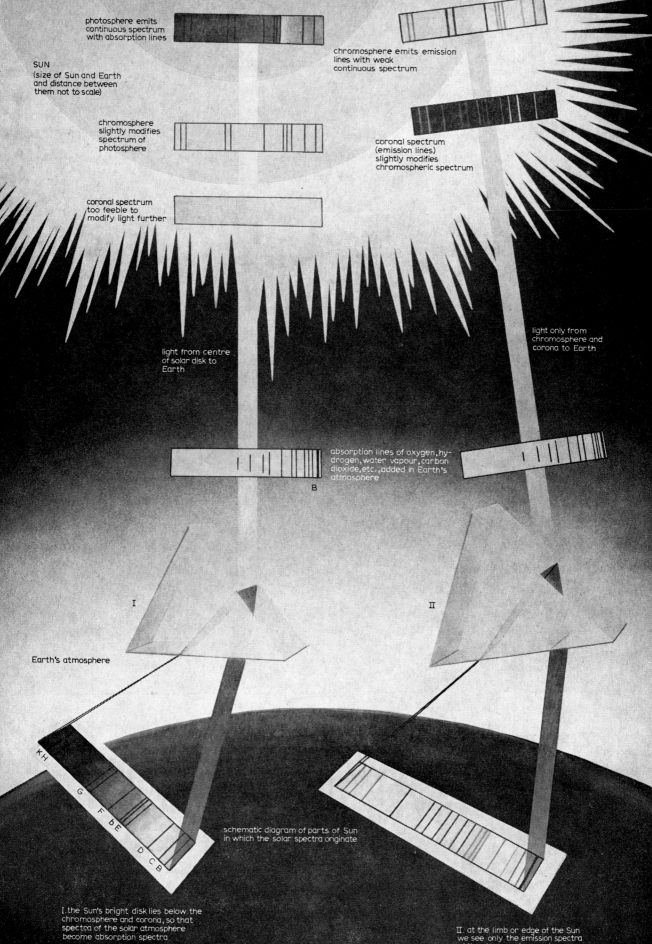

photosphere emits
continuous spectrum
with absorption lines

SUN
(size of Sun and Earth
and distance between
them not to scale)

chromosphere emits emission
lines with weak
continuous spectrum

chromosphere
slightly modifies
spectrum of
photosphere

coronal spectrum
(emission lines)
slightly modifies
chromospheric spectrum

coronal spectrum
too feeble to
modify light further

light only from
chromosphere and
corona to Earth

light from centre
of solar disk to
Earth

absorption lines of oxygen, hydrogen, water vapour, carbon
dioxide, etc., added in Earth's
atmosphere

B

I

II

Earth's atmosphere

K H
G
F
b E
D C B

schematic diagram of parts of Sun
in which the solar spectra originate

I. the Sun's bright disk lies below the
chromosphere and corona, so that
spectra of the solar atmosphere
become absorption spectra

II. at the limb or edge of the Sun
we see only the emission spectra
of the chromosphere and corona

33

THE MULTITUDE OF THE STARS. On a clear night it is possible to see several thousand stars with the unaided eye: approximately one star per ten square degrees. In other words, if we think of the area that 40 full Moons clustered together would occupy in the sky, we can expect to see on the average only one star in that area, which is surprising. In fact, a child's hand can hold more grains of sand than there are stars to be seen in the sky. As soon as the telescope and the camera are called in, however, it is an entirely different story. Just above the centre of the photograph on the left, taken with an exposure of 10 minutes, is the star η Carinae; this is the only star in the Plate which is visible with the naked eye. The second photograph is of the same area, with an exposure of 30 minutes. It reveals a much greater profusion of stars. The third shows not only still more stars but also some luminous gaseous nebulae, while the last photograph is nearly filled with detail. This small piece of the sky, hardly as large as a full Moon, is now seen to contain some 8,000 stars. The Plates are not only proof of the overwhelming number of stars in the sky, but they show what a powerful aid Sir David Gill introduced when he photographed a comet with a portrait camera at Cape Town in 1882, to enable his colleagues in England to enjoy the spectacle. That photograph led to the first photographic star atlas. The photographs above were taken at the Union Observatory in South Africa.

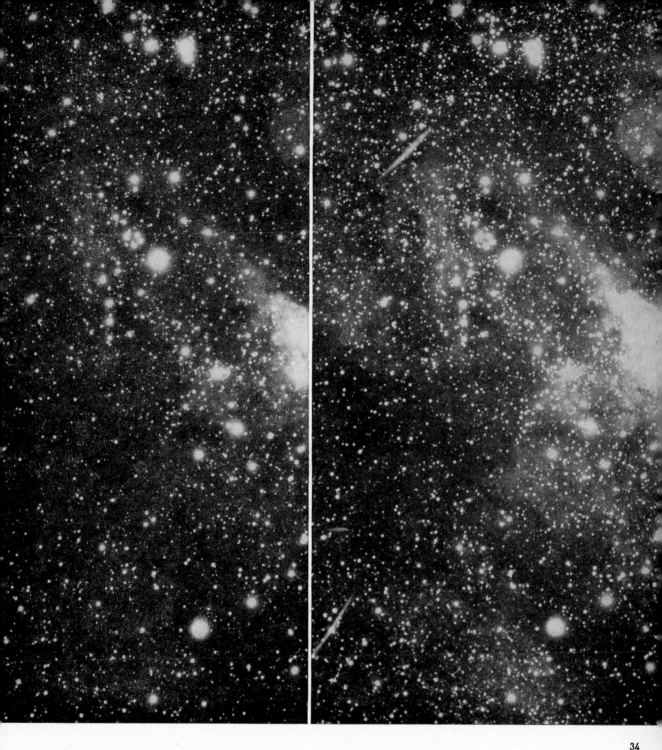

It was a very long time before astronomers took any real interest in the so-called 'fixed stars', which they long regarded as the permanent backcloth against which the movements of the Sun, Moon and planets were enacted. In the second century A.D., Ptolemy recorded the positions and magnitudes of 1,024 stars, but it was not until the eighteenth century that it became possible to widen the study of the fixed stars with the aid of new scientific ideas and better instruments. In Ptolemy's 'Almagest' we find a division of the stars into 6 classes of brightness (magnitude). Stars of the 1st magnitude are the brightest; those of the 6th are only just visible with the unaided eye. The star η Carinae is approximately of the 5th magnitude or, to be more precise (and to give the reader an idea of the great accuracy of modern measurements), it varies between magnitudes of 5·26 and 5·75. A star of the 1st magnitude is exactly 100 times as bright as one of the 6th and approximately 2·5 times as bright as the 2nd, and similarly along the scale. Under this system the Sun has a magnitude of —27, the full Moon —12, Venus at its brightest —4, Sirius —2 and the Pole Star 2. The Hale telescope (sited in the very clear air of Mount Palomar in California: see Pl. 1 and 87-8) can photograph stars as faint as magnitude 23; these are stars which radiate to Earth less than a millionth part of the light radiated by a star just visible to the naked eye.

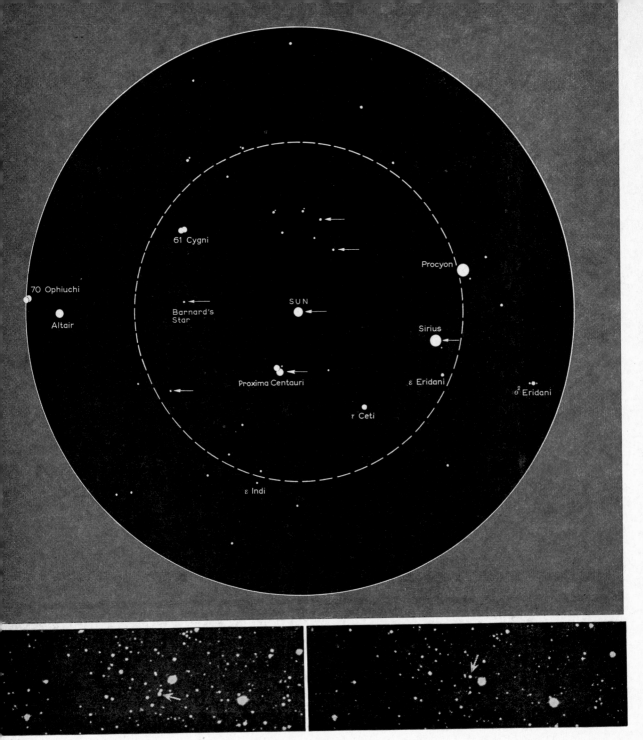

NEAREST STARS. According to Oort, the farthest fragments of our solar system—the nuclei of future comets—may be found one light-year from the Sun. From that distance the Sun can be seen only as a very bright star. How much farther must we go to reach another star? Bessel was the first to measure accurately the distance of a star. He realized that his method, the same as that used by terrestrial surveyors, but with the Earth's orbit round the Sun as his baseline, had no chance of success if the star was too far away. Which star was he to choose? Halley had discovered that stars have a proper motion. It seemed logical to assume that near-by stars have a larger proper motion than distant ones. Bessel knew that the star 61 Cygni has a very large proper motion: in 400 years it moves a distance equivalent to the apparent diameter of the Moon! The choice of 61 Cygni proved an excellent one. In 1838 he found its distance to be 11 light-years. Barnard's Star has an even greater proper motion; the two lower photographs taken respectively in 1894 and 1916, clearly show its displacement. Its distance is 6 light-years. The Sun's nearest neighbour is Proxima Centauri, a distance of 4·2 light-years away. Only 8 stars (arrowed in the smaller circle) are found within a radius of 10 light-years. The illustration as a whole represents a radius of 16^1/$_2$ light-years and yields the following count: 24 single stars, 13 double stars and 3 triple stars.

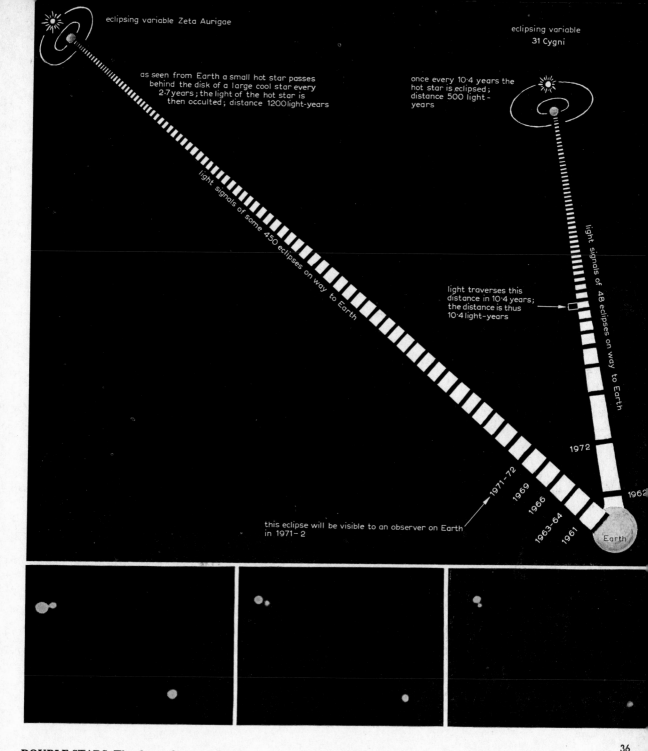

eclipsing variable Zeta Aurigae

eclipsing variable
31 Cygni

as seen from Earth a small hot star passes
behind the disk of a large cool star every
2.7 years; the light of the hot star is
then occulted; distance 1200 light-years

once every 10.4 years the
hot star is eclipsed;
distance 500 light-
years

light signals of some 450 eclipses on way to Earth

light signals of 48 eclipses on way to Earth

light traverses this
distance in 10.4 years;
the distance is thus
10.4 light-years

1972

1971-72
1969
1966
1963-64
1961

1962

Earth

this eclipse will be visible to an observer on Earth
in 1971-2

DOUBLE STARS. The three photographs above were taken in 1908, 1915 and 1920 respectively. It is obvious that the 2 top stars are physically associated and move around the same centre of gravity. The pair (Krueger 60) take 44$\frac{1}{2}$ years to complete a revolution. Spectrographic studies show that possibly as many as 20% of all stars consist of such pairs. The majority are so far from us and so close to each other that the individual stars cannot be seen separately. If their orbital plane happens to be edgewise to the Earth, the stars will eclipse each other in the course of every revolution. In 1780 Goodricke discovered that Algol in the constellation of Perseus is an eclipsing variable of this kind. For 2 consecutive days it is relatively bright (2nd magnitude), then it fades within a few hours to the 4th magnitude. Another remarkable eclipsing variable is ζ Aurigae, one of the 3 small stars (The Kids) close to Capella. A bright, blue star (7 times the size of the Sun) and a weaker, red star (200 times the size of the Sun) revolve round each other every 2.4 years. The eclipse of the blue star by the red lasts about 50 days. Since this binary is 1,200 light-years away from us, the light which will tell us of 450 eclipses is journeying across space to the Earth. If an eclipse chances to be taking place at this moment, it will be 1,200 years before it can be observed on Earth. Also illustrated is 31 Cygni with a period of 10.4 years and a distance of 500 light-years.

36

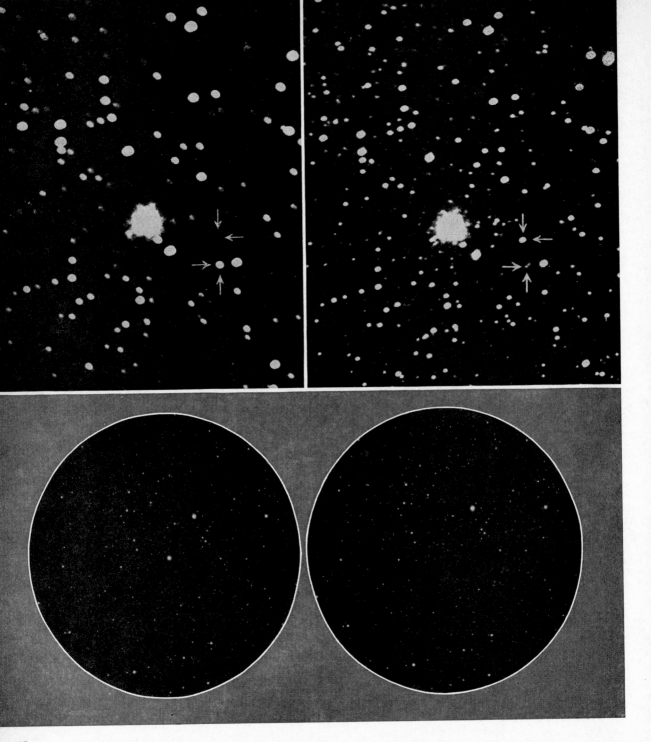

PULSATING STARS. In October, 1596, the Dutchman, David Fabricius, found that there was something amiss in the constellation of Cetus. Where 2 months earlier he had clearly seen a star of the 3rd magnitude there was now nothing to be seen. He saw this strange star (now called Mira) again in 1609. Mira can, in fact, attain the 2nd magnitude and when at its faintest can only be observed with a good telescope, having then decreased to magnitude 10. A cycle of these variations takes about 330 days. At the same time its surface temperature drops from 2,600° to 1,900°C. It is known with certainty that these changes are not due to 2 stars eclipsing each other, but may be due to the contraction and expansion of a single star. Very many variable stars are now known; the top photographs show two in Scorpius (see arrows). The lower illustrations have the star R Coronae Borealis at their centre; on the left it is clearly visible (6th magnitude) and on the right it is hardly perceptible (12th magnitude). Betelgeuse in the left shoulder of Orion varies between magnitudes of 0.2 and 1.2. It is sometimes brighter, sometimes fainter, than Rigel in Orion's foot. These variations are somewhat irregular. Particularly interesting are the regular variations in magnitude of the Cepheids, called after their prototype δ Cephei. Miss Leavitt discovered that the periods of these stars are very closely related to their actual luminosities.

EXPLODING STARS. In November, 1572, Tycho Brahe saw in Cassiopeia a star brighter than Venus, so bright that it remained visible in the daytime. By 1574 this 'new star' had disappeared. Kepler observed a similar phenomenon in Ophiuchus in 1604. Stars of this kind which suddenly blaze forth with brightness 10 million times that of a star like the Sun, are nowadays called supernovae. In our Galaxy such powerful explosions occur on an average of once in 400 years. The phenomenon occurs more often on a reduced scale. In 1901 a bright star of magnitude 0·1 was suddenly seen in Perseus. Shortly afterwards it was invisible to the naked eye, yet a photograph taken 48 years later (bottom) shows matter, ejected from the star, moving away from it at high speed. In 1918 a star in Aquila suddenly became as bright as Sirius; in 1934 a star in Hercules, not previously visible with the unaided eye, suddenly attained a magnitude of 1·5. The two top photographs show this star after and before the explosion. For nearly a year it remained directly visible, then suddenly dwindled to the 13th magnitude. This was followed by a second explosion, less powerful than the first (magnitude attained: 6). Stars which thus suddenly acquire a luminosity 100,000 times that of the Sun are called novae. It is probable that 25 such explosions occur annually in the Milky Way, but on the average only two of these are observed.

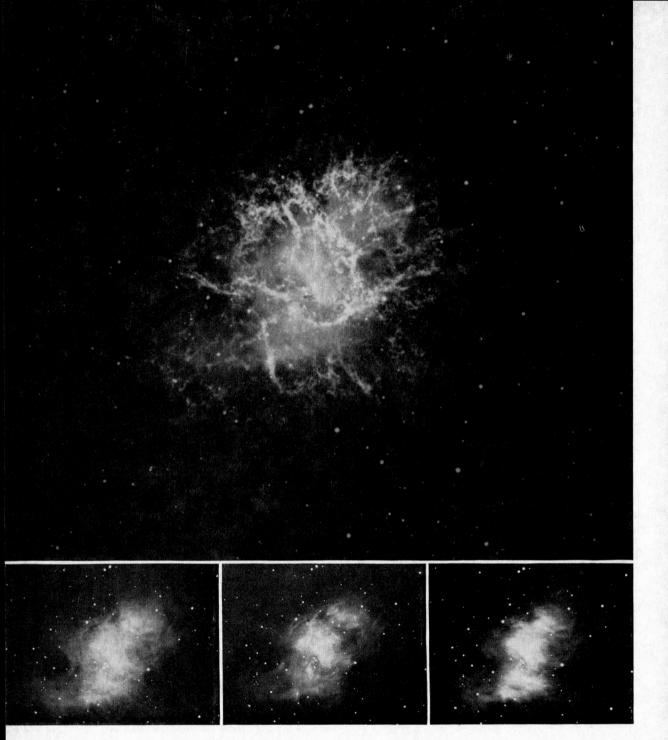

39

THE CRAB NEBULA. Close to the star ζ Tauri lies the nebula M1 with which Messier opened his list of 103 ill-defined objects. How rightly the small crab-like nebula (top picture) occupies this privileged position has only been realized in recent years. When Duncan compared photographs of the Crab nebula with others taken 30 years earlier, he noticed that the nebula was expanding at a speed of about 600 m.p.sec. Its entire mass must have been concentrated round the central point 900 years ago. There was great surprise when Chinese and Japanese chronicles revealed that at that time (1054) a star more brilliant than Jupiter had appeared at this spot. The Crab nebula is thus the remains of the supernova explosion that was seen in 1054. It actually occurred about 2,300 B.C., for the nebula is some 3,300 light-years from Earth. The outer filaments have the spectrum of a tenuous gas (as was expected) but the extensive inner area shows a spectrum suggesting an incandescent solid body or a gas under high pressure, although it is known that the nebula must have very small density. The light from the nebula also proved to be polarized (the lower three photographs show the nebula for three different positions of the polarization filter). Only in 1956 was the explanation discovered: the light of the Crab nebula is radiated by electrons circulating at very high speeds in a magnetic field. The nebula is a powerful source of radio radiation.

THE PLEIADES. In the evening sky in winter the Pleiades form the most striking of all the star clusters. They have been known since antiquity along with the Hyades, which lie close to the Pleiades in the constellation of Taurus (see Pl. 3 and 4), the fainter group Praesepe (the 'Beehive') in Cancer, and the double star cluster in Perseus (see Pl. 41). Many nations have legends about this remarkable little group (the Pleiades), which actually consists of over 300 stars. According to the Greeks, they were the seven daughters of Atlas and Pleione. It is remarkable that so many nations speak of them as 'seven' sisters, although only 6 stars are clearly visible. All the legends, therefore, have a postscript to account for the missing seventh. She is said to have run away from her sisters and become Alcor, situated near the sixth star in the Great Bear. The real explanation is that one of the 7 stars is variable and is much less bright than it used to be. The brightest stars in the photograph above are over-exposed and surrounded by a series of radiating lines which show as a blur at the centre of the image. This is due to unavoidable optical errors in the telescope. The large nebulous veils round the brightest stars will be dealt with more fully in subsequent photographs. These stars, which are about 300 light-years from Earth, have the same proper motion through the sky, which shows that physically they form a single whole.

41 DOUBLE STAR CLUSTER IN PERSEUS. Double and multiple stars are very numerous; in a relatively small space round the Sun it is possible to count more than 500 open star clusters, such as the Pleiades or the double star cluster in Perseus, shown above. The latter cluster lies in the Milky Way, on the borders of the constellations of Perseus and Cassiopeia, and is visible with the naked eye as a faint, luminous patch. Seen through a small telescope it is a magnificent object, both clusters of numerous stars being simultaneously within the field of vision. An inch and a half from the top edge of the photograph there is another smaller star cluster, NGC 957. Not long ago a new type of stellar grouping was discovered, called a stellar association. Such groups are difficult to recognize because they are much less closely concentrated than open star clusters. The fact that stellar associations exist might have remained unnoticed but for some special observational work by the Russian astronomer, V. A. Ambartsumian, who has discovered and examined many of them. The stars in this type of group are receding from each other, are in the Milky Way, and are always enveloped in extensive clouds of hydrogen, the so-called 'interstellar gas clouds'. The speed at which some stellar associations are expanding has been measured. The study of these groups contributes to our knowledge of the age and evolution of the stars.

BIRTH AND LIFE OF THE STARS. If we work back we find that each stellar association must have originated from a central point a relatively short time ago—between 1 and 20 million years. That is a very short time when we realize that the Earth is probably at least 5,000 million years old! This theory is neatly confirmed by the fact that most individual members of a stellar association are blue giants, radiating their energy in such a spendthrift fashion that they cannot have been doing it for long. These generally accepted conclusions, based on observational data, bring us face to face with the question, 'How did the stars originate?' Let us first look at the photograph above, of nebula M16 in Scutum. The bright cloud (of which more later) consists mainly of hydrogen gas made luminous by very hot stars. These clouds are transparent: the light of stars behind them can be seen shining through. Their capricious shape is usually only apparent. It is caused by dark, opaque clouds hiding large parts of the bright cloud from view. The small, very black clouds, called globules, are striking. They are found all over the Milky Way and it is strongly suspected that it is from them that new stars are in process of being formed. They can also be clearly seen in M8 in Sagittarius (Pl. 43). The smaller they are, the more opaque they are. It has been found that their masses are very close to that of the Sun.

43

BIRTH OF A STAR. The tiniest globules on the small photograph (part of the constellation Centaurus) are about 15 times as large as our entire solar system. Continued contraction will eventually increase the pressure and temperature at the centre to such a degree that nuclear reactions may be triggered. The original material, hydrogen, is then converted into helium, releasing vast quantities of energy. The great radiation pressure from the very hot stars created at the nucleus may form new condensation nuclei in the surrounding clouds and a stellar association is created. What happens then to the individual stars depends mainly on the quantity of matter concentrated in them. Man's knowledge of the origin and evolution of the stars is still very fragmentary and the explanation sketched out here is not to be regarded as conclusive.

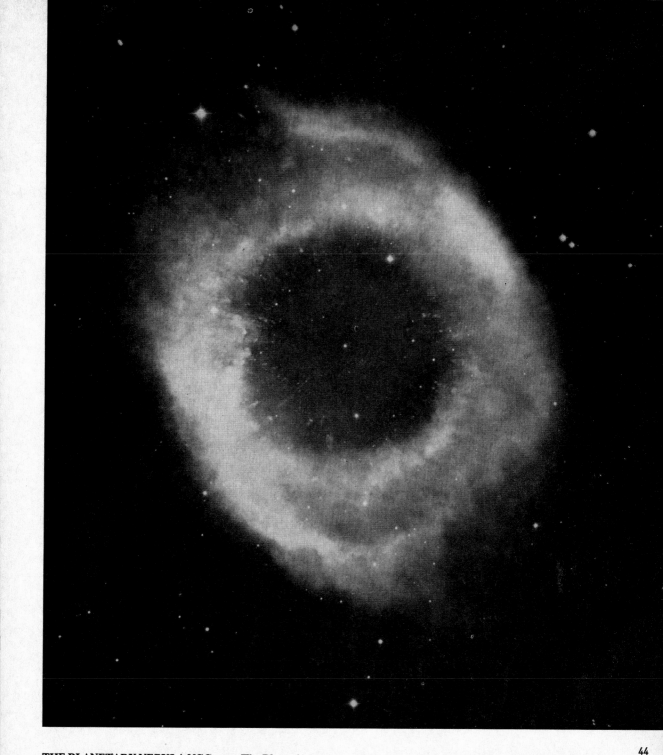

THE PLANETARY NEBULA NGC 7293. The Plate shows a small, faint central star, surrounded by a gigantic spherical cloud with a diameter of about 2 light-years which is more rarefied than any vacuum that man can create on Earth. This huge gaseous cloud, made luminous by powerful ultra-violet radiation from the central star, has scarcely a tenth of the mass of our Sun. About 370 of these strange objects are known in the vicinity of the Sun, and it is estimated that the Milky Way contains 60,000. The best known is the Ring nebula in Lyra, which is visible with a small telescope; it is slightly brighter than a 9th-magnitude star. Planetary nebulae were so named by W. Herschel from their resemblance, when viewed through a telescope, to planetary disks. It has been suggested that planetary nebulae may be the remains of nova explosions—the central star is very similar to former novae as regards spectral type and absolute magnitude—but it is now thought that they represent a later stage in the life of red supergiants. If so, the spherical cloud would then be the star's repelled atmosphere and the central star the nucleus of the former supergiant. All the evidence suggests that stars are not the simple balls of incandescent gas they were formerly thought to be. The confused interplay of atoms, electrons, and electromagnetic waves creates great diversity in the star world and this branch of astrophysics is still in its earliest stages.

PANORAMA OF THE MILKY WAY. The Milky Way, which on clear nights is draped round the firmament like a faintly luminous sash, is accurately reproduced above with the aid of a large number of photographs. The 7,000 brightest stars have also been drawn in. The original map was over $6^{1}/_{2}$ ft. long. The projection chosen was the one most suitable for displaying the Milky Way. Constellations more than 20° north or south of it, however, are considerably distorted. The Auriga pentagon on the extreme left is easily recognized, but some effort is necessary to identify the Pleiades in the group of stars round point 1·2, 2·5, i.e. 1·2 inches from the left edge, 2·5 inches above the lower. If we proceed right from Auriga, we come to Cassiopeia (2·2, 4) whose stars are hidden in bright nebulae. Deneb in Cygnus is in position (3·6, 4). After Cygnus, the Milky Way is divided into two by dark nebulae stretching from Deneb to beyond the centre of the Plate. The bright star north of the bright nebulae in Cygnus is Vega in Lyra (4·4, 4·7). The brightest part of the Milky Way occurs at the middle of the Plate, where we find the dense star clouds in Sagittarius. North of this are the stars of Scorpius (7·2, 4·6). Then comes the part of the Milky Way which is never visible from Europe or North America. It is unfortunate that this includes the brightest and most interesting regions. One striking object is the Coal Sack (9·8, 4) in the constellation Crux. The bright star at 12·8, 3·6 is Sirius. The rest of the

Milky Way from here on is visible in our latitude. At a point 0·8 inches diagonally below and to the right of Sirius, the 3 stars of Orion's Belt can be recognized (14·2, 2·8). In the lower right-hand quadrant are two bright nebulae looking like shreds torn from the Milky Way. These are the Large and Small Magellanic Clouds, which are visible only in the southern hemisphere. In the lower left-hand quadrant, 20° south of the Milky Way, can be seen another luminous patch, oblong in shape—the Andromeda nebula. The position of the Pole Star is 2·6, 5·4. The first telescopes revealed that the diffused light of the Milky Way was produced by a multitude of stars that could not be seen separately with the naked eye. The theory that all these stars formed a closed system was first advanced by Thomas Wright. In 'An Original Theory of the Universe' (1750) he attempted to explain the crowding together of stars in the Milky Way by assuming that all stars occupy a lens-shaped space. From irregularities in the brightness of the Milky Way he deduced that the Sun does not lie at its centre. Somewhat later, on the basis of Wright's brilliant intuition, Kant concluded that the Sun in fact lies slightly to the north of the galactic plane. Sir William Herschel was the first to try to collect the observational material needed to prove these theories correct. The fact that our Earth is itself part of the galactic system is a great handicap to investigations into the structure of the system.

47

STAR CLOUDS, GAS AND DUST. Attempts to investigate the Milky Way are everywhere hampered by clouds of dust and gas. In the plane of the Milky Way only our immediate neighbourhood can be viewed directly. How astronomers finally succeeded in discovering the structure of the system as a whole will be told later. First, however, let us examine in detail some parts of the Milky Way—in the constellations of Cygnus, Auriga and Orion. The Milky Way is brightest in Sagittarius and Cygnus. But because Sagittarius never comes much above the horizon in our northern latitudes and Cygnus is high in the evening sky throughout autumn, the Milky Way, so far as we are concerned, is most beautiful in Cygnus. Deneb, or α Cygni, will be found at 2·6, 5·9; γ at 4, 4·2, δ at 6·4, 6; and ε at 2·0, 1·7. The other stars of Cygnus are lost in bright patches of luminous nebulae. To the left of Deneb we find the bright North America nebula and alongside the latter the start of dark clouds which continue to the lower right-hand edge of the Plate. Plates 49 and 50 show this area. In the lower left corner of Plate 47, with point 1·6, 0·8 as centre, two fine wisps of cloud, the Veil nebula, can be seen. The lower photograph of Plate 48 reproduces this area enlarged, while the upper one shows the delicate structure of the right-hand part of the nebula on a still larger scale, with star 52 Cygni alongside. The distance between the two bright parts of the nebula is about 3°.

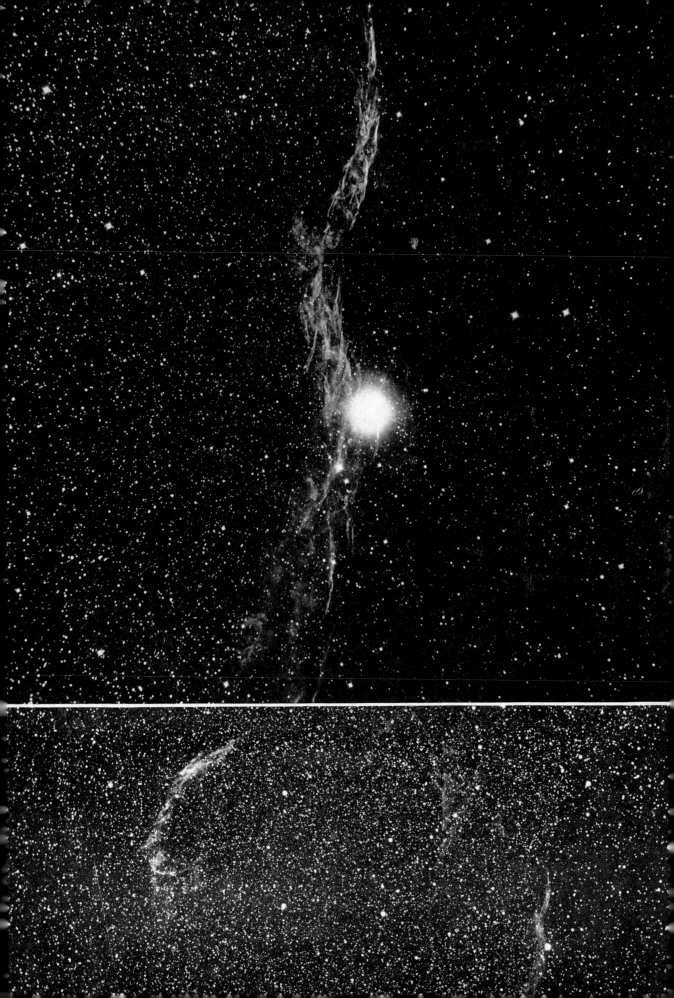

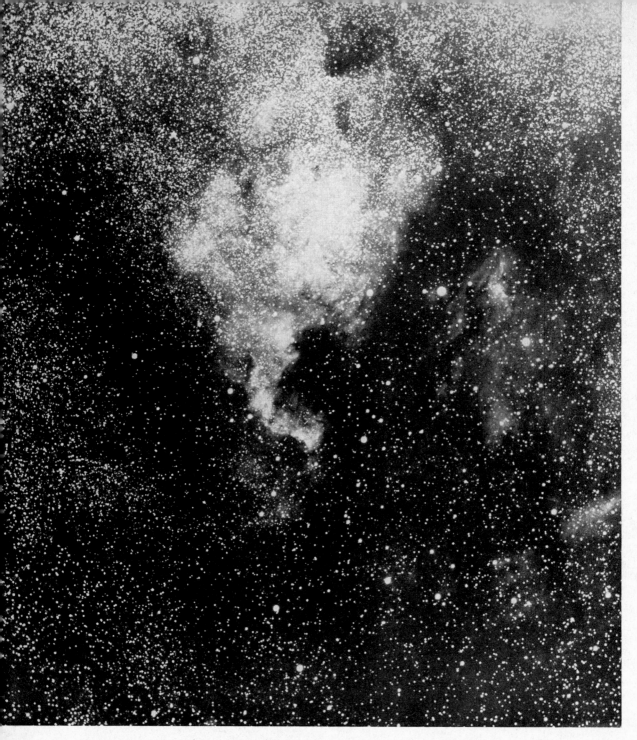

49

THE NORTH AMERICA NEBULA AND THE PELICAN NEBULA. If the Veil nebulae (Plate 48) were extended to join up, they could be thought of as outlining an enormous gas cloud with a diameter of about 50 light-years. Some astronomers think that these gaseous masses are expanding from a point, and they assume that they are the remains of a supernova explosion which must have taken place 30,000 to 100,000 years ago. This theory is probably not correct, but if it is, the Crab nebula can be expected in 5,000 years to look as the Veil nebula looks now. The photograph above shows the area to the left of Deneb. The bright luminous cloud is called the North America nebula, because of its shape. To the right of this can be seen the much smaller Pelican nebula (shown greatly enlarged on Plate 50, where much more detail is visible). With a little imagination it is possible to see in it some resemblance to a pelican. In examining the photographs of nebulae in the Milky Way it is difficult to rid oneself of the impression that one is seeing luminous clouds against a dark background. In many cases, nevertheless, the brighter clouds are the more remote, and take on weird shapes because they are partly obscured by dark clouds. Fewer stars can be counted in the dark parts than in the light, for the only stars visible in the former are those that are nearer than the nebulae, whereas the luminous gases of the latter allow the stars behind them to shine through.

GROUP OF OPEN CLUSTERS IN AURIGA. All the 500 open clusters known are found in or near the plane of the Milky Way. In this photograph of the constellation of Auriga, 5 are clearly visible: M36 at 2·7, 2·4; M37 at 1·3, 1·8; M38 at 3·3, 3; and immediately below, NGC 1907 and NGC 1893 at 4, 2·2. Stars α Aurigae (Capella, magnitude 0) and β Tauri (magnitude 2) lie at 4·2, 7·1 and 3·5, 0·2 respectively. Open clusters consist of younger stars of Population type I. The stars composing an open cluster are kept together by the force of mutual attraction. Since, however, the combined gravitational forces of the stars and other compounds of the Milky Way are also acting on these groups, these clusters will eventually be disrupted. When the American astronomer, Trumpler, found the distances of open clusters by two independent methods in 1930, he came to the surprising conclusion that the results of the two methods accorded well for the nearer clusters, but showed much greater discrepancies for the distant clusters than could be expected on theoretical grounds. From this he concluded that the light from the remote clusters appeared redder than it really was, as a result of selective absorption by diffuse matter in interstellar space. This was one of the earliest indications that there must be some very tenuous matter in interstellar space which did not appear on photographs as either dark or bright clouds.

THE MILKY WAY IN ORION. Although, owing to the long exposure, the photograph is nearly filled with myriads of stars and an extensive, faintly luminous nebula, the stars of Orion can still be made out clearly at the centre. The star at the bottom left-hand corner is Sirius. Various stars in Orion belong to the 'Orion group', a stellar association of the kind mentioned under Plate 41. The very hot stars in this group ionize the surrounding hydrogen and make it luminous. It has been calculated that a star with a surface temperature of 60,000° can ionize hydrogen within a radius of 160 light-years. The star λ Orionis (3·4, 5·2) has a surface temperature of 35,000° and ionizes a hydrogen sphere with a radius of 140 light-years. In the photograph that means the bright area within nearly 1 inch of λ Orionis. But, near stars with a much lower temperature, it is possible for visible nebulae to be formed by the reflection of starlight on small particles of dust. Examples of these are the nebulae round the brightest stars of the Pleiades (Pl. 40). Reflection nebulae show the same spectra as the stars whose light they reflect. Emission nebulae, however, such as the nebulae in Orion, have a line spectrum. The hydrogen in areas devoid of such hot stars remains invisible in photographs but, as we shall see later on, radio astronomy has made it possible for us to observe non-ionized hydrogen up to very great distances.

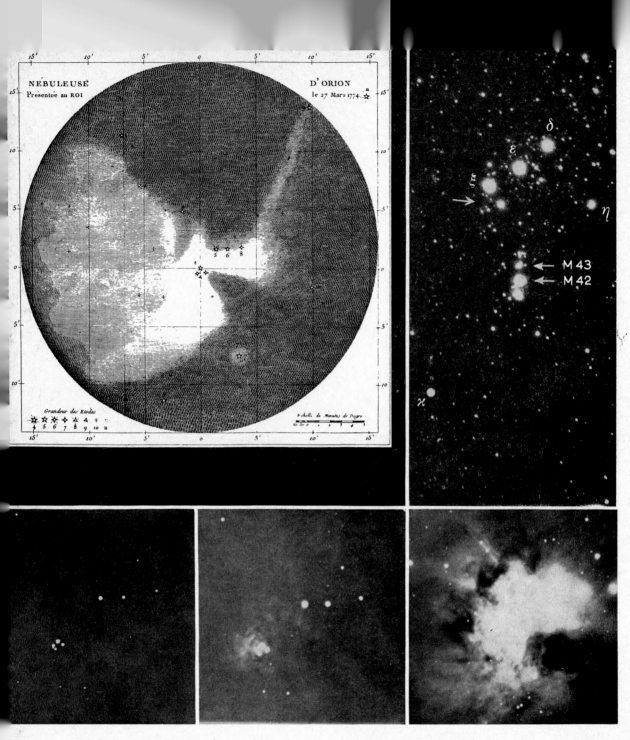

THE GREAT AND THE SMALL NEBULA IN ORION. It is strange that Huygens, and not Galileo, was the first to see this nebula through a telescope. The luminous patch under the three stars in Orion's Belt is so striking, even to the naked eye, that it merits closer examination. With a medium-sized telescope we see a trapezium of small stars surrounded by a pale green, fan-shaped, luminous nebula —the Great nebula in Orion, M42. Messier drew this nebula accurately in 1774 (top left). His main purpose was to be able to trace any change that took place in it in the course of time for, as he said, 'If we compare this drawing with those of Huygens, Picard, Mairan and Le Gentil, we see such an alteration that we can scarcely imagine it to be the same nebula.' Since then it has been shown that such changes as may take place in the nebula in one or two centuries are hardly, if at all, perceptible. The differences between the various drawings mentioned by Messier are definitely not factual. Its gaseous nature was first revealed spectroscopically, in the last century, by Huggins. Chaotic movements involving differences of velocity of as much as 25 m.p.sec. (40 km/sec.) or over, occur in the nebula. On a short exposure the trapezium stars are the first to appear; a longer exposure brings out the nebula, which eventually outshines the small stars completely (below). Plate 54 shows M42 (below) and M43 (above) in all their glory.

THE HORSE-HEAD NEBULA. Round the most easterly star in Orion's Belt (ζ, see Pl. 53) there is yet another richly variegated nebular area. The luminous matter here seems to dash against the dark coast like a long line of breakers. The dark 'horse's head' at 3·4, 4·1, from which the nebula derives its name, looks like a solitary rock. Plate 56 shows a very detailed photograph of just the horse's head. It is very difficult to observe visually, even with a large telescope and good observing conditions. This picture was taken with the Hooker telescope (which has a 100-inch mirror and was, until 1948, the largest in the world; it is situated at Mount Wilson near Los Angeles). The profusion of stars on the bright right-hand side of the Plate is very striking. The bright matter obviously obscures the stars behind it less than the dark matter does. The Horse-head nebula is catalogued as IC434. On Plate 55 another nebula can be seen at 3·2, 5·0 while M43, the Small nebula in Orion, is visible at the bottom, to the right (cf. also Plate 54). The horse's head is outlined on the bright side by an even brighter edge. This edge is probably formed as follows: the dark matter is fairly cold, while the hydrogen ionized by ultra-violet radiation from the hot stars has a temperature of about 10,000°. Because of the difference in temperature the hot gas flows towards the colder and is piled up against it. Only once has a dark nebula been observed to change into a bright one as a result of a nova explosion.

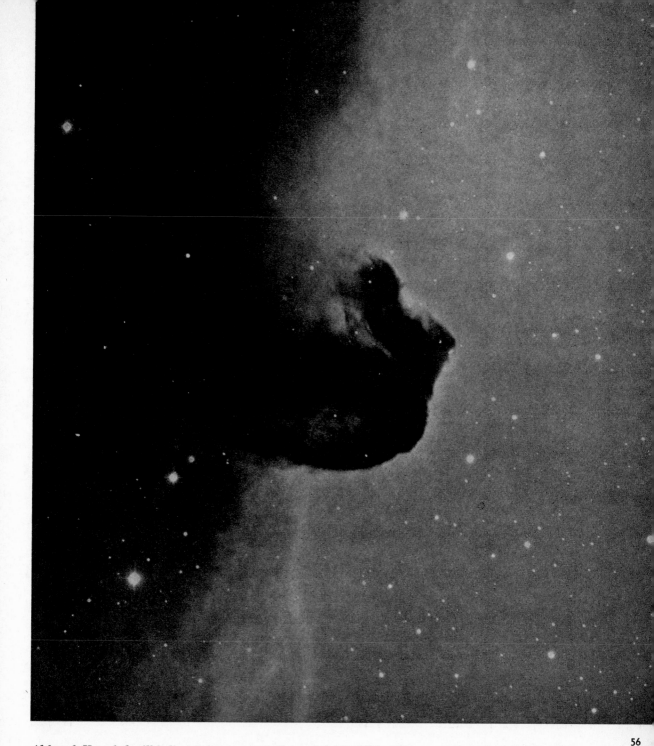

Although Herschel still believed that a very dark patch in the Milky Way was a kind of window through which it would be possible to peer into the empty depths of space, it is now known that such dark patches are in fact dark matter among the stars. On the basis of what has been said above, the picture that can now be formed of interstellar matter is as follows. There are bright or emission nebulae in the galactic plane. Their spectra show that they consist mainly of hydrogen and helium in the gaseous state. The hydrogen is ionized and rendered self-luminous by ultra-violet light from very hot stars. Dark nebulae partly or wholly obscure stars situated behind them. They consist of very fine particles of dust. The dark clouds also contain much hydrogen gas, though the latter does not contribute in any way to the obscuring effect of these clouds. Sometimes the dark matter is more densely concentrated, forming globules. It is suspected that stars originate in these globules, which have diameters of the order of light-years. All these kinds of interstellar matter are directly visible in photographs. Nevertheless, they immediately suggest two sorts of interstellar matter which are invisible: hydrogen clouds in whose vicinity there are no hot stars, and dust clouds which are so tenuous that they do not entirely obscure the stars behind them, or which do not attract attention because they form no contrast with bright emission nebulae.

VISIBLE AND INVISIBLE CLOUDS OF DUST. Kapteyn suspected the existence of these as long ago as 1904. He thought it probable that the luminosity of distant objects was underestimated because part of their light was absorbed by interstellar matter before it reached us. In 1905 Hartmann discovered a remarkable, well-defined dark line, due to ionized calcium, in the spectrum of the double star δ Orionis (the most westerly star in Orion's Belt). This line could not possibly originate in the atmosphere of the two stars, because the spectral lines of both showed periodic shifts as a result of their motion round a common centre, while this calcium line was stationary. In 1930 Trumpler discovered that the dust clouds attenuated blue light more than red. Plate 58 will help to illustrate this point. The top photograph was made on a normal photographic plate, sensitive to blue light-rays. The lower photograph shows the same area, but taken through a filter which allowed only infra-red light to pass and on a plate which was very sensitive to this type of radiation. Far more stars are now visible. That even a distant globular star cluster is also visible is due to the fact that the brightest stars in globular clusters are red. Not all the spectral absorption lines of interstellar matter have yet been identified. Plate 57, a wonderful spectacle of dark and luminous matter in the constellation of Monoceros, and Plate 58 are the last of those dealing with interstellar matter.

59

GLOBULAR STAR CLUSTER M3. Globular clusters frequently contain over 100,000 stars. About 100 are known in the neighbourhood of our Galaxy. The two brightest, ω Centauri and 47 Tucanae are visible only in the southern hemisphere. In the northern, M13 in Hercules is clearly visible with the naked eye as a faint hazy spot, and, with a small telescope, as a small glowing sphere. Larger telescopes reveal a magnificent 'star-flower' like M3 in Canes Venatici, shown above. Globular clusters of stars are much more stable than stellar associations or open clusters. No young stars at all are found in them. In 1917 Shapley, in order to gauge the dimensions of our Galaxy, took advantage of the fact that their luminosity makes these objects visible at much greater distances than individual stars. He determined the distances of all the globular clusters with the aid of the Cepheid variables that occur in them. His conclusion was: all the globular clusters form a system with a diameter of 100,000 light-years and with its centre in the galactic plane. It was a simple matter to identify the centre of this system with the centre of the Galaxy. Since almost all globular clusters were found in one half of the sky, the centre of the Milky Way cannot lie in the vicinity of the Sun. In fact, it lies very far from it, in the direction of Sagittarius. This had already been suspected, for that is where the Milky Way is brightest.

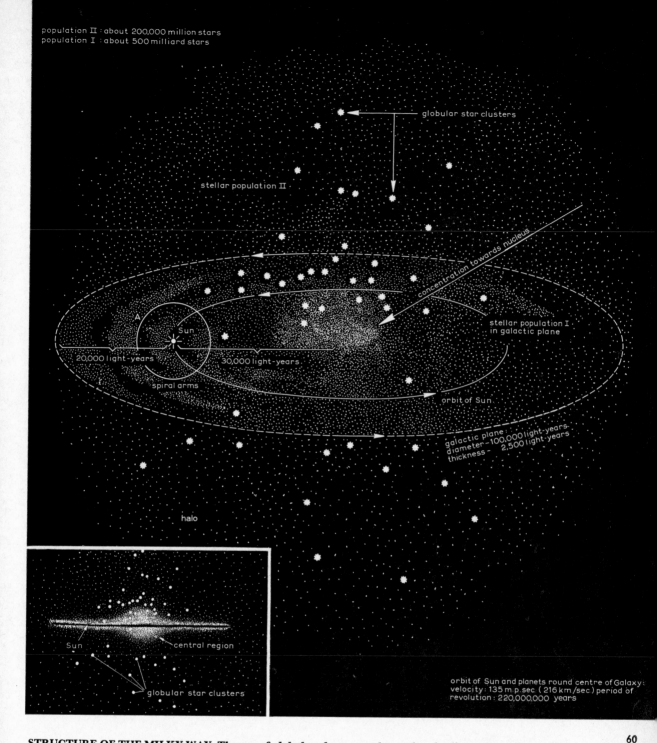

population II : about 200,000 million stars
population I : about 500 milliard stars

globular star clusters

stellar population II

concentration towards nucleus

stellar population I
in galactic plane

A

Sun

20,000 light-years

30,000 light-years

spiral arms

orbit of Sun

galactic plane :
diameter—100,000 light-years
thickness— 2,500 light-years

halo

Sun

central region

globular star clusters

orbit of Sun and planets round centre of Galaxy:
velocity: 135 m.p.sec (216 km/sec) period of
revolution: 220,000,000 years

STRUCTURE OF THE MILKY WAY. The use of globular clusters to determine the dimensions of the Milky Way and our place in it, was a very important step forward. It was as if some city-dwellers who knew only the streets in their immediate vicinity, had been given a map, though only a rough one, of the entire city, showing where their street, the Earth, was situated. Circle A, really a sphere with the Sun at its centre, encloses nearly all the stars that can be seen with the largest telescopes. Visibility in the galactic plane is more restricted than at right angles to it because of interstellar dust and gas. Spiral arms originate from a nucleus thickly populated with stars, and form a flat disk with a diameter of 100,000 light-years and a thickness of 2,500 light-years. These arms consist partly of young stars and partly of interstellar matter. The plane of the spiral arms, shown above in perspective, is surrounded by the spherical system of older stars and globular clusters. Photographed from various points of the universe, the Milky Way would show a striking similarity to other spiral galaxies, such as the Andromeda nebula (Pl. 66); compare the inset (a section through the Milky Way at right angles to the galactic plane) with the galaxy shown on Plate 72. The rotation period depends on the distance from the centre. A star at the extreme outer edge would take 370,000,000 light-years to make one circuit of the galaxy.

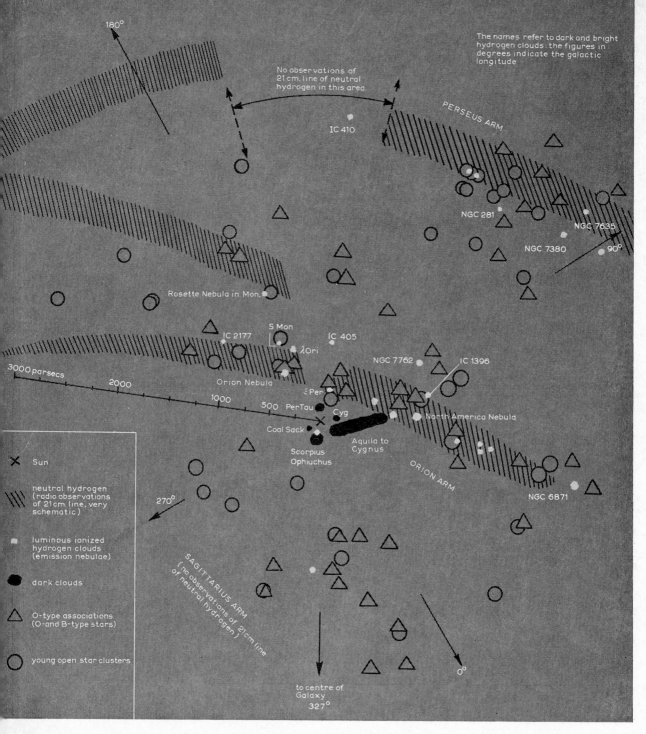

The names refer to dark and bright hydrogen clouds: the figures in degrees indicate the galactic longitude

180°

No observations of 21 cm. line of neutral hydrogen in this area.

PERSEUS ARM

IC 410

NGC 281

NGC 7635

NGC 7380

90°

Rosette Nebula in Mon.

IC 2177

S Mon

IC 405

NGC 7762

IC 1396

λ Ori

3000 parsecs

2000

Orion Nebula

ξ Per

1000

500   PerTau

North America Nebula

Coal Sack

Cyg

ORION ARM

Scorpius
Ophiuchus

Aquila to
Cygnus

NGC 6871

270°

Sun

neutral hydrogen
(radio observations
of 21 cm. line, very
schematic)

luminous ionized
hydrogen clouds
(emission nebulae)

dark clouds

O-type associations
(O- and B-type stars)

young open star clusters

SAGITTARIUS ARM
(no observations of 21 cm. line
of neutral hydrogen)

0°

to centre of
Galaxy
327°

61

MORE DETAILED EXPLORATION OF THE IMMEDIATE VICINITY. The limit of our directly explorable surroundings in the Milky Way is about 3,000 parsecs or 10,000 light-years from the Sun. (The position of the Sun is marked X.) If the hatched strips are ignored, what we see are the results achieved by optical methods before the recent advent of radio astronomy. The main aim of the investigations was to find out whether spiral arms of the kind found in many extragalactic nebulae occur also in our own Galaxy. It was known that young open clusters of stars are always associated with spiral arms, so these and O associations were mapped. The picture obtained did in fact suggest a spiral arm, the Orion arm, situated close to the Sun, and so named because the Orion nebula and the O star associations in Orion lie within it. The figure also shows that the dark and light clouds of Cygnus are part of it. A second arm, the Perseus arm, some 3,000 parsecs away, could also be clearly recognized. The search for spiral arms was pursued in various other ways, but the greatest obstacle to more distant observations were the arms already discovered. To understand how radio astronomy broke through these frontiers and enabled the spiral structure of the Milky Way to be plotted as far as its actual limits, we must return to earlier investigations. Kapteyn discovered that the stars in our vicinity moved in two opposite directions in relation to the Sun. Then more systematic knowledge of the movements of these stars was acquired. Lindblad (Stockholm) and Oort (Leiden) showed that all these

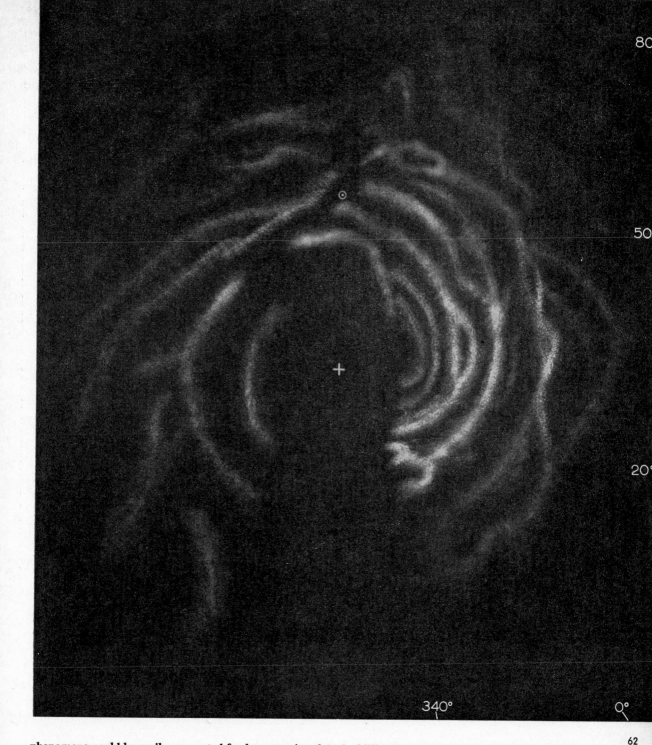

340°

0°

phenomena could be easily accounted for by assuming that the Milky Way rotates, and in such a way that the angular speed of rotation increases towards the centre of the system. The orbital velocity reaches a maximum of 140 m.p.sec. at a distance of 21,000 light-years from the centre, and diminishes both nearer and farther from the centre. This speed in the neighbourhood of the Sun is 135 m.p.sec. and the time required for a single revolution there is 220 million years. Because of this rotation the speeds of the various parts of the spiral arms in the direction of the Sun will vary according to their distance from the centre of the Milky Way. Inversely, if we were able to measure the velocity of a gas cloud, we could also calculate its distance from the centre. In 1944 Van der Hulst, on theoretical grounds, predicted that neutral hydrogen would emit electro-magnetic radiation with a wavelength of 21·1 cm. This radiation was first detected in 1951. Because of Doppler effect the wavelength received from clouds moving towards the Sun is slightly shorter, and that of clouds moving away from the Sun slightly longer. From the different values of wavelength thus obtained, it is possible to determine the velocities of the clouds and hence their distances. This was the method employed by the Leiden astronomers, under the leadership of Oort, to map the spiral arms that are observable from Holland (right). The remaining part (left) has been mapped by Kerr (Australia). The centre of the galaxy is shown by a cross and the position of the Sun by a circle.

63

THE MAGELLANIC CLOUDS. In the southern hemisphere two extensive nebular areas are visible with the naked eye (see Pl. 46). Portuguese seafarers called them the Cape Clouds. They owe their present name to the Portuguese navigator, Magellan, who described them in 1521. These objects do not belong to the Milky Way but are independent galactic systems (extragalactic nebulae). The Large Magellanic Cloud (left half of Pl. 63 and top photograph on Pl. 64) has a diameter half that of the Milky Way while the Small Cloud (lower right on Pl. 63) is half as small again. They are in fact very close neighbours of the Milky Way: their distance from us is about 150,000 light-years, or just $1^1/_2$ times the diameter of the Milky Way. Numerous details of the Clouds can be made out, Dreyer's 'New General Catalogue' listing no fewer than 301 star clusters and nebulae in the Large Cloud alone. In the huge Tarantula nebula, in fact, a certain amount of structural detail is visible with the unaided eye (Pl. 64: 2, 4). In the first two photographs at the bottom of Plate 64 this nebula is shown separately with the exposure times of 3 and 30 min. If it were situated where the Orion nebula is in the Milky Way, it would hide the entire constellation and cast distinct shadows on Earth. In the centre of the third photograph lies S Doradus, the most luminous star known. It can be found in the Large Cloud at $3\cdot4$, $3\cdot6$. It is about a million times as bright as the Sun! Probably this star is an eclipsing variable.

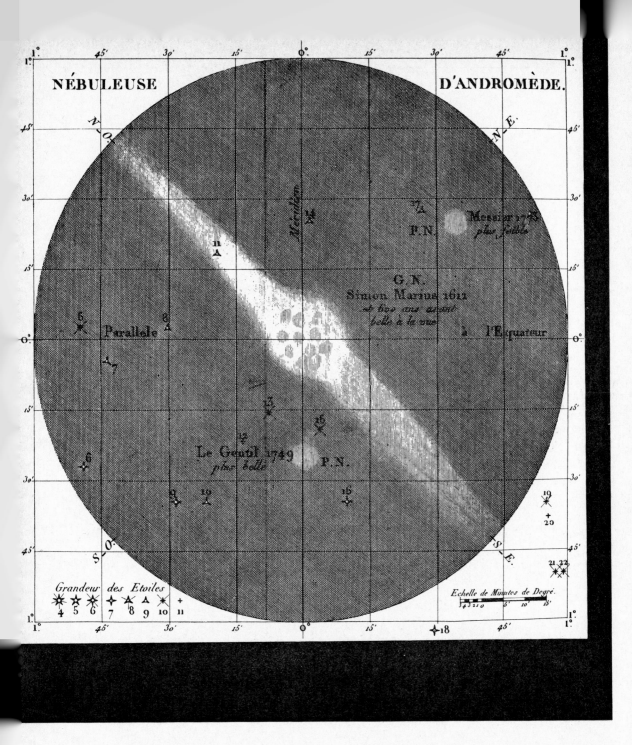

NÉBULEUSE   D'ANDROMÈDE.

THE ANDROMEDA NEBULA. 'Deceptive Glow' No. 31. In 1784 the French astronomer, Messier, completed a list giving accurate positions for over 100 'deceptive glows' liable to confuse searchers after comets, because they could be mistaken for these. Messier, jokingly named the 'comet ferret' by Louis XV (he discovered 21 comets!), had undertaken this task for the sole purpose of facilitating the search for comets. Later, he became so enthusiastic about these nebulae that he devoted extensive researches to them. In 1807 he wrote an article illustrated with the above engraving and entitled 'Observations and drawing of the great and beautiful nebula in the Belt of Andromeda, the first to be discovered, and of the small nebulae, one above, the other below the great nebula, as can be seen on the drawing'. In the article he also gave the following description: 'In the great nebula I saw not the slightest trace of stars. Yet its light appeared to me uneven or knot-like, if I may be forgiven the expression.' In 1612 Simon Marius had been the first to see the Andromeda nebula with a telescope; it looked like 'a candle flame shining through horn'. In 1749 Le Gentil discovered a smaller nebula below the large one, and this appears in Messier's list as No. 32. The nebula above and to the right was discovered by Messier himself: 'On 10th August, 1733, I discovered a small nebula that had never been observed previously. It was very difficult to make out and looked quite different from that discovered by Le Gentil.

The three nebulae occurred simultaneously in the field of the telescope and their centres were approximately in line. It is strange that neither Le Gentil nor I myself, when I was engaged on my catalogue of nebulae, saw the small nebula. Probably the brighter light of the great nebula played tricks on us; to see it properly, the great nebula must be kept out of the field of the telescope. The surrounding stars, whose position I determined accurately, provide more than enough means of observing changes of shape or position in the course of time.'
If a very recent photograph (Pl. 66) is compared with Messier's drawing, we are immediately struck by the care with which Messier made his drawing so long ago. The numbered stars can all be found on the photograph. All the individual stars visible in the picture are foreground objects belonging to our own Milky Way. The photograph, however, gives a wealth of detail outside the centre of the great nebula which Messier could not possibly have observed. Only since 1924 has it been known for certain that No. 31 in Messier's catalogue (known as M31 to this day), M32 (discovered by Le Gentil), and the nebula NGC205 (discovered by Messier) are in fact independent stellar systems far beyond the Milky Way. In the photograph, therefore, we see three galaxies hovering in space. The large nebula M31 is more than twice as large as the Milky Way. Even more interesting than all these facts is the way in which they were discovered.

ASTRONOMERS AT WORK. On evenings in winter the square of Pegasus stands in the western sky. Slightly higher and to the south is the constellation of Andromeda. If the night is clear and moonless, alongside star ν in this constellation a faintly luminous spot can be seen with the naked eye—the Andromeda nebula (lower photograph). Inspired by the brilliantly intuitive picture that Wright had drawn of the Milky Way as a system (see Pl. 46), Kant considered that, seen from a very great distance, the Milky Way would look exactly like the nebula in Andromeda. He added, 'Here lies a vast field for exploration.' A wealth of observational data had to be accumulated before Kant's 'island universe' hypothesis could be confirmed. The spiral structure of the Andromeda nebula was discovered in 1887 on a photograph taken by I. Roberts with a 20-inch telescope and an exposure of 3 hours. The first question that arose was whether it was a gaseous mass or a collection of stars which was too far off for the individual stars to be seen. Sir William Herschel originally assumed that all nebulous objects were unresolved star clusters because he had been able to resolve a few into stars with his largest telescope. Sir William Huggins, however, proved this assumption to be wrong: 'On the evening of August 29th (1864),' he wrote, 'I directed the telescope for the first time to a planetary nebula in Draco. I looked into the spectroscope. No spectrum such as I expected! A single bright

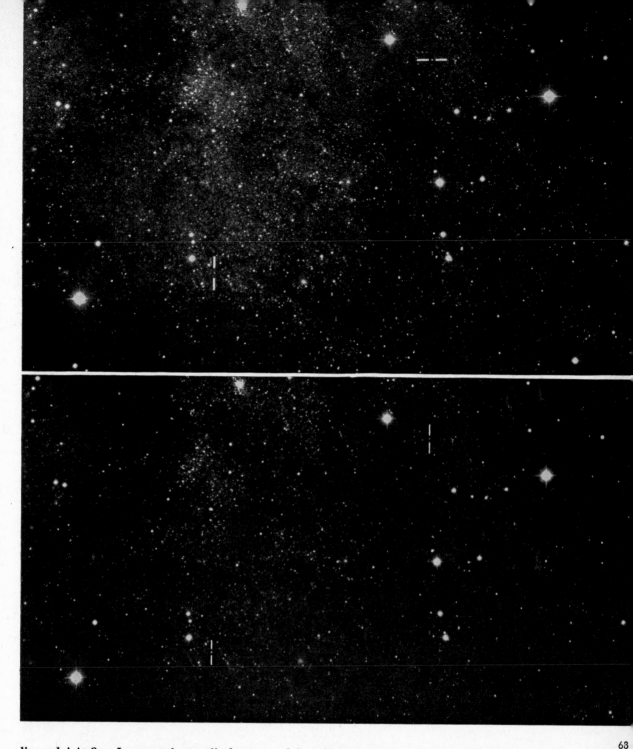

line only! At first I suspected some displacement of the prism and that I was looking at a reflection of the illuminated slit from one of its faces. This thought was scarcely more than momentary; then the true interpretation flashed upon me. The riddle of the nebulae was solved. The answer, which had come to us in the light itself, read: Not an aggregation of stars, but a luminous gas.' But the problem was not quite as straightforward as that, either, for when Huggins examined the spectrum of the Andromeda nebula it proved to be a continuous spectrum, suggesting that the light was indeed stellar light. In 1885 there suddenly appeared in the nebula a new star which attained a brightness equal to $1/10$ that of the entire nebula. If this was a nova of the kind that occurs in the Milky Way, it would be possible to calculate the distance of the nebula. In that case it must be relatively near. Two more novae were discovered in 1917 but these were thousands of times weaker than the 1885 nova. If these were the normal type of nova the Andromeda nebula must indeed be an island universe far beyond our own. Hubble provided the solution in 1924 when he resolved the outer part of the nebula into stars (Pl. 67, top left). These included Cepheid variables which enabled the distance to be determined. Plate 68 shows two details from the top left photograph on Plate 67. Two variables are marked with dashes. The Andromeda nebula is actually an island universe.

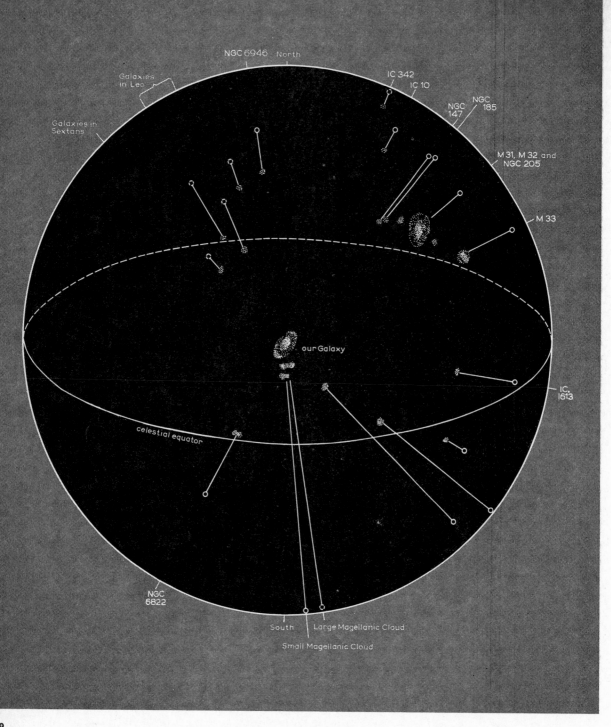

The labels on the figure, clockwise from top:

NGC 6946 · North

IC 342

IC 10

NGC 147

NGC 185

M 31, M 32 and NGC 205

M 33

IC 1613

Galaxies in Leo

Galaxies in Sextans

our Galaxy

celestial equator

NGC 6822

South · Large Magellanic Cloud

Small Magellanic Cloud

THE LOCAL GROUP OF GALAXIES. The Magellanic Clouds are our neighbours; the Andromeda nebula, its companions, and the magnificent spiral M33 in Triangulum (Pl. 70) are more than 10 times as far off. Including the Milky Way, there are about 20 galaxies within a radius of 3 million light-years. Probably there are more hidden behind the dust of the Milky Way, and perhaps some are too faint to be observed. The diagram shows the positions of the known local galaxies in space. A radius from the Milky Way as centre passes through each of the galaxies to the surface of the sphere, but is actually drawn only for the latter part of its length. The shorter the line, therefore, the greater the galaxy's distance away (allowance being made for the fact that this is a perspective drawing). If the radius cuts the front hemisphere, the point of intersection is marked with a full circle; if it cuts the rear, a broken circle is used. The names of the galaxies are shown round the edge. Very roughly we can think of each of the local galaxies as being, on the average, one million light-years from its neighbour. Is it a fortunate coincidence that we are surrounded by so many galaxies which are comparatively easy to observe? Are there other similar clusters in the universe? Do these galaxies affect each other? Are there perhaps connecting links inside the local group? We must venture still farther into space before we can attempt to frame an answer to these questions.

GALAXY M33 IN TRIANGULUM. Close to point 2·4, 0·4 on the lower photograph on Plate 67 is M33 which is shown above. It is invisible with the naked eye and since it is, as we see from Plate 69, about as far from us as the Andromeda spiral is, it must be smaller than the latter. The spiral arms can be clearly seen emerging from the brighter central portion. The brightest stars in the arms are individually visible, and extensive bright nebulae can also be made out here and there between the arms. The largest is at point 1, 5·4. One way of estimating the mass of an external galaxy is on the basis of its absolute luminosity. The average galaxy is so found to have a mass approximately 100 million times that of the Sun. This figure, however, makes no allowance for the mass of non-luminous matter, which also absorbs a considerable part of the light, so that the estimate is very much on the low side. A more reliable method of calculation is found in the theory that these great conglomerations of mass rotate. The Doppler effect gives us velocities of the various parts of a galaxy. The total mass can then be calculated from these rotational velocities. For an average nebula we arrive at a mass 100 million to 100,000 million times that of the Sun. Our own Galaxy has a mass equivalent to 200,000 million Suns and the Andromeda nebula has a mass nearly double that. Our own Galaxy and one of our nearest neighbours are thus far bigger than the average.

71

BAADE DISCOVERS TWO STELLAR POPULATIONS. Until 1943, no-one had succeeded in resolving the nuclei of spiral nebulae into stars. Elliptical nebulae, too, were visible only as diffuse luminous patches in photographs (cf. Pl. 66, on which the central portion of the Andromeda spiral and its two companions can be seen as hazy patches of light). Baade knew that the brightest stars are blue giants. In the autumn of 1943 he therefore attempted to photograph these blue giants in the nucleus of the Andromeda nebula with the aid of the Hooker telescope (100-inch reflector). On a night of particularly good visibility, further improved by the compulsory wartime black-out in the near-by towns of Los Angeles and Pasadena, he made his experiments, using a new type of blue-sensitive plate. Alas, the nucleus was still unresolved. Then he tried a red-sensitive plate. He had immediate success; instead of the luminous spot, he obtained thousands of pin-point stars on his plate. This led him to the discovery that there are practically no blue giants in the central portion of the nebula but only a large number of red stars, brighter than the red giants in the Milky Way. Globular clusters are the only other places where these luminous red stars occur. The elliptical nebulae, such as NGC147 illustrated above (and the companions of the Andromeda nebula: see Pl. 67) were thus shown to consist at least partly of red giants of this type.

Subsequently the stars of the Milky Way were classified into stellar Populations I and II. The former contains main sequence and supergiant stars in close association with clouds of gas and dust; the Sun is included amongst these. The latter contains the stars of the halo and those of globular clusters. Stars of Population II occur in those regions which are quite free of interstellar dust, as is clearly shown by Plate 71, in which an extremely distant galaxy can be seen shining through the dust-free NGC147 at 2·4, 3·7. It is much more difficult to demonstrate that Population type II occurs also in the central part of the Milky Way, the stars of which are hidden from view by thick banks of cloud. In 1953, at the Haute Provence Observatory, Jean Dufay succeeded in obtaining direct infra-red photographs of the central region of the Milky Way. Infra-red rays are less subject to absorption by gas and dust than visible radiation is. The galaxy shown above, M104 in Virgo, does not belong to the Local Group, being situated, in fact, at a distance of some 20 million light-years. The structure of a spiral nebula can be clearly distinguished here; the central flat disk is clearly to be seen from an edgewise-on position. In view of the large amount of dust it contains it shows up black against the surrounding halo of unresolved stars. The white spots scattered through the halo are globular clusters of stars.

M81 IN URSA MAJOR. Far beyond the Local Group of galaxies, the stellar system M81 hovers like a pearly spiral in the depths of the universe. As seen from Earth it is situated in the constellation of Ursa Major. By comparison with M81, which is about 10 million light-years from us, the stars in the foreground, belonging to the Milky Way, are very near. The photograph was taken at the Mount Palomar Observatory, with the 48-inch Schmidt telescope which can record a relatively large area of the sky. Three other remote galaxies can also be seen on the Plate: the spiral nebula NGC2976 in the bottom right-hand corner, the irregular galaxy NGC3034 (M82) at the top and another irregular galaxy, NGC3077, near the left-hand edge. In the original photograph dozens of even more distant galaxies can be made out. This once more raises the question of the limit of the universe. It is certainly possible to see much farther still with larger telescopes. Plate 74 shows the wealth of detail with which the 200-inch Hale telescope on Mount Palomar can photograph M81. The brighter points of light in the spiral arms are frequently but wrongly taken for stars. No doubt there will be some giant star among them, but mostly they are gaseous nebulae or clusters of stars. It is interesting to compare Plate 74 with Plate 73. The halos surrounding the bright stars on Plate 74 are caused by scattering and reflection in the photographic plate. The stars are all in the Milky Way.

Three of them are clearly visible against the background of the nebula itself, while three double stars can be very readily seen to the side of the nebula. Only a very short time ago, in 1956 to be precise, Münch determined the mass of M81 by measuring the speed of rotation of some parts of the nebula. He found it to be about 80,000 million times that of the Sun. If we examine the distribution of galaxies in the sky, their numbers appear to increase the farther we go from the band of the Milky Way, while not a single one is visible in the 'Zone of Avoidance' from 10° to 40° in width in the vicinity of the Milky Way. The reason for this has now been discovered. It is that the thick layer of dust in the spiral arms of our Galaxy obscures all the remote objects in that direction whereas space at the two galactic poles is practically transparent. Towards the end of the last century quite a different belief was held on this matter. The symmetrical arrangement in relation to the galactic plane seemed to suggest that these hazy nebulae in fact belonged to our stellar system. A limited number of these galaxies including some belonging to the Local Group can be seen in considerable structural detail on photographic plates but most are such vast distances away that it is possible to describe their shape only in very general terms. The classification most commonly used (Hubble's) is illustrated on the next few Plates.

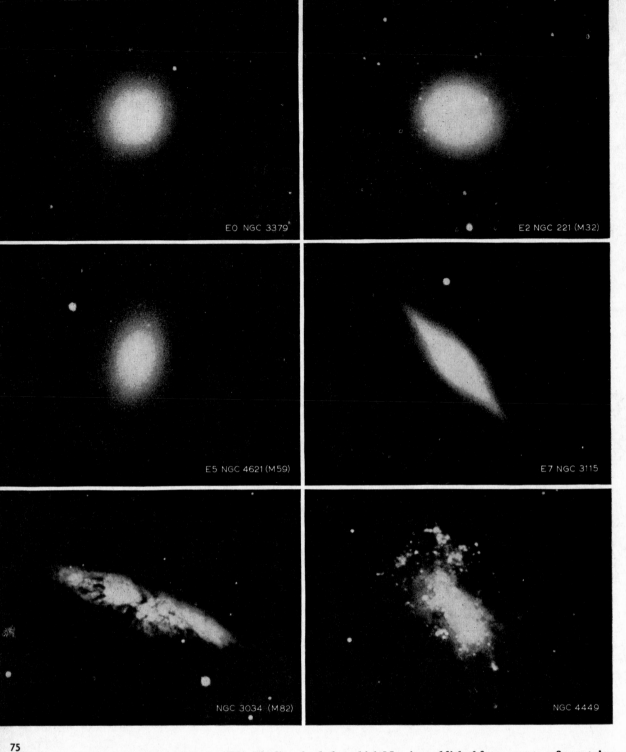

EO NGC 3379

E2 NGC 221 (M32)

E5 NGC 4621 (M59)

E7 NGC 3115

NGC 3034 (M82)

NGC 4449

CLASSIFICATION OF GALAXIES. The list of nebulae which Messier published from 1771 to 1784 contains 103 objects visible with a reasonably large telescope. In 1888 Dreyer brought out the 'New General Catalogue' (NGC) in which 7,840 objects are described. Two later enlarged editions, the Index Catalogues (IC), brought this total to over 13,000. Hubble devised a classification of the numerous extragalactic nebulae that occur among these objects. He distinguished between regular and irregular galaxies, subdividing the former into elliptical, normal spiral and barred spiral nebulae. Elliptical systems (E)—see the first four illustrations on Plate 75—have no clearly defined limits and reveal no definite internal structure. The outward shape may range from spherical to lenticular. Spherical galaxies are denoted by the combination Eo and the most flattened type by E7. In elliptical galaxies red stars predominate and interstellar matter seems to be almost completely absent. Normal spiral nebulae (S) have a pronounced bright central region from which the spiral arms seem to originate. The following classes are distinguished (Pl. 76, left, top to bottom): Sa, which have a bright, extensive central part with the spiral arms wound tightly round it; Sb, with a smaller central region and less tightly wound arms; and Sc, with a still smaller nucleus and even looser spiral arms. An apparent discontinuity between ellipticals and spirals was filled by a new class, designated by So.

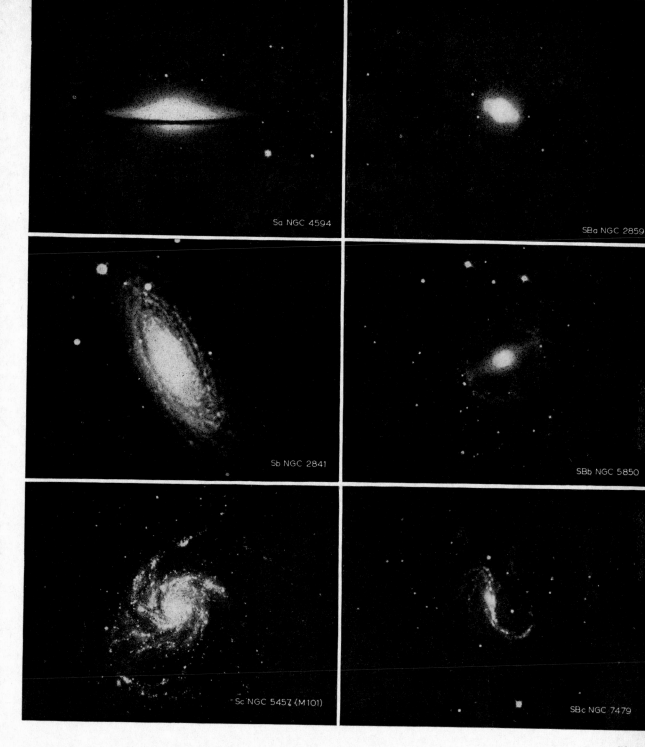

Sa NGC 4594

SBa NGC 2859

Sb NGC 2841

SBb NGC 5850

Sc NGC 5457 (M101)

SBc NGC 7479

In barred spirals (SB) the two spiral arms do not start from the edge of the central portion but from the extremities of a bright star projecting from either side of the central portion. Like normal spirals, barred spirals are divided into three classes, SBa, SBb and SBc, depending on the size of the central region in relation to the bar (Pl. 76, right, top to bottom). The irregular galaxies show no symmetry of construction (Pl. 75, bottom two illustrations). About 78% of all classified galaxies are spirals, one quarter of these being barred spirals. Eighteen per cent are elliptical nebulae and the remaining 4% are irregular nebulae. On the average, irregular nebulae are smaller than elliptical nebulae, which in turn are smaller than spiral nebulae. Hubble originally believed that elliptical nebulae were an early stage of spiral nebulae, i.e. that the elliptical body was the nucleus from which the spiral arms developed. Elliptical nebulae, however, consist mainly of red stars, while stars found in the arms of spiral nebulae are predominantly blue. It is now known that blue giants are young and red giants are old, which suggests the more plausible explanation that the elliptical nebulae are formed from spiral nebulae whose entire spiral matter has been transformed into stars and whose blue giants have long since ceased to shine. But all speculation as to the evolution of the galaxies must still be regarded as extremely uncertain.

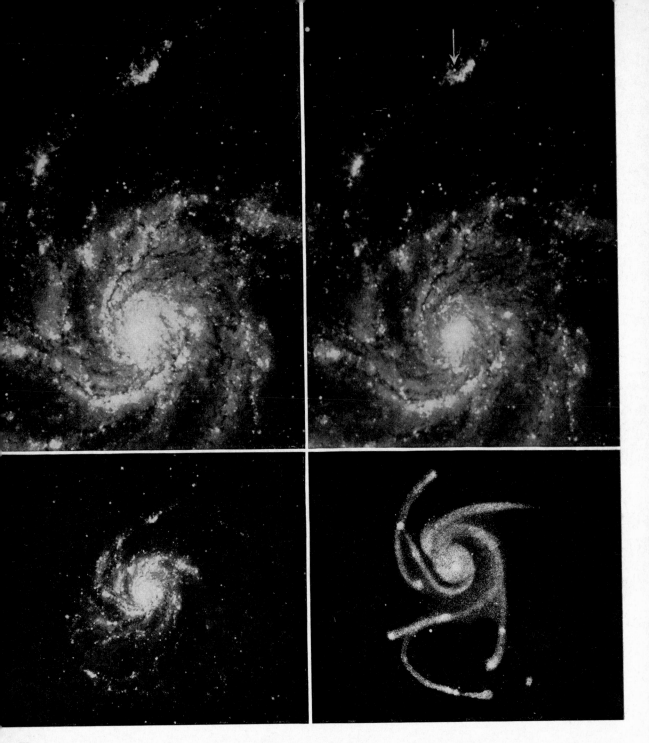

SUPERNOVAE IN DISTANT GALAXIES. Once the distance of the Andromeda spiral had been found, it was then possible to decide that the bright star which Ritchey had seen in it in 1885 could not have been a common nova of the kind observed among stars of our own Galaxy. It was realized that he had seen a supernova (see Pl. 38): the star concerned must have attained a brightness of ten million Suns! Plate 78 gives a picture of a similar vast explosion which was photographed in IC 4182 on 10th September, 1937. The top photograph was exposed for 20 minutes. The supernova is marked with an arrow. All other points of light in this print are foreground stars belonging to our Galaxy. Absolutely the only part of IC 4182 that is actually visible is the supernova, which was thus much brighter than all the stars in the entire system put together! The middle photograph was taken one year and two and a half months later, with an exposure of 45 minutes. The same stars can be recognized. The supernova is not so bright, but because of the longer exposure the brightest parts of the system are just visible. The last photograph was taken on 19th January, 1942, with an exposure of 85 minutes. The supernova has disappeared! In 1936, Zwicky began searching systematically for supernovae in distant galaxies, using a powerful Schmidt telescope capable of photographing extensive areas of the sky.

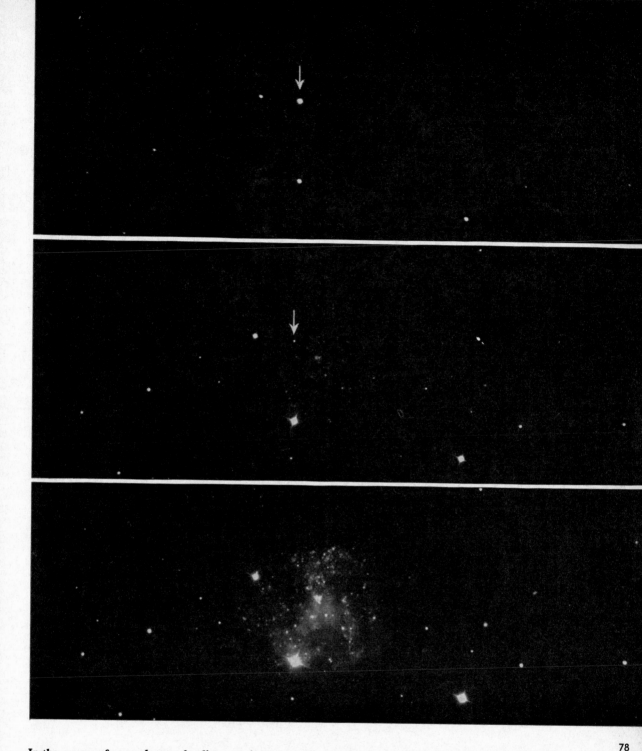

In the course of several years he discovered some more supernovae, which Baade and Humason studied
further with the aid of the great Hooker telescope. They noted that the spectrum of a supernova is entirely
different from that of any other known source of light. The origin of the radiation is still a mystery, though
it is generally agreed that the spectrum suggests extremely high temperatures and velocities. In 1940 Zwicky
deduced from his observations that these fantastic stellar explosions are extremely rare: only two or three
can be expected to occur in any galaxy within 1,000 years. The subject of Plate 77 is an ordinary nova explosion in M 101, a spiral nebula (Sb) in Ursa Major. The first photograph was taken on 9th June, 1950, and the
second on 7th February, 1951. An arrow on the second indicates a bright star which is not visible in the first.
The whole galaxy can be seen on a smaller scale in the lower left photograph; alongside it is a drawing made
by Lord Rosse with the aid of his giant telescope (see Pl. 85). The amazing resemblance is due to the same
peculiarity of human observation which has already been discussed in connection with the canals on Mars:
the bright spots have been joined to form complete spiral arms which Lord Rosse could never have seen,
for some parts only show on a plate that has been exposed for hours on end. What the eye cannot see in a
fraction of a second it will never see, but a photographic plate can register incoming light hour after hour.

79

MORE GALAXIES THAN STARS! Plate 80 (upper) is a photograph taken with the big 48-inch Schmidt telescope of Mount Palomar and shows part of the constellation of Coma Berenices. It contains more galaxies than stars. The lower photograph shows the centre of the upper one, taken this time with the 200-inch Hale telescope. Every spot that is not perfectly circular and sharply outlined is a galaxy. The other objects are all foreground stars of our own Galaxy. This cluster of galaxies was known as long ago as 1865. Photographic research revealed that the cluster of galaxies observable in this direction comprises about 1,000 members. The centre of the cluster is 240 million light-years away from us. At present some 2,700 such clusters, large and small, are known. Plate 79 shows several details from other clusters of galaxies, photographed with the Hale telescope. Above, part of the Leo cluster (distance 650 million light-years). Top left, an elliptical galaxy (E2); top right, a type SBc barred spiral; top centre, a normal spiral (Sb); and bottom right, another barred spiral (SBa). The lower photograph is of a normal spiral (Sb) in the Pegasus cluster at a distance of 100 million light-years. The Palomar 'Sky Atlas', completed in 1956, is a rich source for the study of clusters of galaxies. Its 1,758 Plates were made with the 48-inch Schmidt telescope. A single Plate (representing an area of 7 × 7°) sometimes contains more than 50,000 galaxies!

81

AT THE LIMITS OF THE OBSERVABLE UNIVERSE. The photograph above shows Edwin Hubble peering through the viewfinder of the 48-inch Schmidt telescope at Mount Palomar. In 1936 Hubble succeeded, with the aid of the Hooker telescope, in plumbing the extent of the universe approximately. He determined the distances of the nearest galaxies (M31 and M32) by means of the Cepheid variables photographed in them. In galaxies slightly farther away, he only just managed to photograph the brightest 'stars' (now known to be bright hydrogen regions), and he worked out their distances from their estimated absolute magnitudes and their observed apparent magnitudes. In the case of galaxies too remote for stars to be photographed, he reasoned along similar lines. The farther the galaxy is, the smaller is its apparent magnitude, and it should be possible to calculate its distance likewise from the estimated absolute and the observed apparent magnitude. Although it is now known that the distances thus obtained by Hubble have to be multiplied by a factor 5 and further corrections have constantly to be made, Hubble, with his bold method, was the first to give a reasonable estimate of the size of the universe. Plate 82 shows part of the cluster of galaxies in Corona Borealis which are 700 million light-years distant. The Hale telescope has photographed galaxies which are more than twice that distance from us.

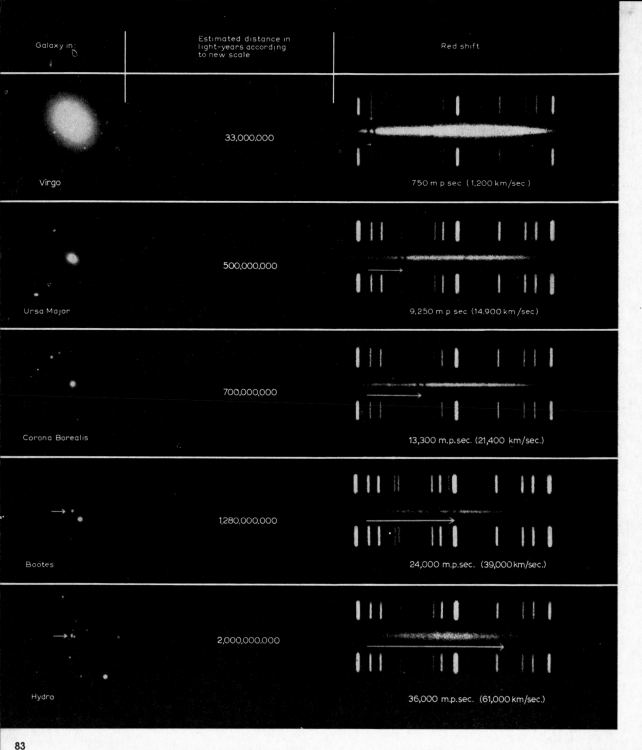

Galaxy in:	Estimated distance in light-years according to new scale	Red shift
Virgo	33,000,000	750 m p sec (1,200 km/sec)
Ursa Major	500,000,000	9,250 m p sec (14,900 km/sec)
Corona Borealis	700,000,000	13,300 m.p.sec. (21,400 km/sec.)
Bootes	1,280,000,000	24,000 m.p.sec. (39,000 km/sec.)
Hydra	2,000,000,000	36,000 m.p.sec. (61,000 km/sec.)

83

EVIDENCE OF AN EXPANDING UNIVERSE. It is extremely difficult to photograph the spectra of distant galaxies. They are so faint that they cannot be observed visually, even with the largest telescopes. The correct aim of the telescope must therefore be calculated from the nebula's position in a photograph. Then the telescope has to be kept directed at the object for hours on end in order to photograph its spectrum which, in the end, may only measure 2 mm. by 1 mm. The spectrum obtained is like that of an average star (spectral type G), viz. continuous, with absorption lines. But the absorption lines are very indistinct, forming as they do the average for all objects in the entire galaxy. By 1917 Slipher had managed to photograph the spectra of 15 spiral nebulae. He was surprised to find that the absorption lines in 13 of these spectra were displaced towards the red. This would suggest that the galaxies were moving away from us. From the shift observed it was possible to calculate that they were receding at 400 m.p.sec. (640 km/sec.), on the average. In 1929 Hubble discovered that all external galaxies whose spectra had been photographed and distances determined, are moving away from us at velocities proportional to their distances from us. This was once more very amply proved within the next few years by the observational material which Humason amassed using the Hooker and Hale telescopes.

Plate 83 shows some of these spectra. On the extreme left is the galaxy as it appears on the photographic plate. This is followed by its distance. On the right we have its spectrum greatly enlarged, a trace tapering at both ends. Above and below each spectrum, and photographed with it, is a comparison spectrum of a terrestrial light-source, against which the displacement of the spectral lines can be measured. Absorption lines H and K of calcium are the easiest to make out in these spectra. Their position for a stationary source is indicated at the top. A horizontal arrow shows the red shift of the H and K lines in each spectrum. It can be calculated from the amount of shift that the galaxy in Hydra is receding from us at one-fifth the speed of light! The conclusion, accepted nowadays almost without question, is that we are living in an expanding universe. The galaxies are like dots drawn on a balloon which is being blown up—they are moving away from each other. Plate 84 deals with some recent discoveries of strange events in distant island universes. Above: NGC5128 is really two galaxies colliding at a distance of 400 million light-years; it is a powerful source of radio radiation, like the two galaxies on the lower right which were first discovered as the 'Cygnus A radio source'. The jet of matter shooting from the galaxy at the bottom left (the elliptical M87 in the Virgo cluster), is emitting polarized light.

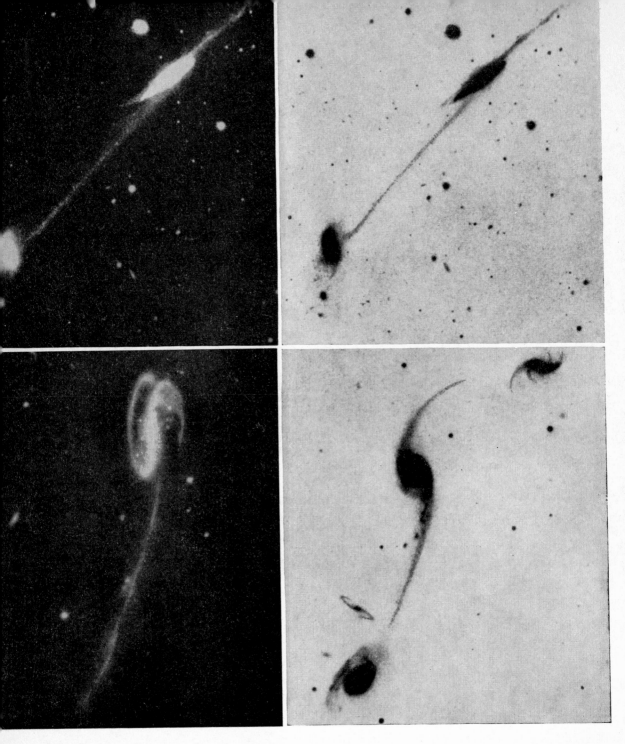

ENCOUNTERS BETWEEN GALAXIES. In 1845, after more than ten years of experimenting, in which neither money nor effort was spared, Lord Rosse finally succeeded in building a reflecting telescope with a bronze mirror ground to a parabolic shape and 6 ft. in diameter. For three quarters of a century this was the largest telescope in the world. With it Rosse discovered objects of a hitherto unknown kind—spiral nebulae. His instrument was the only one with which it was possible to make out details of spiral arms visually. The inset on Plate 86 shows the drawing he made of the remarkable double galaxy in Canes Venatici. The photograph was taken with the Hale telescope and gives an extremely detailed picture of the structure of this galaxy, which we see at a very favourable angle. It is 10-15 million light-years away and the red shift of the H and K lines of calcium indicates a velocity of recession of 300 m.p.sec. (480 km/sec.). Part of this (100 m.p.sec. or 160 km/sec.) is accounted for by the rotation of our own Galaxy. The large nebula is joined to the smaller by a spiral arm. Zwicky has now discovered several thousands of similar multiple galaxies on plates taken with the Mount Palomar Schmidt. On Plate 85 (lower right) can be seen a triple system discovered by Wild. Their fairly similar red shifts and the fact that their spirals point approximately at each other suggest that the three systems are physically associated.

These spiral arms were formed by the tidal effect of the galaxies on each other. Their distance from us is about 140 million light-years. Some even more distant galaxies are visible in the photograph. Plate 85 (top right and left) shows the same pair of galaxies twice, once as a positive and once as a negative, in which the details stand out more clearly. The two galaxies are joined by a bridge of astonishing length. The first spectra of these luminous bridges (which are very difficult to obtain) seem to show that they are mainly composed of stars. A remarkable thing about the top galaxy is that the 'counter-arm' is turned away from the lower galaxy. This is a clear indication that tidal effect is involved here. It has been suggested on occasion that all these multiple stellar systems and connecting arms were formed by systems, originally far from each other, which have come close to one another as a result of their own motion. That this should happen within a cluster of galaxies is very much more probable than that two stars in the neighbourhood of the Sun should come so close together by their own motion as to produce tidal effects on one another. Plate 85 (lower left) shows a spiral nebula with an unusually long arm. Perhaps another galaxy has passed this way. It must, nevertheless, have been very long ago, even by astronomical standards, for there is no longer any trace of the second galaxy.

87

A USELESS SCIENCE? High in the mountains of California, far from the disturbing lights of any city, lies the Palomar Observatory. On the left we can see the small dome of the 18-inch Schmidt telescope and in the middle the dome of the big 48-inch Schmidt. The most expensive stellar telescope in the world is installed in the dome on the right; it is the Hale telescope, a reflector with a 200-inch parabolic mirror (see Pl. 1). In 1928 the final decision was taken to build this instrument, which it was hoped would solve many of the riddles concerning the structure of the universe left by the powerful Hooker telescope on Mount Wilson. A suitable 20-ton disk of pyrex glass, which had taken eight months to cool, was ready for further processing in 1936. This disk took $11^1/_2$ years to grind to a mirror, a total of some 30 tons of abrasive being used up in the process. In December 1947, Anderson became the first to gaze at the heavens through it. To the anxious query as to whether he could see anything he made the laconic reply, 'Yes, a few little stars'. Many of the photographs in this atlas were taken with the Hale telescope (which came into general service in 1949), and much of our present knowledge of the universe is due to its use. Why do men spend so much effort and time and such vast sums of money on anything so seemingly futile as the exploration of the universe? The practical value of astronomy does not go much beyond the accurate determination of time and the fixing of positions on Earth.

Far less expensive instruments could do both these jobs more than adequately. As long ago as 1596 Kepler answered this question in words which need no further comment even in our day and age: ' "But tell me", they will say, "of what use is all your astronomy to a hungry belly?" The wise man does not even listen to the fool who loudly proclaims that its study must be abandoned. Men suffer painters because they gratify our eyes, musicians because they charm our ears, although they serve no other useful purpose. The pleasure that their works procure man not merely befits him but even does him honour. How injudicious, therefore, how foolish it is to wish to deprive the mind of a pleasure which belongs rightly to it, yet to grant that same pleasure to the eye and to the ear. He who grudges man that pleasure is at strife with nature! For the infinitely good God who created nature out of nothing has given every creature not only what is necessary but also beauty and joy in abundance. Would He deprive the human mind, the king of creation, His own image and likeness, of that great joy? We do not dream of asking what the bird hopes to gain by singing, for we know that singing is its very life, because it was created to sing. Likewise, we must not ask why the human mind devotes so much effort to penetrating the secrets of the starry sky.'

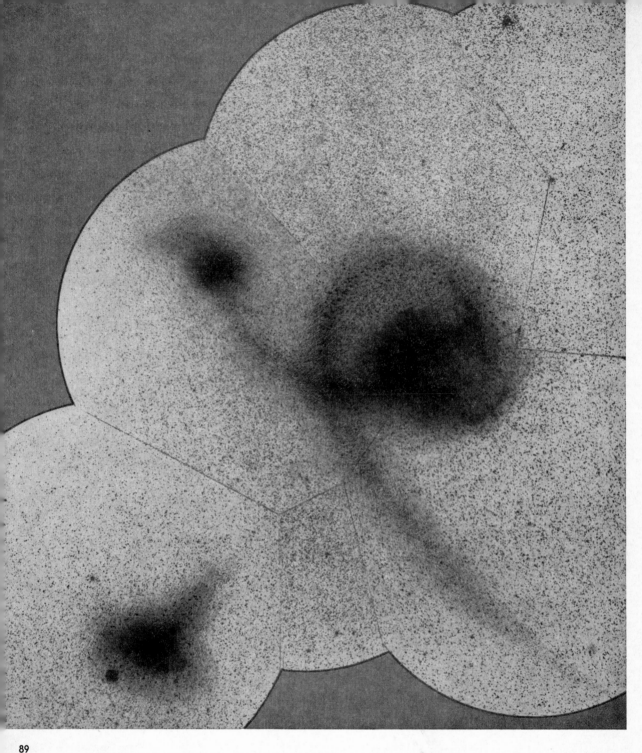

89

THE GALAXY, A MEMBER OF A TRIPLE SYSTEM. Zwicky's investigations revealed that multiple galaxies linked by bridges of matter are not uncommon. This sets us thinking about our own Galaxy and wondering whether perhaps it forms a triple system with the Large and Small Magellanic Clouds. Recent observations by G. de Vaucouleurs in Australia have in fact revealed tidal arms extending from the Large Cloud (which he believes is a one-armed barred spiral rather than an irregular galaxy). The arm most clearly visible in the above photograph is turned away from our Galaxy. Man lives in a strange cosmos and is scarcely aware of the vast universe about him. If we represent the part of it known in 1915 as a hazel-nut in size, the universe as it is known today would, on the same scale, be a sphere with a diameter of 100 miles. When we gaze out of more than four thousand million light-years into outer space we are also looking back more than four thousand million years into time! Every new item of information, every new certainty acquired raises new problems. Questions which only a short time ago lay in the realm of pure speculation, such as the size and shape of the universe or the origin and evolution of galaxies, now have general interest focussed on them. The results achieved by modern astronomy have exposed a new field for research that is considerably larger than that of half a century ago.

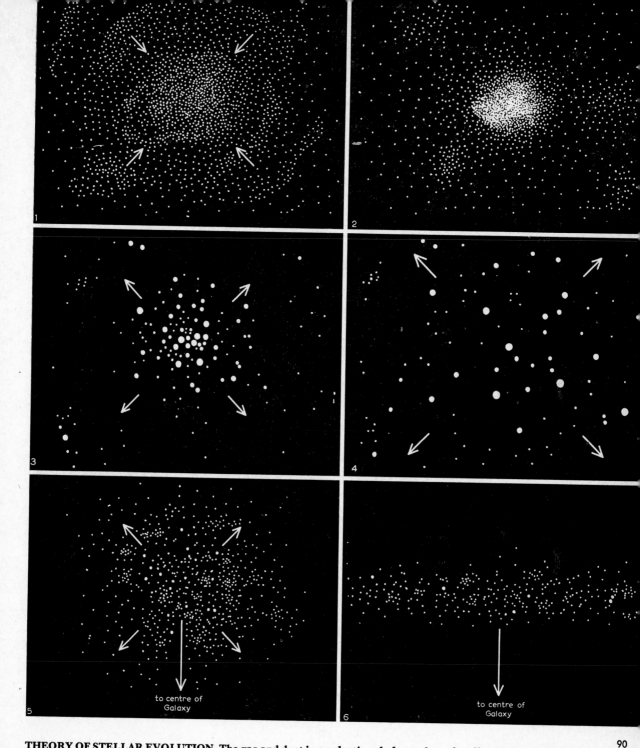

THEORY OF STELLAR EVOLUTION. The gas and dust in a galactic nebula condense locally to form clouds which attract more near-by matter by their own gravitation (Fig. 1). Further contraction results in very compact concentrations, or globules (diameter less than 1 light-year, Fig. 2 and Pl. 43). Condensation continues, increasing pressure causing the temperature of the mass of gas to rise until, eventually, such high temperatures are attained near the centre, that nuclear reactions begin. Once started, these will continue, and a star is created. It is probable that stars usually form in groups, such as the smaller trapezium system (Pl. 53) or the larger O associations, which are systems consisting of young O-type stars. Immediately after their formation these groups start to disperse (Figs. 3 and 4). Even the stars in the larger systems (diameter several hundred light-years) are receding from each other (Fig. 5). Component stars which lie at different distances from the centre of the galaxy will have different periods of revolution. Rotation of this galaxy will, therefore, in the course of some tens of millions of years, cause every stellar association to spread out in the direction of rotation and assume an oblong shape (Figs. 5 and 6). The fact that associations expand means that their lifetime as groups is relatively short; in a few million years they will have entirely disappeared among the other stars and the group will have become completely unrecognizable as such.

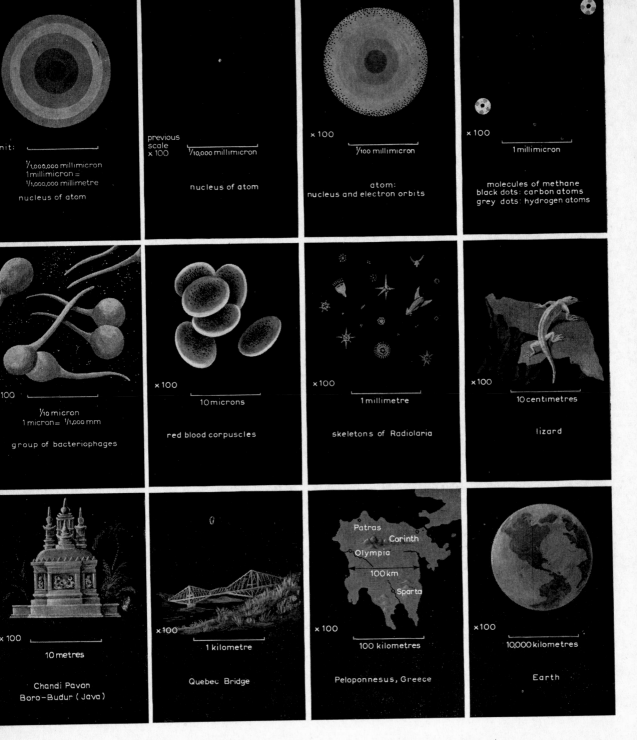

nit: $\frac{1}{1,000,000}$ millimicron
1 millimicron = $\frac{1}{1,000,000}$ millimetre

nucleus of atom

previous scale × 100 — $\frac{1}{10,000}$ millimicron

nucleus of atom

× 100 — $\frac{1}{100}$ millimicron

atom:
nucleus and electron orbits

× 100 — 1 millimicron

molecules of methane
black dots: carbon atoms
grey dots: hydrogen atoms

100 — $\frac{1}{10}$ micron
1 micron = $\frac{1}{1,000}$ mm

group of bacteriophages

× 100 — 10 microns

red blood corpuscles

× 100 — 1 millimetre

skeletons of Radiolaria

× 100 — 10 centimetres

lizard

× 100 — 10 metres

Chandi Pavon
Boro-Budur (Java)

× 100 — 1 kilometre

Quebec Bridge

Patras
Corinth
Olympia
100 km
Sparta

× 100 — 100 kilometres

Peloponnesus, Greece

× 100 — 10,000 kilometres

Earth

91

MICROCOSM AND MACROCOSM. A survey of the universe and the forms that matter assumes from objects of the smallest known dimensions, through distances that are most easily understood by man, to the greatest distance that has any meaning. In addition to matter, space also contains radiation (not shown in the Figures). In this 'chart' man stands nearer the limit of the microcosm, but the boundaries are drawn in accordance with the present state of knowledge. In the last 50 years the known universe has grown considerably: in 1900 the subjects of the first four Figures were things of which men had only a vague idea, and the series would have ended at the eighteenth Figure. A similar survey made then would have consisted of 15 stages instead of the 22 nowadays. Knowledge of the immense forces lurking in the atom has developed only in the last few decades. The structure of the Galaxy was first deduced by Shapley, between 1915 and 1920, when ideas about the external galaxies were also very vague. Man's immediate surroundings, from the animal kingdom to his abode in the universe, occupy only 6 drawings in all. If the usual views are correct, this fragment represented the entire known universe at the start of the Renaissance. Other celestial objects were naturally known, but they were thought to be in the vicinity of Earth. Ideas as to their true distances were extremely hazy. Even the survey above will undoubtedly have to be extended still farther at some

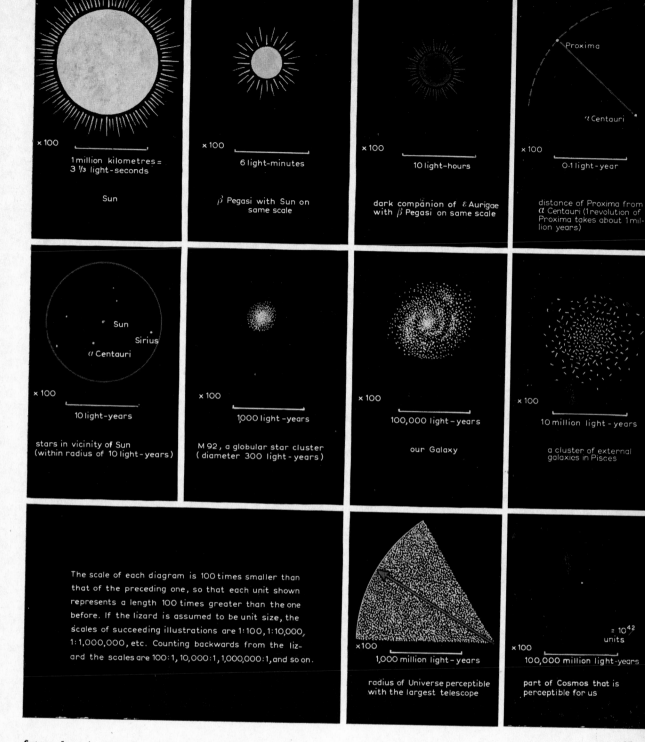

× 100

1 million kilometres =
3 ⅓ light-seconds

Sun

× 100

6 light-minutes

β Pegasi with Sun on
same scale

× 100

10 light-hours

dark companion of ε Aurigae
with β Pegasi on same scale

× 100

0.1 light-year

distance of Proxima from
α Centauri (1 revolution of
Proxima takes about 1 million years)

× 100

10 light-years

stars in vicinity of Sun
(within radius of 10 light-years)

× 100

1,000 light-years

M 92, a globular star cluster
(diameter 300 light-years)

× 100

100,000 light-years

our Galaxy

× 100

10 million light-years

a cluster of external
galaxies in Pisces

The scale of each diagram is 100 times smaller than
that of the preceding one, so that each unit shown
represents a length 100 times greater than the one
before. If the lizard is assumed to be unit size, the
scales of succeeding illustrations are 1:100, 1:10,000,
1:1,000,000, etc. Counting backwards from the lizard the scales are 100:1, 10,000:1, 1,000,000:1, and so on.

× 100

1,000 million light-years

radius of Universe perceptible
with the largest telescope

$= 10^{42}$
units

× 100

100,000 million light-years

part of Cosmos that is
perceptible for us

future date. As we proceed from the smallest to the largest, each form shown is succeeded by a new phenomenon, which in turn is reduced to comparative nothingness. In the last drawing, in fact, the entire perceptible universe has shrunk to a pinpoint and all that remains is a black rectangle, which merely means a
region entirely unknown to man. The question is, 'Can this represent space?' We do not know, for this
universe depends on the forms of the cosmos. If the universe extends to infinity in all directions, the black
rectangle is indeed space, and the survey might be pursued to infinity. Some theoreticians, however, favour
a finite universe, which would thus have a fixed, perhaps even 'measurable' volume. Space would then be
'curved' and unlimited in the same way that, for instance, the surface of a sphere is bounded and has no
limits. The idea that space is curved and finite was suggested by Einstein in 1917. One of its most powerful
advocates was the famous British astronomer, Sir Arthur Eddington. This kind of space, however, is a
mathematical abstraction and it is impossible to form a mental picture of it. If perceptible space does in
fact form a considerable part of this finite universe, some of the area of the black rectangle may not represent space at all; in that case the above survey very probably takes us close to the limit of the macrocosm,
although the possibility of other universes beyond our own still remains an open question.

92

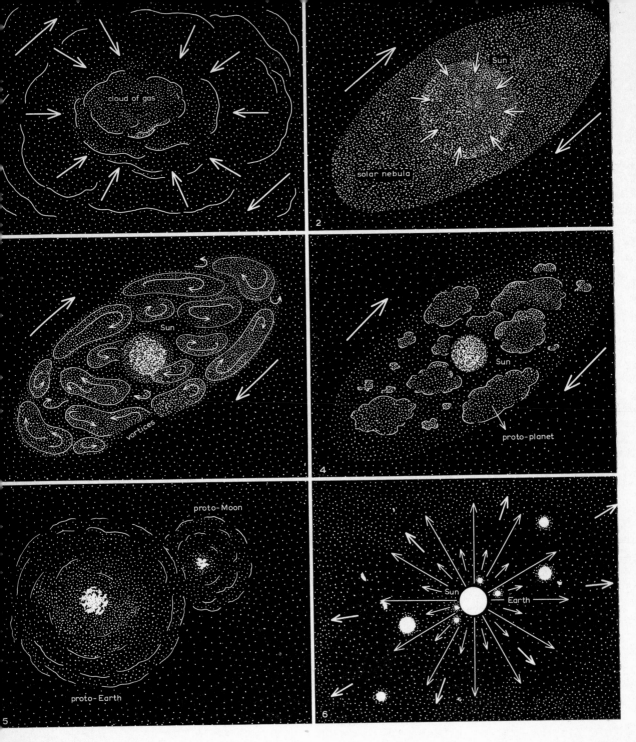

THE ORIGIN OF THE SOLAR SYSTEM. There are at present many different theories concerning the origin of the solar system. One of the most satisfactory is that of G. P. Kuiper (1949): the Sun was formed by the contraction of a rotating cloud of gas (Fig. 1), part of the original matter remaining behind in the form of a flat disk —the solar nebula (Fig. 2). The latter contained gaseous vortices of varying size which kept re-forming and disappearing (Fig. 3). The nebula broke up into clouds, the proto-planets, whose masses and dimensions depended upon local condensations of the nebular matter (Fig. 4). The bodies of the planets and satellites were formed round and near the centres of the proto-planets by condensation. The proto-Earth may possibly have divided into two, thereby giving rise to a double planet (Fig. 5). When the Sun started to radiate, the heat drove off a large part of the mass of the proto-planets, because the outer atmosphere attained extremely high temperatures. Part of the mass of the proto-planets was lost by evaporation and this matter has now disappeared. Kuiper assumes that it was ionized by solar radiation, the ions then being driven into interstellar space (Fig. 6). The proto-planets must therefore have been formed before the Sun started to radiate, i.e. when it was still in the state of a contracting gaseous nebula. The entire process may have taken roughly 10^8 or 10^9 years to complete.

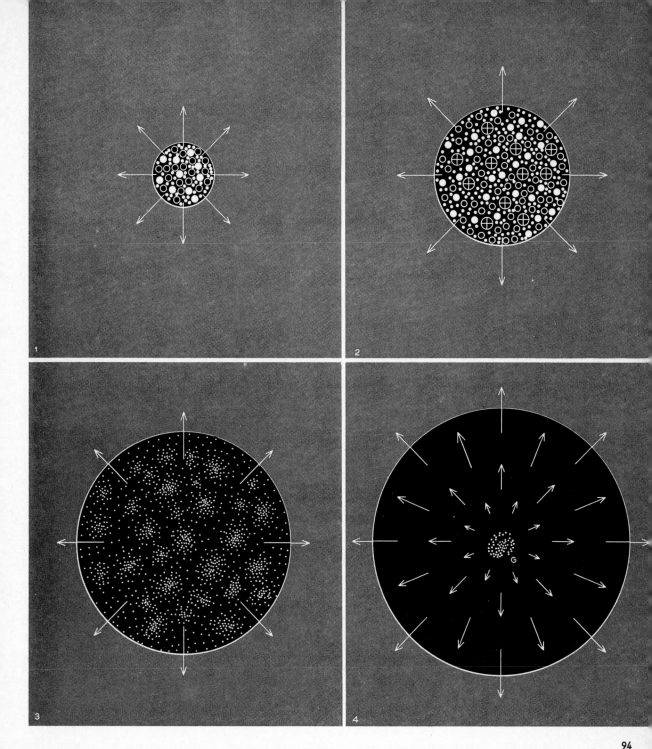

THE ORIGIN OF THE UNIVERSE. According to Lemaître all matter was originally combined in the 'prime-val atom' (diameter 100 million miles). Matter consisted of neutrons (open circles), protons (white circles) and electrons (white dots), packed extremely close together. More than 20,000 million years ago this gigantic atom exploded, hurling its contents into space. In Lemaître's view, the evolution of the universe may be likened to fireworks that have just gone off. 'We', he says, 'are on a cooled-down cinder, watching the suns slowly dying out and trying to recall the bygone magnificence of the origin of the world.' Fig. 1: a few minutes after the explosion, temperature several billion degrees. Fig. 2: one hour later, the universe is still ex-panding, temperature 1,000 million degrees. Particles are combining to form nuclei (circles with crosses). Fig. 3: 30 million years later. The temperature has dropped to a few thousand degrees, part of the gas has condensed into dust. Gravitation gives rise to chance accumulations. From these condensations are formed the clouds which are the origin of the subsequent galaxies. Those portions of the universe to which the ex-plosion imparted the greatest velocities relative to each other, are now the parts that are farthest from one another. Fig. 4: the expanding universe of today. The lengths of the arrows indicate the relative velocities of the receding galaxies.

The following symbols are used in the star charts:

✸ Brighter than magnitude 2   ✦ Magnitude 4 to 5

◐ Magnitude 2 to 3   • Magnitude 5 and fainter

◉ Magnitude 3 to 4   ⁘ All other objects (external galaxies, globular star clusters, gaseous nebulae and planetary nebulae).

The Milky Way is shown shaded on the star charts. For the symbols and Greek letters used in the charts, see the articles Constellations, Star atlas and Greek alphabet.

Cross-references are indicated by an asterisk (*) if the word concerned occurs in running text. Cross-reference to a head-word which does not so occur inside an article is indicated by an italic v (*v*). An arrow is used to refer readers to an illustration. When the reference is to an illustration occurring in the same article, this arrow is placed in brackets with the number of the figure, where applicable, e.g. (→ 1). If there is only one illustration, a reference in the form (→, 3) means: see part or item 3 of that illustration. The titles of subjects have been abbreviated within each article to the initial letter or letters.

The plates to which references are made are those in the front section of this volume.

Dec. : Declination

R.A. : Right Ascension

The compilers of this book tender their grateful thanks to Prof. M. G. J. Minnaert, Director of the Utrecht Observatory, for his co-operation and advice; to Dr C. de Jager, Astronomer of the Utrecht Observatory; to Mr J. Damen Sterk, Utrecht Observatory Librarian; to Dr G. I. Thompson, Senior Scientific Officer, Royal Observatory, Edinburgh; to Mr R. G. Lascelles, Special Assistant to the Department of Radio Astronomy in the University of Manchester; and to the many who placed photographs at their disposal—The Associated Press Ltd., London – Prof. D. P. Avigliano, Wheaton (Illinois) – Commonwealth Observatory, Mount Stromlo (Canberra) – Flower and Cook Observatories, Philadelphia – Griffith Observatory, Los Feliz Section, Los Angeles – Harvard College Observatory (Mass.) – Instituto e Museo di Storia della Scienza, Florence – S. Kesküla, Lund – Lick Observatory, Mount Hamilton (California) – Lowell Observatory, Flagstaff (Arizona) – K. Lundmark, Lund – *Manchester Evening News*, Manchester – W. A. McCalla, Pittsburgh (Penn.) – *Minneapolis Star*, Minneapolis – Mount Wilson and Mount Palomar Observatories, Pasadena (California) – Observatoire de Paris, Meudon – Observatoire du Pic-du-Midi, Bagnères-de-Bigorre – Observatory, Leiden – Osservatorio Astrofisico di Arcetri, Florence – Radcliffe Observatory, Pretoria – Royal Astronomical Society, London – Sonnenburgh Observatory, Leiden – Spijkerbosch Observatory, Olst (Netherlands) – *St Paul's Dispatch*, Minneapolis – United States Naval Observatory, Washington, D.C. – United States Navy, Washington, D.C. – Tj. E. de Vries, Oud-Zuilen (Netherlands) – Warner and Swasey Observatory, East Cleveland (Ohio) – Yerkes Observatory, Williams Bay (Wisconsin).

A or **Å,** abbreviation for Ångström*, the unit in which wavelengths of light are frequently expressed.

Aberration (Lat. *aberratio,* diversion). 1. The light from star S reaches the telescope at point P(→). It still has to cover the distance AB. While it is doing so, the Earth is displaced slightly to the right (viz. by its revolution round the Sun). The light reaches the eye not at a point vertically beneath P, but at point Q, slightly to the left. We see the star therefore in the direction QR, i.e. slightly displaced in the direction of the Earth's motion. In other words, we see it not in direction S but in direction S′. The angle α is called the aberration.

We distinguish daily, annual and secular *A.* Daily *A.* is caused by the Earth's rotation on its own axis and is very small, not exceeding 0·3″. Annual *A.* is due to the Earth's revolution round the Sun, and does not exceed 20·47″. Secular *A.* is caused by the motion of the solar system in the universe.

In determining the position of a celestial object, *A.* must be allowed for. *A.* was discovered by Bradley in 1728 when he was trying to find the parallax* of the nearest star. The velocity of light can be found from the *A.*

2. In optics* the term *A.* is applied to various lens defects whereby the image is blurred, e.g. chromatic *A.*,

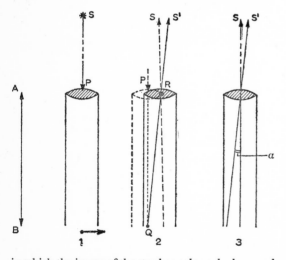

in which the image of the star has coloured edges, and spherical *A.,* in which the image of the star is not seen as a point.

Absolute magnitude, *v.* Star.

Absorption, the stopping and reduction of light by the matter it encounters on its path. The atmosphere of the Earth absorbs a part of the light from celestial objects. *A.* is more pronounced on the horizon than in the zenith. A star which is of the first magnitude in the

zenith has an apparent magnitude of 2 when 15° above the horizon. Red light is less subject to *A.* than is blue; celestial bodies on the horizon appear redder than they actually are.

Also very important in astronomy is the interstellar* *A.* caused by matter between the stars.

When light passes through a gas certain wavelengths may be absorbed from it, giving rise to absorption lines* in the spectrum* of the light.

Absorption lines in the spectrum* of a star are dark lines caused by the outer layers of the star which absorb or scatter light of particular wavelengths. The *A.l.* of the solar spectrum are called Fraunhofer lines* after their discoverer. They enable us, among other things, to identify the chemical composition of the outer layers of the stars (*v.* Pl. 32).

Achernar, the star α in the constellation of Eridanus and one of the brightest stars in the sky: apparent magnitude 0·6, distance 66 light-years, spectrum B5. Not visible in the northern hemisphere.

Achilles, a member of the Trojan group of asteroids*, which move round the Sun in the same orbit as Jupiter. *A.* was the first of the Trojans* to be discovered (1904).

Adonis, one of the asteroids* which pass very close to the Earth, was discovered in 1936. Only its occasional proximity to Earth enables it to be seen at all, for it is small, about a mile in diameter. In perihelion* its distance from the Sun is slightly greater than Mercury's average distance from the Sun.

Air Pump, *v.* Antlia.

Albedo of a planet, asteroid or satellite is the ratio of the light it reflects in all directions to the light it receives from the Sun. The *A.* thus represents the body's reflecting power. The sunlight not reflected is absorbed and heats the surface. The *A.* and comparison with known materials enable us to make deductions as to the materials composing the surface. For instance, Europa, one of the large moons of Jupiter, is as white as snow.

The *A.* is also used to estimate the size of small celestial objects. The diameters of the fainter asteroids, for instance, are found approximately from the *A.* and the observed luminosity. It is assumed that their *A.* is roughly the same as the average *A.* of the four brightest asteroids, whose diameters are known. Approximate albedos: Mercury 0·06, Venus 0·64, Earth 0·39, Moon 0·07, Mars 0·15, Jupiter 0·42, Saturn 0·45, Uranus 0·46, Neptune 0·53, Ceres 0·06, Pallas 0·07, Juno 0·12, Vesta 0·26; clouds 0·65–0·72; snow 0·70–0·78.

Albireo, the star β in the constellation of Cygnus, which slight magnification reveals as a double star*. Its components show a marked contrast in colour— yellow and blue. Apparent magnitudes 3·2 and 5·3.

Alcor, i.e. 'the little rider', or 'the weaker one', the star 80 Ursae Majoris, forms with Mizar (ε Ursae Majoris) a double star visible with the naked eye (distance apart 12′, i.e. at least ¼ light-year with both stars 72 light-years away).

Alcyone, η Tauri, the brightest star in the Pleiades, the galactic cluster* in the constellation of Taurus. Apparent magnitude 3·0, spectrum B5.

Aldebaran, α Tauri, visually one of the brightest stars in the sky. Apparent magnitude 1·06, distance 57 light-years, spectrum K5. Further data: temperature 3,400°C., diameter 43 × Sun's, luminosity 105 × Sun's, mass 4 × Sun's, density 0·00005 × Sun's. *A.* is a red giant*.

Algol, β Persei, the prototype of the Algol-type variables. The name means demon star and was bestowed many centuries ago by the Arabs, to whom its variable luminosity was familiar. Its variability was rediscovered in 1782 by Goodricke, who supposed that it consisted of two stars very close to each other and following the same orbit round a common centre, and that the plane of this orbit was edgewise to the Earth, so that the stars appeared to occult each other. This hypothesis proved correct. The combined stars appear as one which is variable in its luminosity: when the brighter star is eclipsed by the fainter, we see a sharp drop in the luminosity of the system; when the fainter star is occulted by the brighter, we observe only a slight decrease in luminosity (*v.* Double stars). *A.*'s period is 69 hours, its variation in magnitude from 2·2 to 3·5, its spectrum B8. *A.* has a surface temperature of 15,000°C., its companion only 5,800°C. The system also includes a third star, which orbits round the system once every 23 months. At present some 200 similar systems are known.

Algol-type variables, *v.* Algol, Double stars.

Alidade, *v.* Astrolabe.

Almagest (Arabic: *al-Magisti,* the greatest, i.e. the greatest treatise on astronomy) is a primer of astronomy written in the second century A.D. by the Alexandrian astronomer, Ptolemy. It describes the motion of celestial objects on the assumption that the Earth is at rest (the Ptolemaic system*). The *A.* is also the earliest magnitude catalogue known and lists the magnitudes of 1,025 stars. It was not known in Europe until A.D. 867. The first Latin translation dates from 1175.

Almanac, a summary of astronomical data for the current year. The almanacs most familiar to us are the *American Ephemeris and Nautical Almanac* (Washington), the *Astronomical Ephemeris* (London), the *Connaissance des Temps* (Paris), the *Astronomisch-Geodätisches Jahrbuch* (Heidelberg), the *Astronomical Ephemeris* of the Soviet Union. The work involved is allocated to various institutes on an international basis.

The *Astronomical Ephemeris* includes: the predicted positions of the Sun, Moon, planets and some of the main asteroids at daily intervals; the apparent diameters of these bodies; the Moon's position in right ascension and declination at hourly intervals; the daily distances of planets and asteroids from the Earth; the positions of the most important stars for the current year; solar and lunar eclipses; the daily position of the terminator* on the Moon; the central meridian at daily intervals in connection with the rotation of the Sun, Mars and Jupiter; data on the satellites of Mars, Jupiter, Saturn, Uranus and Neptune; conjunctions* and oppositions*; times of rising and setting of the Sun and Moon, and tables of all kinds as aids to astronomical calculations.

Since 1960, the *American Ephemeris and Nautical Almanac* and the *Astronomical Ephemeris* have been completely identical in content.

Alphard, the Arabic name for the star α Hydrae. Apparent magnitude 2·2, spectrum K2.

Alphecca, the Arabic name for the star α Coronae Borealis. Apparent magnitude 2·3, spectrum Ao. Also known as Gemma.

Altair, the Arabic name for the star α Aquilae, which, because of its relatively short distance from the Sun, is one of the brightest stars in the sky. Apparent magnitude 0·89, absolute magnitude 2·4, distance 16 light-years, luminosity 9 × Sun's, spectrum A5. *A.* is one of the 40 or so stars within 5 parsecs of the Sun and, like Sirius and Procyon, considered to be in our 'immediate vicinity' (*v.* Pl. 35).

Altar, *v.* Ara.

Alt-azimuth mounting, a method of mounting a telescope so that it can be rotated about both a vertical axis and a horizontal axis. A theodolite is so mounted (*v.* Telescope).

Altitude, one of the co-ordinates in the system based on the horizon and the vertical circle (*v.* Celestial sphere). *A.* is the angular distance of an object above the horizontal.

Amor, one of the smaller asteroids*, occasionally comes close to the Earth. Discovered in 1932, shortest distance from the Earth 10,000,000 miles.

Andromeda, a constellation in the northern hemisphere, named after the daughter of the Ethiopian king Cepheus*, and Cassiopeia*. To preserve her country from disaster, Andromeda was tied to a rock as a sacrifice to a sea monster. Perseus slew the monster

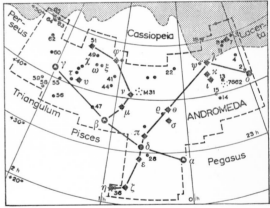

The constellation of Andromeda

and freed her. *A.* went with him to Tiryns in the Peloponnesus and after her death was accorded a place in the heavens. The constellation lies between 22 h. 55 min. and 2 h. 35 min. R.A., and between 21° and 53° N. Dec. (→)

Andromeda nebula (M31) (*v.* Pl. 66), an external galaxy* of spiral structure near star ν in Andromeda. This 'nebula' was described as long ago as the ninth century by a Persian astronomer and rediscovered by Simon Marius in 1612, after the invention of the telescope. This system is similar in form to our Galaxy, but considerably larger. Its distance, according to latest research, is 2·2 million light-years (1956), its diameter about 200,000 light-years. Its mass is $3·3 × 10^{11}$ times that of the Sun, or about 65% more than the mass of our Galaxy. The plane of its spiral arm lies at an angle of about 15° in space to the line of sight from Earth (→). Its structure is like that of the

Galaxy; we find luminous nebulae and dust clouds in its spiral arms. Stars of Population type* I which, with the dust clouds, form the spirals, produce 90 % of the system's light but comprise only 20 % of its mass. Even on photographs made with the Hale telescope* only the giant stars can be resolved. The system's light comes mainly from stars which are smaller than our own Sun, and which cannot be seen individually because of their great distance. By comparing photographs it is possible to identify variable stars, including Cepheid variables*. A large number of globular star clusters* belonging to this galaxy can also be seen. The distance is found by measuring the apparent luminosity of the various known objects (v. Distance finding).

The spiral arms of M31 begin some 3,000 light-years from the centre. The central portion is very transparent, indicating that there is no dust there.

A large number of novae have been discovered photographically in M31, and the number of nova explosions in the galaxy as a whole has been estimated at 26 per year. The novae seem to occur mainly in the vicinity of the central region. The Andromeda galaxy appears to be approaching us due to the effect of the rotation of our Galaxy (so that the Sun is at present moving towards M31). M31 has two satellite systems (v. Pl. 66, 67), both examples of elliptical galaxies: NGC221 (or M32) and NGC205. Recently NGC205 has also been resolved photographically into stars. When parts of M31 and NGC205 were compared on photographs, the individual visible stars counted and the surface brightness of these parts measured photoelectrically, it was found that the stars forming NGC205 are similar in type to those forming the globular star clusters in the Galaxy (Population type II), while the spiral arms of M31 contain stars similar in type to those in the vicinity of the Sun in our Galaxy (Population type I). The elliptical galaxy therefore seems to consist at least partly of a different kind of star from those of the spiral arms of M31.

The galaxy M31 may be described as follows. The relatively small central region is an ellipsoid with its major axis in the same direction as the main axis of the galaxy. The spiral structure is observable even in the central region. The first spiral emerges from the latter and divides into two after one circuit. Confused clouds of gas and dust give the start of the innermost spiral arm a complicated appearance. The first stars, blue supergiants, as well as luminous hydrogen clouds, are visible in the second spiral arm, 3 kiloparsecs from the central portion. The third arm consists mainly of dust and supergiants. The fourth comprises giants and supergiants and some luminous hydrogen clouds in, or on the edge of, dark clouds. Most of the gas and dust here has already condensed into stars. Arms 6 and 7 (1·5° and 2° from the central region) are tenuous, for many distant external galaxies can be seen behind them. They therefore contain little dust but consist of numerous blue and red supergiants and variable stars, including Cepheids. Still further from the centre can be seen remains of former

spiral arms. These include a group of B-stars 29 kiloparsecs from the central region.

Ångström, the unit in which wavelengths of light are normally expressed. $1 \text{ Å} = \frac{1}{100,000,000}$ cm (or 10^{-8} cm). The wavelength of red light is about 6,500 Å, that o violet light about 4,000 Å.

Annular eclipse, v. Solar eclipse.

Anomalistic period, v. Period.

Ansae are the extremities of Saturn's rings when they project like handles from the planet.

Antapex of the Sun's motion (→ Apex).

Antares, the star α Scorpii, appears one of the brightest stars in the southern sky and is a visual binary or double*. The main star is red, the companion green, (apparent magnitudes 1·2 and 6·8). The companion is difficult to detect in the bright light of the main star. Antares was so named by the Greeks because its predominantly red colour made it resemble Mars (called Ares by the Greeks). The main star is a supergiant* (spectral-type M1) with a diameter of 300 solar diameters and a variable with a period of several hundred days. Absolute magnitude —3·2, temperature 3,100°C., luminosity 1,660 × Sun's, mass 15 × Sun's, density 0·0000004 × Sun's.

Antlia (the Air Pump), an inconspicuous constellation in the southern hemisphere, between 9 h. 25 min. and 11 h. 5 min. R.A., and —24° and —40° Dec. (→)

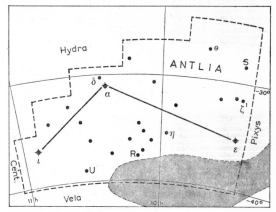

The constellation of Antlia

Apastron, the point on the orbit of the fainter component of a double star at which this component is farthest from the main star.

Aperture of a telescope is the clear diameter of the objective. The resolving power* depends on the size of the A.

Apex of the Sun's motion is the point on the celestial sphere towards which the Sun, in its motion relative to the neighbouring stars and interstellar matter, appears to be heading. This motion is due to the fact that the stars, including the Sun, are moving round the centre of the Galaxy at different velocities. These orbits are so vast that they are practically straight lines. The Sun is moving at a rate of 12 m.p.sec. in relation to the other stars. Seen in perspective, it appears as if the stars are moving radially over the celestial sphere in all directions from the A. as centre. The A. lies in the constellation of Hercules and near Lyra, at right ascension 18 h. and declination 30° N. The antapex is the point on the celestial sphere diametrically opposite the A. (→).

line of sight from Earth

Plane of spiral arms

15°

section through spiral arms

M31

Position of M31 in space in relation to Earth

Aphelion, the point on the elliptical orbit of a planet, asteroid or comet, at which the body is at its greatest possible distance from the Sun.

Apogee, the point on the Moon's orbit where the Moon is farthest from the Earth. *A.* is also used with reference to artificial satellites.

Apollo, a small asteroid* discovered in 1932. Its perihelion* lies within the orbit of Venus, and the

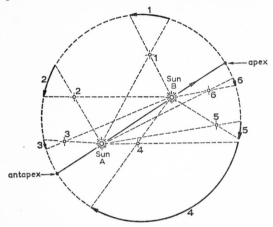

The motion of the Sun from A to B, i.e. in the direction of the apex, makes the surrounding stars, as seen from the Sun (or Earth), appear to move away from the apex. The Sun's displacement from A to B corresponds here to the apparent movements of stars 1–6 as indicated by black arrows

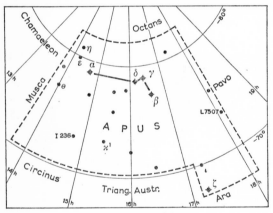

The constellation of Apus

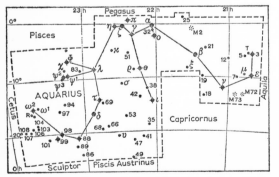

The constellation of Aquarius

asteroid on occasion comes within 3,100,000 miles of the Earth. *A.*'s diameter is not more than about a mile.

Apparent magnitude, *v.* Star.

Apus (the Bird of Paradise), a southern constellation situated between 13 h. 45 min. and 18 h. 10 min. R.A. and between —68° and —82° Dec. (→)

Aquarius (the Water-bearer), is one of the zodiacal* constellations and is therefore astride the ecliptic*. It is situated between R.A. 20 h. 35 min. and 23 h. 55 min. and between Dec. 3°N. and 25°S. (→)

Aquila (the Eagle), a constellation in the Milky Way, which is cut into two in this region by dark interstellar clouds. It lies between 18 h. 40 min. and 20 h. 35 min. R.A. and + 18° and —12° Dec. *A.* is easily found in summer in the southern sky with the aid of the

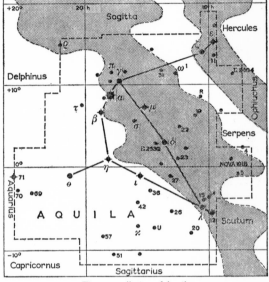

The constellation of Aquila

bright star Altair*. It is an interesting region which, if viewed even through small opera-glasses, can be seen to be teeming with stars. (→)

Ara (the Altar), a constellation situated in the southern hemisphere between R.A. 16 h. 30 min. and 18 h. 10 min., and Dec. —45° and —67°.

Archer, *v.* Sagittarius.

Arcturus, the star α Boötis, a red giant*. Spectrum Ko, apparent magnitude 0·24, distance 41 light-years, temperature 4,200°K., diameter 24 × Sun's, absolute magnitude — 0·1, luminosity 96 × Sun's, mass 4 × Sun's, density 0·0003 × Sun's.

Argo, old name for Puppis*, Vela* and Carina*.

Ariel, one of the moons of Uranus, discovered by Lassell in 1851. Average distance from planet 120,000 miles, period 2 d. 12 h. 29 min., diameter 300 miles (?), magnitude at opposition* 15·2.

Aries (the Ram), a northern zodiacal* constellation, situated between 1 h. 45 min. and 3 h. 25 min. R.A. and between 10° and 31° N. Dec. (→facing)

Arizona Crater, a crater made by a meteorite in Arizona (*v.* Meteorites and Pl. 25, 26).

Arrow, *v.* Sagitta.

Artificial satellite (*v.* Pl. 6), a manned or unmanned projectile which moves for some considerable time in an orbit around the Earth (*v.* also Space travel). To fire a satellite into a particular orbit round the Earth a certain velocity is necessary. If the velocity is too low, the satellite falls back to the Earth's surface. A velocity of about 5 m.p.sec. (8 km/sec.) produces a circular orbit which returns to the point of departure. If the velocity is increased, the satellite will describe an ellipse, on which the point of greatest elevation is diametrically opposite the point of departure, and will return to the point of departure. If the satellite is given a slight extra impulse at the highest point of its orbit, it will pass over its starting point, and so continue to make circuits of the Earth.

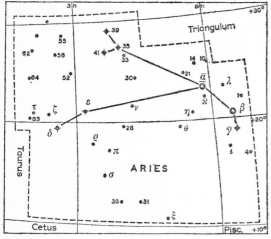

The constellation of Aries

The orbit of an *A.s.* at any moment approximates to an ellipse with the centre of the Earth at one focus. If there were no air resistance, the movement in an orbit would continue indefinitely. However, even at heights of 100 miles and upwards, there is enough atmospheric friction to slow up the *A.s.* The immediate effect of this is to cause the height of the apogee* to decrease. The height of perigee* also decreases, but by a smaller amount. The consequence is that the *A.s.* spirals down, the orbit becoming progressively more circular and lower until the *A.s.* suddenly enters much denser atmosphere and burns up or breaks up.

The following table shows the relevant orbital data for Sputnik 2 (1957 β).

VARIATIONS OF ORBITAL ELEMENTS
OF SPUTNIK 2 (1957 β)

Date	Period (minutes)	Eccentricity	Perigee height (miles)	Apogee height (miles)
1957 Nov. 4	103·8	0·099	139	1,040
1958 Jan. 4	100·5	0·080	136	850
1958 Feb. 21	97·1	0·060	130	655
1958 Mar. 25	93·8	0·040	122	463
1958 Apr. 9	90·8	0·021	109	293

We see that during the first two months of its life, the height of the apogee decreased by 190 miles, while the height of the perigee decreased by only 3 miles. These variations became faster as the date of disintegration approached. In the case of Vanguard 1 (1958 β2), which was launched on 17 March 1958 and had a height of perigee of 405 miles, the variation of its period is imperceptible. After one year of life, its eccentricity had changed from 0·191 to 0·190, its period from 134·2 to 133·9 minutes and its height at apogee from 2,460 to 2,446 miles. The lifetime of this *A.s.* is estimated at about one century.

The flattening of the Earth produces a rotation of the plane of the orbit round the Earth's axis (→ 1). In the case of Sputnik 2, the speed of this precession of the orbital plane was 2° 38' a day at the beginning of its life (3 Nov. 1957); the nearer the satellite approached the Earth, the more the rotation of the plane speeded up; it reached 2° 48' on 31 Dec. 1957 and 3° 09' on 10 March 1958.

Theoretically, the inclination α of the orbit to the terrestial equator remains constant during this precession. However, in practice, a very slow diminution of the angle is observable. For Sputnik 2, $\alpha = 65°$ 20' on 3 Nov. 1957; 65° 15' on 3 March 1958; 65° 12' on 10 April 1958. This diminution, of one thousandth of a degree each day, is probably due to the rotation of the Earth's atmosphere.

The precession of the orbital plane must not be confused with the apparent rapid movement of the trajectory towards the west, which is due to the rotation of the Earth. After one revolution, the *A.s.* reappears at a more westerly position than on its previous round, because while making the orbit, the Earth has rotated through an appreciable angle.

Another change is to be seen in the orientation of the ellipse in the orbital plane. It has been shown that this speed of rotation of the major axis depends on the orbital inclination, being zero when $5 \cos^2\alpha = 1$, i.e. when $\alpha = 63°$ 26'. It is in the same sense as the movement of the satellite if $\alpha < 63°$ 26' (Explorer) and in the opposite sense for the larger angles (Sputnik). The orbital inclination of the first three Russian *A.s.s* was about 65°, little different from 63° 26'. Consequently, the rotation of the major axis was slow and difficult to measure (about 0·4° a day).

A satellite can only be observed when it is still lit up by the Sun's rays (*v.* Pl. 6) and when the observer's sky is dark. So an *A.s.* near the Earth is only observable for two or three hours after sunset or before sunrise.

The satellite is designated by the year of its launching followed by the Greek letter corresponding to the order of launching; finally, a suffix distinguishes its particular components, the brightest having the first numbers; e.g. Sputnik 3, the fourth satellite of 1958, is 1958 δ 2; its rocket, being brighter, is 1958 δ 1.

NOTES ON CERTAIN ARTIFICIAL SATELLITES. *The First Earth Satellite*, Sputnik 1, was launched on 4 Oct. 1957 by the U.S.S.R. The final stage, the rocket, became a satellite along with the sphere (diameter 23 inches, weight 184 lb.). All the naked-eye observations were made of the rocket, a cylinder several yards long. The nose cone also became a satellite. The sphere was provided with 4 antennae; 2 radio transmitters sent out signals on 15 metres and 7·5 metres wavelength respectively. The initial period of Sputnik 1 was 96·2 minutes; its height above the Earth varied between 140 and 500 miles (→ 2). The rocket descended on 1 Dec. 1957, having made 879 revolutions in 58 days: Sputnik 1 descended after 1,400 revolutions, about 4 Jan. 1958. This satellite travelled 44 million miles round the Earth, equivalent to the distance between the orbits of the Earth and Mars.

The Second A.s., Sputnik 2, was likewise launched by the U.S.S.R. one month after the first. The satellite was not separated from its rocket. Sputnik 2 contained

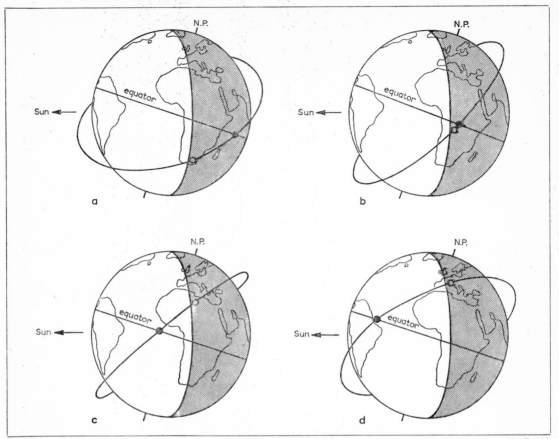

Fig. 1. Diagram showing how the orbit of an artificial satellite rotates. The black circles show where the orbit intersects the Earth's equator in four successive weeks (a–d). This point of intersection moves from east to west. The diagram is based on a daily displacement of 4¾° (Sputnik I). At the same time the point where the satellite is visible (white circle close to Earth's terminator) is moving to the north

detectors of cosmic rays, photo-electric cells for measuring solar X-rays and ultra-violet radiation, radio transmitters and instruments for measuring temperature. It also contained an hermetically sealed cabin containing a living dog (Laika), with apparatus for registering biological phenomena. Sputnik 2 ended its career on 14 April 1958, having made 2,368 revolutions in 162 days; in all, its total path was 75 million miles. The entry into the atmosphere took place over the Caribbean. Many watchers on land and at sea followed the dazzling meteor.

The First American Satellite was launched on 1 Feb. 1958. 'Explorer 1' was cylindrical: length 80 inches, diameter 6 inches, weight 31 lb. This satellite contained instruments for measuring temperature and cosmic rays as well as two radio transmitters. The inclination of the orbit to the Earth's equator was only 33° (*cf.* 65° for the Sputniks). Explorer 1 was not visible in Europe. Because of the greater height of its perigee (220 miles against 140 miles for the Sputniks), its life will be several years, the fall being expected in 1962. The satellite was launched by the American Army, using a Jupiter C four-stage rocket. On 4 Feb. 1958, the internal temperature of Explorer 1 varied between + 100° C and + 30° C.

Vanguard 1 (1958β) is the lightest of all the *A.s.s.* Launched on 17 March, 1958, it has a very high orbit (perigee 405 miles). So its lifetime must be of the order of 100 years, as we have already mentioned. Vanguard 1 possesses solar batteries; the only data transmitted are those of temperature.

The Third Soviet Satellite, Sputnik 3, was launched on 15 May 1958, weight 2,926 lb., (of which 2,140 lbs. were instruments) base diameter 68 inches, length 12 feet. The detached rocket was also a satellite, 1958 δ1. This rocket fell on 3 Dec. 1958, having made 2,908 revolutions in 202 days; it covered nearly the distance from the Earth to the Sun. Sputnik 3 itself (1958 δ2) fell on 6 April 1960, having travelled 280 million miles. The rocket descended first because its larger surface meant that there was greater atmospheric resistance. The rocket was easily visible to the naked eye, often attaining magnitude 1. It varied in brightness about every 9 seconds, due to the rotation of the cylinder. Sputnik 3 was provided with instruments to measure the Earth's magnetic field, solar radiation, cosmic rays and the impact of micrometeorites as well as exterior and interior temperatures.

Atlas (1958ζ) was the biggest satellite launched by the U.S.A.: weight 8,700 lb., diameter 10 feet, length 80 feet.

The American 'Discoverer' Satellites are 'polar' satellites, the inclination of their orbits to the equator being about 90°. The essential purpose of the Discoverers is to eject a 200 lb. capsule, situated in the nose cone and destined to be intercepted in the air or recovered from the sea. So far, three such capsules have been recovered.

Explorer 6 *(1959 δ)* is named 'Paddlewheel'. Four vanes carry, on each face, cells which transform the Sun's light into electric energy. Altogether, the satellite has 8,000 cells. Each cell, fully illuminated, produces 7 milliwatts; this energy is stored up in batteries. The height of Explorer 6 varies between a minimum of 156 miles and a maximum of 26,000 miles.

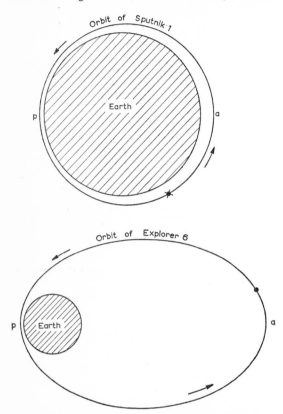

Fig. 2. First orbits of satellites Sputnik 1 (above) and Explorer 6 (below); p = perigee, a = apogee. The height of Sputnik 1 above the surface of the Earth varied between 140 and 590 miles in one revolution. Explorer 6 reached a distance of about 26,000 miles from the Earth. The lower drawing is on a scale three times smaller than that of the upper one

The elements of its orbit are unusual; with the exception of *Lunik* 3 *(1959θ)*, which was really a lunar rocket, Explorer 6 has the most eccentric orbit (0·76), the greatest distance of apogee (¹/₉ of the distance between Earth and Moon) and the longest period of revolution (12 hrs. 54 min.) (→ 2). There is a great variation of speed over its orbit: 6·4 m.p. sec. at perigee and 0·9 m.p. sec. at apogee. Because of its elongated orbit, Explorer 6 can study in detail the Van Allen radiation belts, which it traverses twice in one revolution.

Lunik 3 *(1959θ)* was a lunar rocket. It photographed the 'invisible' side of the Moon (*v.* Space travel). This rocket then became an *A.s.* of the Earth. Its orbit had the greatest height of perigee (greater than the distance Earth–Moon), the greatest eccentricity (0·82) and the greatest period of revolution (15·5 days) of all the *A.s.s.* Such an orbit is not

stable; it is subject to significant perturbations, due to the attraction of the Moon and the Sun. On 26 Oct., the signals from Lunik 3 ceased to be heard, perhaps after the impact of some meteorite. Calculations indicated that the distance of perigee grew rapidly less, and the satellite entered the Earth's atmosphere at the beginning of April 1960.

Tiros 1 *(1960 β₂)*, launched on 1 April 1960, moves in an almost circular orbit at a height of 450 miles. It is a meteorological satellite containing two television cameras, one wide angle and one narrow angle, expressly to collect photographs of the pattern of the clouds on the Earth's surface. The satellite receives orders as it passes over a ground station. Later, it observes and tape records a series of pictures, transmitting them to the ground the next time it passes over a receiving station.

Sputnik 4 (1960 ε) launched exactly two years after Sputnik 3, was intended to be an immediate forerunner of a manned space flight. Not taking into account the last stage of the carrier rocket, Sputnik 4 was the heaviest *A.s.*, to date. The weight of its scientific instruments, including its sources of energy, (chemical and solar batteries) was about two tons.

Echo 1 *(1960 ι)* was launched on 12 August 1960. It is a large spherical balloon 100 feet in diameter, coated with a highly reflecting layer of aluminium and consequently is easily visible. It carries two radio transmitters. The orbit lies between heights of 800 and 900 miles. Its main purposes are to study long distance radio communications by serving as a reflector of radio waves and also to study the air resistance at great heights. Its large size and relatively light weight make it an ideal object for this latter purpose.

Sputnik 5 *(1960 λ)*, launched on 19 August 1960, carried two live dogs. After 18 revolutions round the Earth, at a command from the ground, the capsule containing the dogs was ejected and safely landed in a chosen region.

What we have learned from A.s.s. a. The study of the rotation (precession) of the plane of orbit of several *A.s.s* has allowed the effect of the flattening of the Earth to be determined. The speed of precession has suggested slightly less flattening (1/298) than has hitherto been accepted (1/297).

b. The effect of air-resistance permits the density of air to be determined. Between 110 and 450 miles, the density of the Earth's atmosphere is at least 10 times greater than was believed. The table gives collected data.

MEAN DENSITY OF THE UPPER ATMOSPHERE

Height		Density	Density
Kms.	Miles	g/cc	(Sea Level = 1)
200	125	$3·9 \times 10^{-13}$	$3·2 \times 10^{-10}$
300	187	$3·7 \times 10^{-14}$	$3·0 \times 10^{-11}$
400	250	$8·8 \times 10^{-15}$	$7·2 \times 10^{-12}$
500	312	$2·6 \times 10^{-15}$	$2·1 \times 10^{-12}$
600	374	$8·7 \times 10^{-16}$	$7·1 \times 10^{-13}$
700	436	$3·1 \times 10^{-16}$	$2·5 \times 10^{-13}$

It appears that the density at high altitudes is not constant, the variations increasing with altitude. These variations very probably are related to solar activity. At the same time, the flattening of the Earth must be taken into account, for it reduces the effective altitude of perigee of a satellite when it traverses the equatorial belt.

c. The *A.s.s* and the lunar rockets (*v.* Space travel)

Date of launching	Name	Observations
1957		
4 Oct.	Sputnik 1, 1957 α 2	burned out 4 Jan., 1958 rocket 1957 α 1, burned out 1 Dec., 1957
3 Nov.	Sputnik 2, 1957 β	burned out 14 Apr., 1958
1958		
1 Feb.	Explorer 1, 1958 α	in orbit, radio transmission ended 23 May, 1958
17 Mar.	Vanguard 1, 1958 β 2	in orbit; rocket 1958 β 1 also in orbit
26 Mar.	Explorer 3, 1958 γ	burned out 28 June 1958
15 May	Sputnik 3, 1958 δ 2	burned out 6 Apr., 1960; rocket 1958 δ 1 crashed 3 Dec., 1958
26 July	Explorer 4, 1958 ξ	burned out 23 Oct., 1959
11 Oct.	Pioneer 1	reached point 70,600 miles from Earth and returned to Earth
6 Dec.	Pioneer 3	reached point 63,000 miles from Earth
18 Dec.	Atlas-Score, 1958 ζ	burned out 21 Jan., 1959
1959		
2 Jan.	Mekhta, artificial planet 1	in orbit round the Sun, period 443 days
17 Feb.	Vanguard 2, 1959 α 1	in orbit; rocket 1959 α 2 also in orbit
3 Mar.	Pioneer 4, artificial planet 2	in orbit round the Sun, period 407 days; rocket also in orbit
13 Apr.	Discoverer 2 1959 γ	burned out 26 Apr., 1959
7 Aug.	Explorer 6, 1959 δ 2 ('Paddlewheel')	in orbit, radio contact ended 8 Oct., 1959; rocket 1959 δ 1 also in orbit
13 Aug.	Discoverer 5, 1959 ε	burned out 28 Sept., 1959
19 Aug.	Discoverer 6, 1959 ζ	burned out 20 Oct., 1959
12 Sept.	Lunik 2	hit Moon 13 Sept., 1959; rocket also on Moon
18 Sept.	Vanguard 3, 1959 η	in orbit
4 Oct.	Lunik 3, 1959 θ 1	in orbit round Earth and Moon; rocket 1959 θ 2 also in orbit
13 Oct.	Explorer 7, 1959 ι 1	in orbit; rocket 1959 ι 2 also in orbit
7 Nov.	Discoverer 7, 1959 ϰ	burned out 26 Nov., 1959
20 Nov.	Discoverer 8, 1959 λ	burned out 8 Mar., 1960
1960		
11 Mar.	Pioneer 5, artificial planet 3, 1960 α	in orbit round Sun, period 311 days
1 Apr.	Tiros 1, 1960 β 2	weather satellite; rocket 1960 β 1 also in orbit
13 Apr.	Transit 1B, 1960 γ 2	navigation satellite; rocket (1960 γ 1) and a component (1960 γ 3) also in orbit
15 Apr.	Discoverer 11, 1960 δ	burned out 26 Apr., 1960
15 May	Sputnik 4, 1960 ε	artificial satellite and cabin (1960 ε 1 and ε 3), both in orbit
24 May	Midas 2, 1960 ζ 1	in orbit
22 June	Transit 2A, 1960 η 1 Greb, 1960 η 2	both in orbit; launched by same rocket which is also in orbit
10 Aug.	Discoverer 13, 1960 θ	in orbit
12 Aug.	Echo 1, 1960 ι	in orbit, together with rocket
19 Aug.	Sputnik 5 1960 λ	landed safely 20 Aug., rocket still in orbit

have revealed the existence of permanent radiation belts called Van Allen belts (*v.* Cosmic rays).

d. Counts of micrometeorite impacts have shown that they are much more abundant than hitherto believed.

e. Measurements have been made of the Earth's magnetic field and of cosmic radiation at a high altitude.

f. Biological experiments particularly on the influence of loss of gravity upon living beings (dog Laika), have been carried out.

g. The first meteorological satellite is relaying television pictures of the cloud formations over much of the Earth's surface.

Ascending node, the point where the orbit* of the Moon or a planet intersects the plane of the ecliptic, or the orbit of a star intersects the celestial plane, when the body in question is moving from the south to the north of the plane.

Association of stars, *v.* Star cluster and stellar association.

Asteroids, minor planets or planetoids (*v.* Pl. 22) are small celestial bodies which, like the planets, orbit round the Sun, especially between Mars and Jupiter. Only one is visible with the unaided eye. *A.* are so small (between 440 miles and 1 mile in diameter) that they appear not as disks but, like the stars (hence the name), as pinpoints. Only their motion through the sky distinguishes them from stars. The calculation of their orbits has led to solutions of some special cases of the three-body problem*, and one of the *A.*, Eros*, passes so close to Earth that its distance can be accurately found by the triangulation* method. This datum together with Kepler's laws* enable the most accurate measurement of the Sun's distance from Earth to be made. Towards the end of the eighteenth century Bode's law led astronomers to suspect that there must be a planet, then unknown, between Mars and Jupiter, and search for such a planet went on vigorously in that century. In 1801 Ceres was discovered by the Italian astronomer, Piazzi. This tiny asteroid orbits round the Sun at a distance of about 2·8 A.U. In the following year Pallas was discovered by an observer trying to fix the position of Ceres. By 1891 no fewer than 322 *A.* had been found. From then on the search for *A.* was conducted photographically. A particular area of the sky would be photographed for several hours on end with the telescope following the diurnal motion. The plate then showed the stars as spots, but the *A.*, because of their motion, as traces. At present more than 6,000 *A.* have been discovered and hundreds of new discoveries are reported annually. It is impossible to work out the elements of the orbits of all these 'wandering rocks', though this has been done for more than 1,500 of them. The orbits of most *A.* are roughly circular. That of Hidalgo, however, is very eccentric and inclined at 43° to the plane of the ecliptic. All *A.* revolve round the Sun in the same direction as the planets. Worthy of particular mention are the Trojans*. Their orbit lies close to Jupiter's and their period of revolution is between 11·3 and 12·1 years (Jupiter 11·9 years).

Some *A.* come very close to the Earth: Eros, discovered in 1898, approaches within about 14 million miles of the Earth. Apollo, Amor, Adonis and Hermes come even closer. The largest of the *A.*, Ceres, has a diameter of 429 miles (*v.* table). The total mass of all *A.* is estimated at about $\frac{1}{1000}$ the mass of the Earth. Fluctuations in their brightness (e.g. Eros) suggest that

ORBITAL ELEMENTS OF A SELECTION OF ASTEROIDS

	Name of asteroid	Discoverer	Year of discovery	Average apparent magnitude at opposition	Estimated diameter in miles	Sidereal period of revolution in years	Semi-axis major of elliptical orbit in A.U.	Eccentricity of elliptical orbit	Inclination or angle between orbital plane and plane of ecliptic in degrees	Date of last opposition	
1	Ceres	Piazzi	1801	7·4	429	4·60	2·77	0·076	10·6	19th Aug.,	1960
2	Pallas	Olbers	1802	8·0	281	4·61	2·77	0·234	34·8	6th July,	1960
3	Juno	Harding	1804	8·7	150	4·36	2·67	0·258	13·0	11th June,	1960
4	Vesta	Olbers	1807	6·5	244	3·63	2·36	0·089	7·1	2nd July,	1960
5	Astraea	Hencke	1845	9·9	112	4·14	2·58	0·190	5·3	8th Sept.,	1960
6	Hebe	Hencke	1847	8·5	106	3·78	2·42	0·204	14·8	16th May,	1960
7	Iris	Hind	1847	8·4	94	3·68	2·38	0·231	5·5	30th March,	1960
8	Flora	Hind	1847	8·9	77	3·27	2·20	0·157	5·9	21st April,	1960
9	Metis	Graham	1848	8·9	133	3·69	2·39	0·124	5·6	25th Oct.,	1960
10	Hygiea	De Gasparis	1849	9·5	222	5·60	3·15	0·100	3·8	12th Febr.,	1960
11	Parthenope	De Gasparis	1850	9·3	75	3·84	2·45	0·101	4·6	18th Dec.,	1959
12	Victoria	Hind	1850	9·7	94	3·56	2·38	0·221	8·4	29th April,	1960
13	Egeria	De Gasparis	1850	9·7	123	4·14	2·58	0·086	16·5	7th May,	1960
14	Irene	Hind	1851	9·7	98	4·16	2·59	0·164	9·1	21st Aug.,	1960
15	Eunomia	De Gasparis	1851	8·6	146	4·30	2·64	0·187	11·8	5th Sept.,	1959
16	Psyche	De Gasparis	1852	9·6	201	4·99	2·92	0·139	3·1	3rd Dec.,	1960
18	Melpomene	Hind	1852	9·3	82	3·48	2·30	0·218	10·1	23rd July,	1960
19	Fortuna	Hind	1852	9·8	100	3·82	2·44	0·158	1·5	22nd Sept.,	1959
20	Massalia	De Gasparis	1852	9·2	112	3·74	2·41	0·144	0·7	8th Aug.,	1960
22	Calliope	Hind	1852	9·8	156	4·96	2·91	0·101	13·7	4th Aug.,	1960
27	Euterpe	Hind	1853	9·7	94	3·60	2·32	0·172	1·6	15th July,	1960
29	Amphitrite	Marth	1854	9·0	114	4·08	2·55	0·074	6·1	20th March,	1960
30	Urania	Hind	1854	9·9	56	3·64	2·36	0·127	2·1	30th Oct.,	1960
39	Laetitia	Chacornac	1856	9·5	160	4·60	2·77	0·115	10·4	11th Dec.,	1960
40	Harmonia	Goldschmidt	1856	9·2	56	3·41	2·27	0·046	4·3	14th Dec.,	1960
44	Nysa	Goldschmidt	1857	9·8	62	3·77	2·42	0·151	3·7	10th Sept.,	1960
51	Nemausa	Laurent	1858	9·8	94	3·64	2·37	0·066	10·0	4th April,	1960
63	Ausonia	De Gasparis	1861	9·9	92	3·70	2·40	0·125	5·8	11th Nov.,	1959
192	Nausicaa	Palisa	1879	9·3	120	3·72	2·40	0·246	6·9	16th Oct.,	1959
324	Bamberga	Palisa	1892	9·9	122	4·40	2·68	0·339	11·3	20th July,	1960
349	Dembovska	Charlois	1892	9·8	160	5·0	2·93	0·089	8·3	13th May,	1960
433	Eros	Witt	1898	10·7	11	1·76	1·46	0·223	10·8	13th Sept.,	1958
944	Hidalgo	Baade	1920	17·1	27	13·96	5·79	0·655	42·5	14th Aug.,	1960
1221	Amor	Delporte	1932	18·0	2	2·67	1·92	0·436	11·9	——	
1566	Icarus	Baade	1949	12·0	1	1·12	1·08	0·827	23·0	——	
—	Apollo	Reinmuth	1932	17·0	2	1·81	1·49	0·566	6·4	——	
—	Adonis	Delporte	1936	19·0	1	2·76	1·97	0·779	1·5	——	
—	Hermes	Reinmuth	1937	18·0	1	1·47	1·29	0·475	4·7	——	

the *A.* are not spherical but irregularly shaped masses of rock (→ Eros).

Astrograph, a photographic telescope with which it is possible to take a photograph of a very extensive area of the sky at a single exposure. This used to be done by employing a lens system with a large field of view (often a triplet or even more complicated system). The present-day instrument is the Schmidt camera*, in which a special combination of lens and mirror gives a very wide field.

Astrographic Catalogue (Carte du Ciel), a catalogue listing the positions of about 4 million stars obtained from some 44,000 photographs. The plan was drawn up at the International Congress in Paris in 1887 and the work was allocated to eighteen observatories. It is now approximately half completed. Most of the volumes already published give only the positions of the stars as measured on the photographic plates, and the diameters of the areas photographed, together with formulae for converting this information to Dec. and R.A., and the photographic magnitudes.

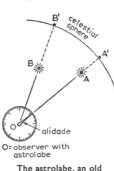

O = observer with astrolabe

The astrolabe, an old astronomical instrument

Astrolabe, one of the oldest astronomical instruments. Used by the ancient Greeks, it remained the chief measuring instrument until the Renaissance. In its simplest form, it consists of a graduated disk and a movable ruler, the alidade. If it was desired to measure an apparent angular distance on the celestial sphere between stars A and B (→), the instrument was held with the disk in the plane of the observer's eye and the two stars. If the ruler was aimed in the direction of A and then in that of B, the difference between the two readings gave the angle AOB, i.e. the distance in degrees of arc between A′ and B′ on the celestial sphere.

Astrology (Gr., study of the stars), a pseudo-science concerned with the relation between the position and motion of celestial objects and life on Earth. Just as modern chemistry arose from alchemy, *A.* gave way to astronomy. In forecasting a person's future *A.* uses the apparent positions of the Sun, Moon, planets and signs of the Zodiac* on the celestial sphere at the time of the person's birth. A very large number of rather arbitrary rules are used, some of which are derived by tradition from ancient Babylon, while others vary from astrologer to astrologer. It is quite certain that the results of *A.* do not as a general rule accord with facts. *A.* is also used in attempts to assess a person's character and hence his prospects in life.

In using the signs of the Zodiac, *A.* takes the positions of constellations as they were at the time of the Babylonians. The stars, however, by their annual motion, have since changed their positions relative to these signs. Moreover, the stars in a constellation have no real connection with each other. Their various distances from Earth mean that they are scattered in space and the groups they form on the celestial sphere are only apparent. It is true, in a general way, to say that *A.* is based on antiquated notions which modern man has abandoned.

Astrometry, the branch of astronomy concerned with the measurement and calculation of the positions and motions of celestial bodies.

Astronautics, *v.* Space travel.

Astronomical constants. Solar parallax 8·80″; constant of nutation 9·21″; constant of aberration 20· 47″; annual precession* 50·27″; obliquity of the ecliptic* 23° 26′ 45″; sidereal day 23 h. 56 min. 4·091 sec.; synodic month* 29 d. 12 h. 44 min. 3 sec.; sidereal month 27 d. 7 h. 43 min. 11·5 sec.; tropical year* 365 d. 5 h. 48 min. 46 sec.; sidereal year* 365 d. 6 h. 9 min. 9·5 sec.

Astronomical unit, unit of length used in measuring distances within the solar system. It is the mean distance from the Earth to the Sun. The *A.U.* = 92,960,000 miles = 500 light-seconds approximately. Neptune's distance from the Sun is about 30 *A.U.*

Astronomy is the science which treats of everything beyond the Earth. It is concerned with the study of the motions and structure of celestial objects and the phenomena observable on the latter.

HISTORY. The history of *A.* provides a survey of the way in which man has discovered the universe. As long ago as the beginning of the seventeenth century Kepler pointed out its importance: 'I am convinced that the manner in which mankind has obtained an insight into astronomical phenomena is no less worthy of admiration than the discoveries themselves.'

Ancient A. The first systematic observations by the Egyptians, the Chinese, and especially the Chaldeans laid the foundations for Greek *A.* The paths of the planets along the Zodiac were observed and the saros cycle of eclipses discovered.

Greek A. developed a logical mathematical explanation of the motions of the Sun, Moon and planets, based on the assumption that the Earth was the stationary centre of the universe (geocentric theory).

Ptolemy (about A.D. 150) wrote the culminating treatise on Greek *A.* His book, called the *Almagest**, after a later Arabic translation, remained the standard work on *A.* until the seventeenth century.

Classical A. The era of classical *A.* started with Newton (1687) but was foreshadowed by Copernicus, Tycho Brahe, Kepler and Galileo*. The year 1543 saw the publication of Copernicus's *De revolutionibus orbium coelestium,* in which he elaborated his heliocentric system. It was more than a century before his revolutionary thesis, that the Sun was the centre of the universe and the Earth only one of the planets, was generally accepted by astronomers. Galileo's first telescopic observations (1610), which revealed the principal satellites of Jupiter and also that the inferior planets show phases, furnished important arguments in favour of the heliocentric theory.

The long-continued and accurate observations of Tycho Brahe enabled Kepler to discover the laws governing planetary motion (1580). Newton in his *Principia* (1687) showed that both Kepler's laws and the motion of a falling body could be derived from his own law of gravitation. In so doing he laid the foundation of classical *A.* The mathematical development of Newton's theory culminated in Laplace's *Traité de mécanique céleste* (1799). In 1846 Galle discovered the planet Neptune very nearly where Adams and Leverrier had calculated it to be on the basis of Newton's theory. Meanwhile, the telescope had revolutionized methods of observation and brought numerous new discoveries.

In 1610, shortly after the telescope was invented, Galileo reaped the first harvest by discovering Jupiter's four largest moons, the lunar craters and the phases of Venus.

In 1668 Newton made the first reflecting telescope. In 1845 the Earl of Rosse built the largest instrument of the first period of classical *A.,* a reflecting telescope with a metallic mirror 6 ft. in diameter—and observed many features of nebulae with it. Foucault made further development of the reflecting telescope possible by his discovery of a method of coating glass reflectors with silver and by his extremely sensitive method of testing the concave mirror for correctness of shape.

Modern A. While classical *A.* was celebrating its greatest triumphs, while new planets and asteroids were being discovered, and the motions of the members of the solar system were being more and more accurately defined, the era of modern *A.* had already started. In modern *A.* new light was thrown on the structure of the universe, as well as on that of our Galaxy and also on the problem of the origin and evolution of the stars.

Structure of the Galaxy. Towards the end of the eighteenth century W. Herschel made an attempt to determine the structure of the stellar system. His work was hampered by his failure to obtain distances. It was not until 1838 that Bessel found the first stellar distance (61 Cygni, approximately 600,000 A.U.). The dawn of this era saw the advent of two powerful aids: spectroscopy and photography. Fraunhofer applied the spectroscope to *A.* in 1815, but this instrument did not come into its own until 1859 when Kirchhoff gave the correct interpretation of the Fraunhofer lines in the solar spectrum. The radial motion of a star was first observed spectroscopically by Huggins in 1868. In 1887 David Gill began to use astrophotography systematically and before long photographic observation became more important than visual. The positions of stars were now recorded in extensive star catalogues. One of the first was the *Bonner Durchmusterung,* which was started in 1862. In 1890 the first part of the Paris *Carte du Ciel* appeared, in which all stars down to the 12th magnitude are photographed. The need for more accurate data persisted and in our own time (1949–57) the most up-to-date photographic record of stars visible in the northern hemisphere has been compiled; it is the *Palomar Sky Survey* and includes all stars down to the 20th magnitude. Kapteyn realized that for knowledge of the structure of the stellar world it was necessary to collect more information about all stars than just their magnitude and position in the firmament. In 1905 he put forward the proposal that 206 areas suitably distributed over the celestial sphere (selected areas) should be studied as fully as possible, as test samples of the Galaxy as a whole. The data thus assembled later proved a valuable contribution to our knowledge of the Galaxy.

In 1912 Miss Leavitt discovered an extremely valuable aid to determining the distance of stars which are so far away that trigonometrical methods are entirely unsuitable. She found that the mean absolute magnitude of a certain type of variable star (cepheid) is related to the period of its variations of luminosity. The distance of the star can therefore be calculated from its apparent and its absolute magnitude.

Shapley applied this method to the distances of globular clusters and found in 1917 that all globular clusters form a system whose centre is far from the Sun. Yet three years later astronomers were still not convinced that Shapley had thereby discovered the centre of the Galaxy. Gradually, however, the idea gained ground that all visible stars form a self-contained whole which looks roughly like a lens-shaped disk. In 1926–27 Oort and Lindblad were able to show how many features of stellar motions could be explained by the rotation of the Galaxy. It was also found that in between the stars there is diffuse matter which is made luminous locally by the presence of very bright stars. In 1904 Hartmann discovered in the spectrum of the double star δ Orionis two stationary lines among the periodically shifting lines of this rotating binary. These lines were presumably caused by a gas situated between the Earth and the stars. Oort calculated in 1932 that the mass of stars in our Galaxy must be roughly the same as the mass of the non-luminous matter there.

Following the development of radio-astronomy, further research revealed that interstellar matter is arranged in spiral arms starting from the centre of the Galaxy. These arms were plotted by Oort, Van de Hulst and others from 1951 onwards.

Extragalactic nebulae*. As long ago as the eighteenth century it was suggested that the universe contained stellar systems other than that to which the Sun belongs. But even as late as 1900 actual knowledge on the subject was so slight that Young took only one and a half pages to deal with the objects which later proved to be far beyond our own Galaxy, as well as with the nebulosities contained in it. He added that we can 'only guess as to the nature of these nebulae'.

In 1925 Hubble furnished definite proof of the existence of such systems. With the aid of the cepheid variables in them, he determined the distances of M31 (Andromeda nebula) and NGC6822. These proved to be considerably greater than the dimensions discovered shortly before for our own Galaxy. In 1926 Hubble published his classification of extragalactic nebulae, and three years later he discovered the now familiar velocity–distance relation according to which exterior galaxies are receding from us at velocities proportional to their distances from us.

This work was made possible by data provided by the Hooker 100-inch telescope* on Mount Wilson which had come into use in 1918. In 1948 an even more powerful instrument (with a 200-inch parabolic mirror) began operations—the Hale telescope*. This was built specially for research into extragalactic nebulae. With this telescope it is possible to plumb the universe to a distance of 2,000 million light-years. Extragalactic nebulae were found to occur usually in clusters. Our own Galaxy belongs to a small cluster of 30 or so. Zwicky found that some extragalactic nebulae are linked by bridges of tenuous matter and that they exert tidal effects on each other (*v.* Pl. 85). The distances previously assigned to the extragalactic nebulae were corrected by Baade in 1952. All distances found had been based directly or indirectly on the period-luminosity law*. It now appeared that there were two types of cepheid, belonging to the two types of stellar population distinguished by Baade in 1943. The distances found were for type I stars, whereas the period-luminosity curve for type II stars had been used to determine luminosity. The result was that all distances found for extragalactic nebulae had to be approximately doubled. The correction does not apply to distances within our own Galaxy. In 1958, Sandage showed that for galaxies beyond the so-called Local Group the correction factor which must be applied to Hubble's scale is 5 or more.

Astrophysics. At the start of the twentieth century the study of astronomical physics was still in its infancy. The spectroscope had revealed that the matter which occurs in the atmosphere of the stars (and the Sun) also occurs on Earth. Spectroscopy could not bear full fruit, however, until the theory of the structure of the atom was developed after 1910.

The interior of stars is not observable, and astronomers therefore have to depend on theoretical investigation. It has been deduced that stars consist mainly of hydrogen and helium and that they derive their energy from nuclear reactions*, in which hydrogen is transformed into helium (Bethe and Weizsäcker, 1938). These discoveries gave a firm basis on which to construct theories relating to the age and evolution of the stars.

Although the discoveries of modern astronomy make all previous work seem insignificant by comparison, many problems still await solution. Radio-astronomy, which made rapid strides after 1945, has provided an enormous mass of new data. Research based on the most modern instrumental aids (photomultiplier, electron image tube, etc.) continues and for all we know we may be on the verge of yet another new era in men's probing of the universe.

Astrophotography, the photography of celestial objects, is employed much more than visual observations at large observatories nowadays. Modern telescopes are specially constructed for photographic use; the observer looks through the smaller auxiliary telescope to check the position of the object and to ensure, in the case of long exposures, that the main telescope is actually following the object's motion in the sky. Both reflecting and refracting telescopes and, more recently, telescopes combining both principles are used for photography (*v.* Schmidt telescope).

Photography has many advantages over visual observation. Light rays from an object make an impression on the retina of the eye which then transmits it direct to the brain. This picture is not retained on the retina and the latter is immediately free to receive new impressions. There is a limit below which light is too faint to activate the retina; such light we are unable to perceive. The photographic plate, however, works differently; impressions made by light are not passed on but retained and accumulated. A series of weak impressions is built up by this cumulative effect into a single picture which can be seen with the human eye. This makes it possible to obtain pictures of very faint objects which can never be observed visually, even through the largest telescopes.

Thus, by using large telescopes which can follow the apparent rotation of the celestial sphere (due to the Earth's rotation) so accurately that it is possible to make exposures extending over several nights, we are able to photograph extremely faint objects enormous distances away from us. All the knowledge we at present possess about extragalactic nebulae* we owe to photography. Even the nearest spiral nebula* can only be seen through the telescope as a hazy spot with no definite structure, and the more remote galaxies cannot even be perceived visually. Not merely distant objects but also numerous details of our own Galaxy, such as faint nebulosities, cannot be observed except by photography. Moreover, the eye is sensitive to light only in a particular range of frequencies.

By correct choice of light-sensitive emulsions, it is possible to take photographs in light that man cannot see, e.g. infra-red light. Similarly, photographs of a single object can be made in various colours. Mars, for instance, is photographed in blue light and red light. If we compare these pictures, we find that the blue light shows the atmosphere of the planet, while the red light pierces the atmosphere and reveals details of the permanent surface (v. Pl. 17, 18).

The method used in photographing the Sun is basically the same: by recording only the light of a particular wavelength, we can obtain different views of the Sun. Spectroheliograms*, as these are called, taken by the light of, for example, the Hα line of hydrogen or the K-line of calcium (v. Spectrum and Sun) yield information about the structure of the outer layers of the Sun. Moreover, the spectra* of celestial objects can be measured and studied only after they have been recorded on a photographic plate. Most modern developments in astronomy* and astrophysics would have been impossible without photography.

Astrophysics, the study of physics as applied to astronomy (v. Astronomy).

Atlas, the star 27 Tauri, one of the brightest stars in the Pleiades*.

Atlas, v. Star atlas.

Atlas, *Photometric Atlas of the Solar Spectrum*, by M. Minnaert, G. Mulders and J. Houtgast (1940), published by the Utrecht Observatory. Gives all the measured absorption lines of the solar spectrum from 3,332 to 8,771 Å. The scale of this Atlas is 1 Å = 20 mm, so that the total length of the solar spectrum is over 100 metres.

Atmosphere (v. Pl. 5) is the gaseous envelope surrounding a celestial body. If a planet's mass is small, it does not exert sufficient power of attraction on the molecules of gas, which therefore gradually disappear into space under their own velocity. The Moon, for instance, has no A. of any consequence. The planet Mercury likewise has practically no A.; it is so close to the Sun and the high temperature imparts such a great velocity to the molecules of gas that the mass of Mercury is insufficient to retain an A. Whether a planet possesses an A. or not thus also depends on its temperature and hence on its distance from the Sun. The greater the distance from the Sun, the more likely it is to have an A. In general, therefore, the possession of an A. by a planet will depend on whether the average velocity of its gas molecules is considerably smaller than the velocity of escape. The presence of an A. round a planet is mainly indicated by absorption lines* in its spectrum* and by clouds or twilight.

ATMOSPHERES OF THE STARS. Our main source of information is the Sun, the only star we can study from close quarters. In the Sun there is no definite boundary between the A. and the body, as there is in the planets, because the entire Sun is in a gaseous state and the various parts merge more or less gradually into each other.

The photosphere, which radiates visible light, is regarded as the Sun's surface. The A. surrounding it is divided into the chromosphere, the K- (or inner) corona and the F- (or outer) corona, and consists of gases, mainly hydrogen, becoming more and more rarefied towards the outside (v. Sun).

The Sun's A. is studied with the aid of the solar spectrum (v. Atlas).

It is quite definite that all stars, like the Sun, possess A. and the spectra of these have been recorded and studied. Some stars have A.s which are expanding rapidly, being fed by streams of gas from the inside of the stars, e.g. Wolf-Rayet* stars and P Cygni type stars. The presence of stellar A.s is sometimes particularly obvious in the case of eclipsing variables. The darker component may have an extensive A. When the brighter star disappears behind the dark one, we do not see a sudden occultation but a very slow passage from light to dark as the rays of the bright star shine through the gradually thickening layers of A. round the occulting star. If the dimensions of the system are known, the thickness of the A. can be worked out with the aid of the orbital velocities. An example of this type of double star is ζ Aurigae.

ATMOSPHERES IN THE SOLAR SYSTEM

	Velocity of escape in m.p. sec. (km/sec.)	Distance from Sun in A.U.	Existence of an atmosphere	Main constituents
Mercury	2·4 (3·8)	0·39	no	
Venus	6·5 (10·4)	0·72	yes	carbon dioxide
Earth	7·0 (11·3)	1·00	yes	nitrogen, oxygen, carbon dioxide
Mars	3·2 (5·1)	1·52	yes	carbon dioxide
Jupiter	37·9 (61·0)	5·20	yes	methane, ammonia, H_2 ?
Saturn	22·8 (36·7)	9·55	yes	methane, ammonia, H_2 ?
Uranus	13·4 (21·6)	19·20	yes	methane, H_2 ?
Neptune	14·8 (23·8)	30·09	yes	methane, H_2 ?
Pluto	6·8 (11·0) ?	39·52	?	*
Moon	1·5 (2·4)	1·00	no	
Io	1·5 (2·4)	5·20	?	
Europa	1·3 (2·1)	5·20	?	
Ganymede	1·8 (2·9)	5·20	?	
Callisto	1·5 (2·4)	5·20	?	
Mimas	0·1 (0·2) ?	9·55	?	
Enceladus	0·1 (0·2) ?	9·55	?	
Tethys	0·2 (0·4)	9·55	?	
Dione	0·3 (0·5) ?	9·55	?	
Rhea	0·4 (0·7)	9·55	?	
Titan	1·7 (2·8)	9·55	yes	methane, ammonia
Iapetus	?	9·55	?	
Triton	1·7 (2·8)	30·09	yes	methane?

Atmospheric absorption. The Earth's atmosphere is not completely transparent to light. Any beam of light entering from outside tends to lose some of its intensity, some colours (or wavelengths) being affected more than others. In the visible region of the spectrum, A.a. is quite small but outside that region, both to violet and to red, it increases greatly. In the ultra-violet, at about 3,000 Å, absorption due to ozone high in the atmosphere sets in and no wavelengths less than 2,900 Å penetrate to the ground. This is fortunate because all the ultra-violet radiation and X-rays* which are injurious to organic life are cut off. In the infra-red, the most important atmospheric absorber is water vapour, but oxygen and carbon dioxide also play a role and relatively little of the infra-red radiation gets through. At still longer wavelengths, the atmosphere again becomes transparent and so radio waves from outer space can penetrate to the ground (v. Radio astronomy).

Atmospheric refraction is the bending of a light beam as it passes through the Earth's atmosphere. It causes celestial bodies, particularly when close to the

AVERAGE ATMOSPHERIC REFRACTION
(Temperature 50° F., pressure 29 1/2 inches of mercury)

Altitude	Refraction	Altitude	Refraction
0°	34′ 50″	10°	5′ 16″
1°	24′ 22″	20°	2′ 37″
2°	18′ 06″	30°	1′ 40″
3°	14′ 13″	40°	1′ 09″
4°	11′ 37″	50°	0′ 48″
5°	9′ 45″	65°	0′ 27″
		80°	0′ 10″
		90°	0′ 00″

horizon, to appear to be higher than they really are. It occurs because the density of the atmosphere decreases with height, so that it acts like a prism and

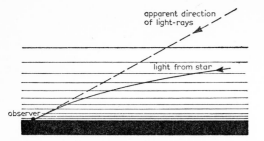

bends rays of light slightly. This is also the reason why the lunar and solar disks appear flattened when on the horizon. Allowance must be made for *A.r.* when the positions of celestial objects have to be worked out accurately. Refraction in the zenith is zero (→).

Refraction varies slightly with temperature, being higher at lower temperatures and vice versa (1 % per 5°F.), and increases or decreases with atmospheric pressure (3 % per inch of mercury).

Atom was, according to views formerly held, the smallest unit into which matter could be divided, and *A.s* were classified into about 90 kinds. Substances composed of *A.s* of the same kind are called elements. All other substances are composed of molecules consisting of a stable combination of different *A.s.* Various investigations, including some into radio-activity, have shown that the *A.* is not indivisible (Rutherford, Bohr). The *A.* is, in fact, made up of a positively-charged nucleus, around which negatively charged electrons revolve in definite orbits, like planets around the Sun. If an electron jumps from one particular orbit to another closer to the nucleus, energy is released in the form of a light-wave of a particular frequency or, according to another view (*v.* Light), of a particle of light (photon) with a definite energy. When this happens, we see a certain emission line in the spectrum*. If light of a certain frequency and wavelength is absorbed by an *A.* (or if a photon with a certain energy impinges on the *A.*) an electron transfers to an orbit farther from the nucleus. This wavelength then disappears from the spectrum and instead we see a dark absorption line.

The nucleus is made up of positively charged protons and electrically neutral neutrons. The nuclei of the various elements differ in the number of protons and neutrons they contain; a hydrogen nucleus consists of a single proton, a helium nucleus of two protons and two neutrons, and so on. These nuclei are not unalterable; by losing or acquiring fundamental particles, or by fusion, they may be transformed into another kind of nucleus. In particular, such processes occur in the interiors of stars (*v.* Nuclear reactions). The number of electrons orbiting round the nucleus is equal to the number of protons in the nucleus, so that the *A.* as such is electrically neutral. If one or more electrons are removed, a positively charged particle called an ion is left. The actual process which goes on in the interiors and atmospheres of stars, and elsewhere, is called ionization. The degree of ionization of a star partly determines the structure of its spectrum. More recent research (particularly on cosmic rays*) has revealed many other fundamental particles such as the meson (positively, negatively or neutrally charged

particle with a mass between that of a proton and that of an electron), the neutrino (an uncharged massless particle) and the positron (positively charged particle with the same mass as an electron).

A.U., *v.* Astronomical unit.

Auriga (the Charioteer), a constellation in the northern hemisphere, extending from 4 h. 35 min. to 7 h. 30 min. R.A., 28° to 56° N. Dec. (*v.* Pl. 51). (→)

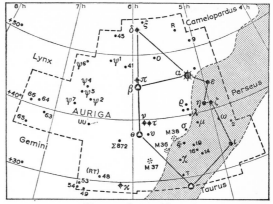

The constellation of Auriga

Aurora, or Polar Lights, a fascinating display of light occasionally visible at night in the polar regions (*v.* Pl. 5). It occurs most frequently in the areas with magnetic inclinations of 75° to 80°—northern Norway, Iceland, northern Canada, Alaska, etc., in the northern hemisphere; round the borders of Antarctica in the southern hemisphere. It extends towards the equator at times of great solar activity. The *A.* can assume many forms: a diffuse milky light (brighter than the Milky Way), a greenish white arc, deep-red rays, flickering draperies of colours ranging from deep-red to blue. Its height has been determined by triangulation; on the average it is from 65 up to 100 miles, but cases have occurred, e.g. on the evening of 25th January, 1938, when it reached 500 miles. This *A.* began at this altitude above the Earth and descended later as low as 50 miles. It extended between Scandinavia and Ireland and was visible even in Africa.

A widespread display of *A.* frequently follows a great solar flare. The disturbed Sun then ejects streams of very attenuated gas, with positive ions and electrons, into space at velocities exceeding 600 m. p. sec. These streams are bent by the Earth's magnetism so that they enter our atmosphere mainly in the polar regions where they collide with the gases of the terrestrial atmosphere and cause them to glow. About 1900 Birkeland reproduced the *A.* with the aid of cathode rays and a powerfully magnetized globe. Mathematical research on the orbits which the solar particles should follow under the influence of the Earth's magnetic field has been carried out by Störmer. Both theory and experiment accord qualitatively with the observational data.

Autumnal equinox, *v.* Celestial sphere.

Azimuth, one of the two co-ordinates in the system used to fix the position of a celestial object in relation to the observer's horizon. It is the angular distance, measured in the observer's horizontal plane from the south point of the horizon westwards to the point where the vertical great circle through the object intersects the horizon (*v.* Celestial sphere).

Barlow lens, a plano-concave lens inserted in the eyepiece holder of a telescope between the objective* and the eyepiece* in order to obtain greater magnification without using powerful eyepieces. It is specially employed for observation of planetary details. Depending on its position, a *B.l.* with a focal distance of, for example,—33 mm can increase the magnification of a telescope by a factor of 2–3. Better than a single lens is an achromatic system.

Bear, Great, *v.* Ursa Major.

Bear, Little, *v.* Ursa Minor.

Bellatrix, γ Orionis, one of the brighter stars in the constellation of Orion. Visual magnitude 1·7, spectral type B2.

Berenice's Hair, *v.* Coma Berenices.

Beta Lyrae stars (β Lyrae-type variables) are very close eclipsing variables (*v.* Double stars and Spectroscopic binaries) with a common atmosphere. They are named after the star β Lyrae. There is still no general agreement about the physical properties of this system. The following explanation is the most acceptable at present.

A gas stream flows between the two closely situated components (→). Part of this gas forms an expanding ring round the whole system, or a stream of gas from the binary enters space with a spiral motion. The system consists of a larger component (spectrum B9) and a small F-type companion. The total mass of the binary is 100 times that of the Sun. The two stars are elongated by their mutual attraction, and have their major axes in line with each other. At the primary eclipse, as seen from Earth, the F-type star is in front of the B9 star.

The system also presents a spectrum resembling that

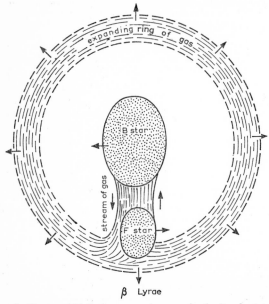

β Lyrae

of a B2 star which shows no change of velocity during the revolution of the two stars. This spectrum comes from the light emitted by the atmosphere enveloping

the whole system and it is either expanding or receding spirally from the binary. The B9 star provides 96% of the system's light; the F-type star is normally invisible. The period is 13 days. With its expanding gases the whole system is as large as the entire solar system. Its structure can only be studied spectroscopically: details cannot be observed by telescope because β Lyrae is about 1,600 light-years away. β Lyrae is thought to be a newly formed system whose components are receding from each other.

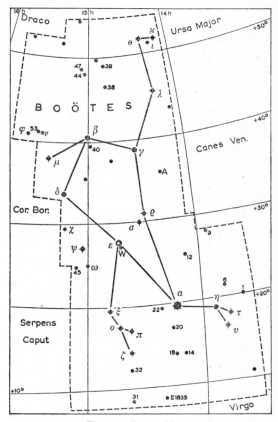

The constellation of Boötes

Betelgeuse, the star α Orionis, with Rigel, one of the two brightest stars in the constellation of Orion. The name was bestowed on it by the Arabs: perhaps originally 'Yad al-Jawza', 'the front paw of the sheep'. The whole constellation was likened originally to a sheep, and only later to the mythological figure Orion. *B.* is a variable red giant* with a period of six years. Its diameter is at most 540 × Sun's; temperature 3,100° C.; density 0·0000001 × Sun's; apparent magnitude 0·92; absolute magnitude —3·4; luminosity 2,900 × Sun's; distance 200 light-years; spectrum M2. This star is one of the few whose diameter has been measured with an interferometer*.

Binary stars, *v.* Double stars.
Bird of Paradise, *v.* Apus.
Blink comparator, or blink microscope, an instrument with which it is possible to detect slight differences between otherwise similar photographic plates. It enables slight displacements of objects in the sky or slight variations in brightness to be traced. The two plates are viewed through an optical system in which they are made visible alternately in rapid succession. Any object whose brightness or position has changed is revealed by a flickering.
Blue sky results from the fact that the Earth's atmosphere scatters blue light more than red light. The scattered light from any sunbeam is thus predominantly blue. Consequently, when the eye looks in a direction away from the Sun, it sees only this blue light scattered from the general sunlight reaching the Earth in the observer's neighbourhood (*v.* Red sunset).
Bode's law is an empirical rule for working out the distances of the planets from the Sun. Many of the distances obtained thereby correspond to the actual distances. It states that if n is the serial number of the planet concerned (see the following table), its distance in astronomical units from the Sun is given by $0 \cdot 4 + 0 \cdot 3 \times 2^n$. The 'law' appears, however, to have no

scientific basis but to be purely fortuitous (*v.* Solar system and table).

	n	Distance by BODE'S LAW	Actual distance
Mercury	— ∞	0·4	0·39
Venus	0	0·7	0·72
Earth	1	1·0	1·00
Mars	2	1·6	1·52
Ceres (asteroid)	3	2·8	2·77
Jupiter	4	5·2	5·20
Saturn	5	10·0	9·54
Uranus	6	19·6	19·19
Neptune	—	—	30·07
Pluto	7	38·8	39·46

Bolide, a brilliant meteor*, or fireball.
Bolometer (Gr. *bolē*, ray and *metron*, a measure) an instrument for measuring radiant heat from the Sun and stars. A blackened platinum wire is exposed to the radiation, which heats it and causes its electrical resistance to change. This change in resistance is a measure of the radiant heat.
Boötes (the Herdsman), a constellation in the northern hemisphere, between R.A. 13 h. 35 min. and 15 h. 50 min. and Dec. 8°N. and 55°N. *B.* appears to be pursuing the bear (Ursa Major) with his hunting dogs (Canes Venatici). (→ facing)
Bull, *v.* Taurus.

C

Caelum (the Chisel), a small, inconspicuous constellation in the southern sky. *C.* is situated between 4 h. 20 min. and 5 h. 5 min. R.A. and between —27° and —49° Dec. (→)
Callisto, one of Jupiter's four brightest moons. Mean distance from Jupiter 1,170,000 miles, period 16 d. 16 h. 32 min., diameter 3,220 miles, magnitude at opposition 6 (→ 3 Solar system).
Camelopardus (Giraffe), is an inconspicuous constellation in the northern hemisphere. The constellation stretches from 3 h. 10 min. to 14 h. 30 min. R.A. and from 53° to 86° N. Dec. (→)
Canals, *v.* Mars.
Cancer (the Crab), a constellation in the northern sky, situated between R.A. 7 h. 55 min. and 9 h. 20 min. and Dec. 7°N. and 33°N. It lies on the ecliptic and is therefore a zodiacal* constellation. (→ p. 120)
Canes Venatici (the Hunting Dogs), a constellation in the northern sky between 12 h. 5 min. and 14 h. 5 min. R.A. and 28° and 52° N. Dec. (→ p. 120)
Canis Major (the Great Dog), a constellation in the southern sky, rich in bright stars. α Canis Majoris, or Sirius, partly owing to its relatively short distance from the Sun, is the brightest star in the sky. The constellation lies between 6 h. 10 min. and 7 h. 25 min. R.A. and 11° and 33° S. Dec. (→ p. 120)

The constellation of Caelum

Canis Minor (the Little Dog) (→ Monoceros), a small constellation in the northern hemisphere, situated between 7 h. 5 min. and 8 h. 10 min. R.A. and 0° and 13° N. Dec.

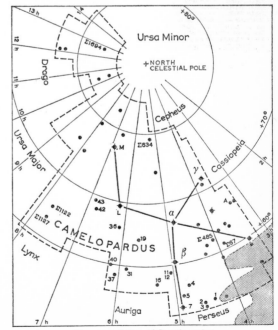

The constellation of Camelopardus

Canopus, α Carinae, visually the brightest star in the sky after Sirius. Because of its southerly position (Dec. —52° 40′), not observable in many northern latitudes.

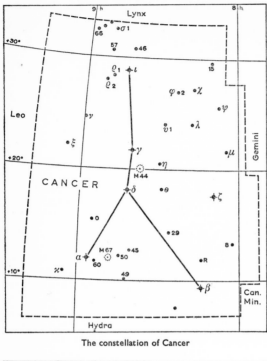

The constellation of Cancer

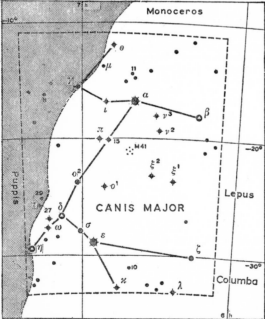

The constellation of Canis Major

Apparent magnitude—0·86, absolute magnitude — 7·4 (?), distance 650 (?) light-years, luminosity 40,000 × Sun's, spectral type Fo.

Capella, α Aurigae, a spectroscopic binary star (Campbell 1899), with a period of 104 days. The masses of the two components are 4·3 and 3·3 times that of the Sun. The system also includes a third star of the 10th magnitude (spectral type M). Apparent magnitude 0·21, absolute magnitude — 0·6, distance 52 light-years, luminosity 150 × Sun's, spectrum Go.

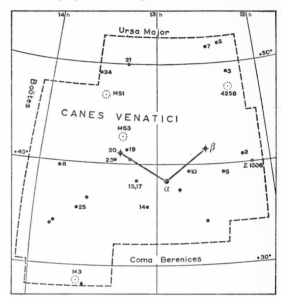

The constellation of Canes Venatici

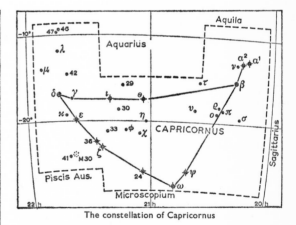

The constellation of Capricornus

Capricornus (the Sea-goat), one of the zodiacal* constellations and therefore astride the ecliptic. It lies in the southern hemisphere and extends from 20 h. 5 min. to 21 h. 55 min. R.A. and from —9° to —28° Dec. (→)

Carina (the Keel), a southern constellation. It is situated between R.A. 6 h. and 11 h. 20 min. and Dec. —51° and —75°. (→ facing)

Carte du Ciel, title of a scheme to compile a photographic atlas, on which work was started in 1887 by 18 co-operating observatories. It is not yet complete (v. Astrographic Catalogue).

Cassegrain focus, a particular arrangement of mirrors in a telescope for the purpose of lengthening the path of the light in the tube, and thereby obtaining a longer focal distance and a greater image (→ Hale telescope, 1).

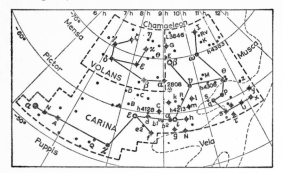

The constellations of Carina and Volans

Cassini's division, a dark band (width about 3,000 miles) dividing the ring of Saturn into rings A and B. A star moving behind Saturn's ring resumes its normal brightness when it reaches *C.d.* From this we may assume that this separating band is devoid of matter (*v.* Pl. 21).

Cassiopeia, a northern constellation situated between 47° and 77° N. Dec. and between 23 h. and 3 h. 35 min. R.A. A large part of the constellation lies in the Milky Way. The name *C.* is taken from Greek mythology. *C.* was the wife of King Cepheus and the mother of Andromeda. *C.* boasted that she was more beautiful than the Nereids. As a punishment, Poseidon sent a sea monster which devoured man and beast (*v.* Andromeda). (→)

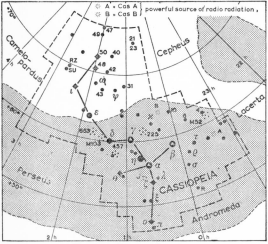

The constellation of Cassiopeia

Castor, the star α Geminorum, discovered to be a double star* in 1719. Its definitive orbit was published by Strand in 1941. Period 511 years; its actual semi-axis major is 105 A.U. Both component stars are themselves spectroscopic binaries with periods of 3 and 9 days respectively. At a distance of 100 A.U. from the visual binaries there is a small third component (spectral type M) which itself is an eclipsing binary with a period of 0·8 of a day. The *C.* system as a whole thus consists of six individual stars. Apparent magnitude 1·59, abso-

lute magnitudes of main components 2·8 and 2·0, distance 43 light-years, luminosities 11 and 23 × Sun's, spectral types both Ao.

Celestial co-ordinates, *v.* Celestial sphere.

Celestial sphere, an imaginary sphere used to describe celestial phenomena and to define the positions of points in the sky. It is thought of as a sphere, of indefinite but large radius with the observer at its centre (→ 2). It is not the actual positions of celestial objects in space which are defined, but the points where radii through them meet this sphere. All objects are therefore regarded as being equally far from the observer. Similarly the orbits of actual and apparent motions are projected on the *C.s.* and form lines on its inner surface (→ 3 and 4). Depending on the type of phenomena to be described, two types of sphere are used.

The static celestial sphere (→ 5, 6, 8 and 9). A vertical line from the observer's position C meets the visible half of the *C.s.* in the zenith and the invisible half in the nadir. Great circles of the *C.s.* which pass through the zenith and nadir are called vertical circles. The plane through C perpendicular to the vertical line intersects the *C.s.* in a great circle, the horizon. The line through the place of observation C, parallel to the axis of rotation of the earth, is called the celestial axis. The celestial axis intersects the *C.s.* at the north and south celestial poles. The celestial pole remains stationary during the diurnal motion of all other objects in the sky (→ 4). The vertical circle through the north celestial pole and the zenith is called the observer's celestial meridian (→ 5). The points of intersection of the meridian and horizon are called the north and south points. The plane through the observer's position at right angles to the celestial axis intersects the *C.s.* in a great circle, the celestial equator or, simply, equator. The points where the celestial equator intersects the horizon are called the east and west points (→ 6). The paths of the stars in their daily motion form, on the celestial sphere, circles parallel to the celestial equator (→ 5 and 7).

The points where a star crosses the observer's meridian are called culminations or transits. A star is at upper transit when it reaches its greatest altitude. This point therefore lies on the celestial meridian. An hour circle is a half great circle of the *C.s.* which joins the two celestial poles and is therefore at right angles to the celestial equator. The zero-hour circle of a star passes through the point of upper transit. The hour circle moves from 0 to 24 hours with the star in its daily motion round the celestial pole (→ 9).

1. The horizon and the vertical circle are used as the bases of a system of co-ordinates for fixing positions in the sky (→ 8).

a. The altitude of a star S is the arc of the vertical circle passing through S, measured from the point of intersection of the horizon and the vertical circle to S.

b. The azimuth of S is the arc of the horizon measured from the south point westwards to the point where the vertical circle of S and the horizon intersect. The diurnal motion of S causes the altitude and azimuth values to change continuously.

2. A second system of co-ordinates is based on the celestial equator and the hour circle of a star at a particular moment (→ 9).

a. The declination of a star S is the arc of the hour circle of S measured from the point of intersection of this hour circle and the celestial equator to the star.

b. The hour angle of star S is the arc of the celestial equator measured from the point of intersection of the celestial equator and the upper branch of the celestial meridian (situated on the visible part of the *C.s.*) to the point of intersection of the star's hour circle and the celestial equator. It is thus measured from the

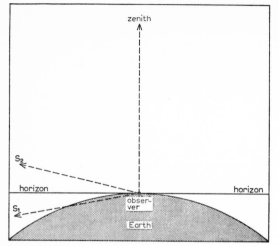

Fig. 1. If a star lies in the direction S₁, i.e. below the horizon, it is invisible. Above the horizon (direction S₂), it is visible

star's zero-hour circle. This hour angle changes continuously owing to diurnal motion, but declination remains the same, because the paths of all stars in their daily motion are parallel to the celestial equator.

The rotating celestial sphere. The various co-ordinates associated with the stationary *C.s.* (except declination) change continuously because of diurnal motion, which is only apparent, and due to the earth's rotation. To fix a star's position irrespective of time, another system, that of the rotating *C.s.*, is used. This is similar in most respects to the stationary *C.s.* but is considered as sharing in diurnal motion. It therefore rotates round the celestial axis once every 24 hours. The celestial equator is used again but it also shares in diurnal motion. Half circles join the north and south celestial poles and are therefore at right angles to the celestial equator; these are called declination or hour circles.

The system of co-ordinates is now as follows (→ 10):

3. *a.* The declination of a star S is the arc measured along the hour circle through S from the point of intersection of the celestial equator and the hour circle to S. It is positive for stars north, and negative for stars south, of the celestial equator. *b.* The R.A. of star S is the arc measured along the celestial equator, in the direction opposite to diurnal rotation, from the vernal equinox to the point of inter-section of the hour circle of S and the celestial equator. The vernal equinox (see next system of co-ordinates) is where the Sun's path intersects the celestial equator, i.e. where the Sun crosses from the southern to the northern half of the *C.s.* Since the vernal equinox is a point on the celestial equator, it thus has diurnal

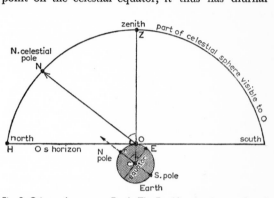

Fig. 2. O is an observer on Earth. The Earth's axis when produced cuts the celestial sphere at the north celestial pole. As the celestial sphere is infinitely distant from the observer, the direction ON, in which the north celestial pole lies, is parallel to the Earth's south-north axis. Since angles ZOH and nCE are each 90°, angle NOH = 90° — angle NOZ = 90° — angle nCO = OCE, i.e. the altitude of the north celestial pole above the horizon is equal to the geographical latitude of the observer's position

motion like the stars. Declination and R.A. therefore remain constant. This system is used, *inter alia*, for defining the positions of stars on charts and in catalogues.

The annual orbit of the Sun on the rotating C.s. As the Sun is higher in the sky in winter than in summer and its

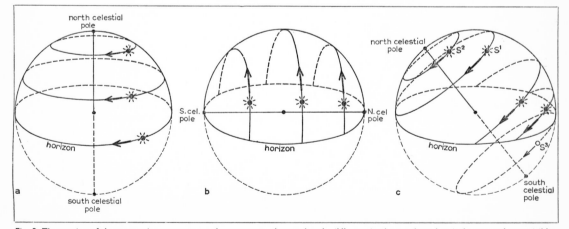

Fig. 3. The motion of the stars as it appears to an observer at: a. the north pole. All stars in the northern hemisphere are always visible, and no star in the southern hemisphere is ever visible. b. the equator. All stars are above the horizon and therefore visible during half of their orbits. c. a latitude of 51½° N. (London). The stars S¹ to the north celestial pole are always visible (circumpolar stars, e.g. S²); those from S³ to the south celestial pole are never visible. The stars between S¹ and S³ are above the horizon for part of their orbits

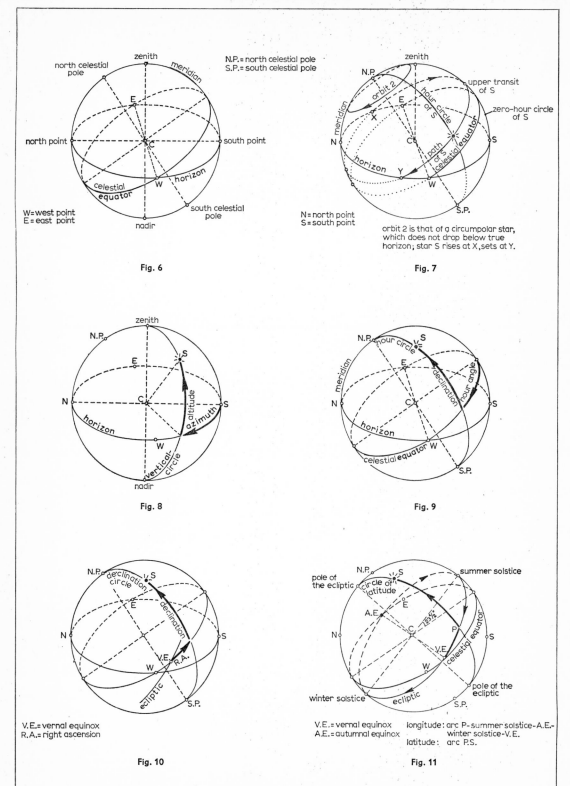

N.P. = north celestial pole
S.P. = south celestial pole

W = west point
E = east point

Fig. 6

orbit 2 is that of a circumpolar star, which does not drop below true horizon; star S rises at X, sets at Y.

N = north point
S = south point

Fig. 7

Fig. 8

Fig. 9

V.E. = vernal equinox
R.A. = right ascension

Fig. 10

V.E. = vernal equinox
A.E. = autumnal equinox

longitude: arc P-summer solstice-A.E.-winter solstice-V.E.
latitude: arc P.S.

Fig. 11

declination is therefore constantly changing, it has an apparent proper motion in addition to diurnal rotation. Its declination and R.A. change in annual cycles

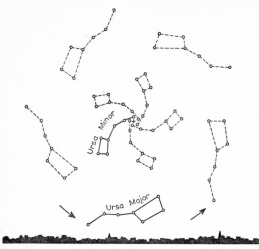

Fig. 4. Apparent diurnal motion of the stars round the celestial pole: various positions of the constellations of Ursa Major and Ursa Minor, as seen from a place with the same latitude as London. The interval between the successive positions is 4 h. 48 min.

as a result of the Earth's revolutions round the Sun. In a year the Sun describes a special path relative to the stars in the sky, the Sun's way or ecliptic (→ 11). The ecliptic is a celestial great circle whose plane is inclined 23 1/2° to the celestial equator and intersects the latter at the vernal equinox and the autumnal equinox (v. also Ecliptic). A line through the centre of the C.s. at right angles to the plane of the ecliptic intersects the C.s. at the poles of the ecliptic. The celestial semicircle joining the two poles of the ecliptic and passing through a star S is called the circle of latitude of S.

4. The ecliptic and circles of latitude can also be used as the bases of a system of co-ordinates.

a. The latitude of a star S is the arc measured along the circle of latitude of S from S to the point of intersection of the circle of latitude and the ecliptic.

b. The longitude of S is the arc measured along the ecliptic in the direction of diurnal rotation from the vernal equinox to the point where the circle of latitude of S intersects the ecliptic.

5. A final system of co-ordinates is used to describe phenomena associated with the structure of the Galaxy. Its basis is the celestial great circle which most closely corresponds to the middle of the Milky Way, i.e. the galactic equator. The line through the earth at

right angles to the galactic plane cuts the C.s. at the north and south galactic poles. The former is situated at 27·4° N. Dec. and 12 h. 49 min. R.A.

a. The galactic latitude of an object is an arc of the great circle passing through the galactic poles and the object at right angles to the galactic equator. It is measured from the galactic equator to the object and is positive in direction of the north, negative in the direction of the south, galactic pole.

b. Galactic longitude is the arc measured in the same direction as R.A. along the galactic equator from a point in the direction of Sagittarius coinciding approximately with the centre of the Galaxy (R. A. 14 h. 42·2 min., Dec. —28° 55′), to the intersection of the object's circle of galactic latitude and the galactic equator. These galactic co-ordinates are also inde-

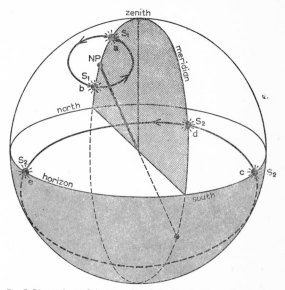

Fig. 5. Rise and set of the stars. Star S1 is close to the north celestial pole (NP) and describes an apparent daily orbit which lies wholly above the horizon. S1 crosses the meridian and attains its greatest and least altitude at a and b (a = upper transit, b = lower transit). Star S2 lies far from the celestial pole and is above the horizon for only part of its apparent orbit. It rises at c, crosses the meridian (transit or culmination) at d, and sets at e

pendent of the observer's position and can therefore be used on star charts.

Centaur, v. Centaurus.

Centaurus (the Centaur), a constellation in the southern sky. C. was a Greek demi-god, half horse and half man. The constellation lies partly in the Milky

LIST OF SYSTEMS OF CO-ORDINATES

1st circle	Poles	2nd circle	Co-ordinates	
Horizon	zenith, nadir	vertical circle	altitude and azimuth	position of a point at a particular moment, depending on the observer
Celestial equator	celestial poles	hour circle or declination circle	declination and hour angle	hour angle dependent on diurnal motion, declination independent of diurnal motion
Celestial equator	celestial poles	hour circle or declination circle	declination and right ascension	independent of diurnal motion
Ecliptic	poles of the ecliptic	circle of latitude	latitude and longitude	phenomena associated with the solar system
Galactic equator	galactic poles	circle of galactic latitude	galactic latitude and longitude	phenomena associated with the Galaxy

Way, between R.A. 11 h. 5 min. and 15 h. and Dec. —30° and —65° (→ Crux).

Central mountain, a mountain with one or more peaks situated near the centre of a walled plain on the Moon. Smaller and miniature craters sometimes found on these peaks form an important link in the series of arguments in support of a volcanic origin for the walled plains (v. Moon).

Cepheid law, v. Period-luminosity law.

Cepheid variables are variable stars* named after δ Cephei, the fourth star in the constellation of Cepheus. Miss Leavitt discovered that the period of this type of star depends on the star's mean absolute magnitude; the more luminous the star, the longer the period (period–luminosity law*). From a graph or a formula it is possible to find the absolute magnitude of a cepheid variable if its period is known. The distance of the star can then be computed from the absolute magnitude and the apparent magnitude (v. Distance finding). The *C.v.* have proved extremely important for astronomy because they enable us to calculate the distance even of objects that are far beyond our Galaxy. Several kinds of *C.v.* are now known (v. Variable stars).

Cepheus, a constellation in the northern sky, largely situated in the band of the Milky Way. It is named after King Cepheus, a character in Greek mythology

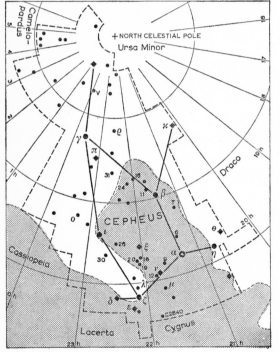

The constellation of Cepheus

(v. Andromeda). R.A. 20 h. to 8 h. 20 min., Dec. 53° to 88°N. (→)

Ceres, the largest of the asteroids* (diameter 430 miles) and the first to be discovered (Piazzi, 1st January, 1801). When Piazzi fell ill, the asteroid was 'lost' until Gauss devised a method of determining the elements of its orbit* from three observations. He forecast the position in which it was rediscovered on 31st December of the same year. Its time of rotation is 9 h. 5 min.

Cetus (the Whale), a constellation on the celestial equator, between R.A. 23 h. 55 min. and 3 h. 20 min. and Dec. 25°S. and 10°N. (→)

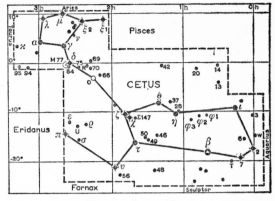

The constellation of Cetus

Chamaeleon (the Chameleon), a constellation in the southern hemisphere, situated between R.A. 7 h. 40 min. and 13 h. 35 min. Dec. —75° and —82°. (→)

Charioteer, v. Auriga.

Chisel, v. Caelum.

Chromatic relates to colour, e.g. the chromatic aberration of a lens.

Chromosphere, part of the Sun's atmosphere situated between the photosphere and the corona. (v. Sun and Pl. 29, 31).

Chronograph, an instrument for recording the exact time at which an event occurs. One type of *C.* uses pens on a moving strip of paper. A clock operates one pen at second intervals. As soon as the observer sees an event (such as an occultation of a star by the Moon) he presses a button which operates the second pen. By comparison of the pen traces on the paper, the time of the event is obtained. More accurate and specialized *C.s.* photograph a cathode ray oscilloscope, the time and event marks appearing as spot movements.

Circinus (the Compasses), small constellation in the southern sky, situated between 13 h. 35 min. and 15 h. 25 min. R.A. and —55° and —70° Dec. (→ p. 126)

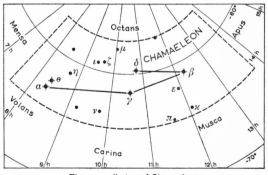

The constellation of Chamaeleon

Circumpolar stars, stars which are so close to the celestial north pole that they do not drop below the horizon in the course of their daily motion. For places with a latitude of 51½° N (London), *C.s.* are stars with declinations greater than 38½° N. (*v.* Celestial sphere).

Cirrus nebula, *v.* Veil nebula.

Clock, *v.* Horologium.

Cluster, *v.* Star cluster. A cluster of extragalactic nebulae is defined as a group of hundreds or thousands of these objects with higher condensation than elsewhere.

Coal Sack, example of a dark galactic nebula, situated in the southern hemisphere in the vicinity of Crux (*v.* Interstellar matter).

Coelostat, (pron. seelostat), is a combination of one moving and one fixed mirror. The moving mirror is mounted parallel to the Earth's axis and is rotated about that axis at one revolution per two days. Light from a star or, more particularly, the Sun, is then reflected in a fixed direction. The second mirror intercepts this beam and can be used to direct it to fixed observing equipment, as required.

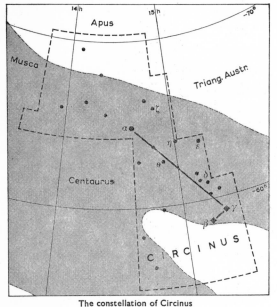

The constellation of Circinus

Collision of extragalactic systems (*v.* Pl. 84) has been deduced from the powerful electromagnetic radiation that is sometimes emitted. The radio source Cygnus A (→ Cygnus) coincides with one of the members of a cluster of galaxies. Photographs show that this galaxy consists of two galaxies passing through each other. The 'collision' of galaxies should be interpreted as follows. Galaxies are so tenuous that there is no possibility of the actual stars colliding; the collision involves only their gas and dust, and gives rise to intensely high temperatures; the latter may then cause, *inter alia*, powerful radio radiation.

Another example is NGC1275, a member of the Perseus cluster. In this case an Sa-type spiral nebula is penetrating an Sc-type nebula whose arms are twisted out of shape by the enormous forces involved. Two more pairs of colliding galaxies have been found in the southern hemisphere: NGC1487 and NGC3256. Both pairs have distorted central regions and are surrounded by extensive veils of luminous matter, which were probably created by mutual tidal effect (*v.* also Magellanic Clouds). These galaxies are not radio

sources. Heavy emission lines of hydrogen and ionized oxygen have been found in the spectrum of NGC3256.

Colour excess, *v.* Colour index.

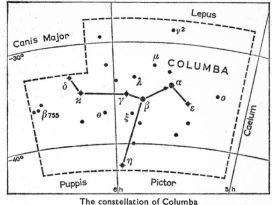

The constellation of Columba

Colour index is the difference between photographic magnitude* and visual magnitude*, i.e. $m_p - m_v$. By convention we put $m_p = m_v$ for spectral* type Ao; then *C.i.* is positive for red stars and negative for blue stars. For the bluest stars the *C.i.* is $-0 \cdot 3$ and for the reddest it is $+2$. The *C.i.* is a measure of the colour of a star and for a particular *C.i.* there is a corresponding spectral type. Thus, if a star in a particular spectral class has too great a *C.i.* (i.e. is too red), it is because its light has passed through interstellar matter which has scattered the violet rays more than the red. The difference between the *C.i.* measured and the *C.i.* appropriate to the spectrum observed is called the colour excess. The latter furnishes a measure of the amount of absorbing matter between the star and the observer.

Columba (the Dove), a small constellation in the southern sky between R.A. 5 h. and 6 h. 40 min. and Dec. $-27°$ and $-43°$. (→)

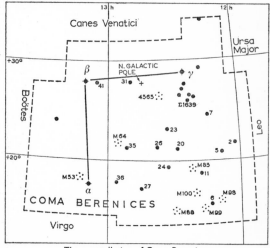

The constellation of Coma Berenices

Coma Berenices (Berenice's Hair), constellation (→) in the northern sky, situated between R.A. 11 h. 55 min. and 13 h. 35 min. and Dec. 14° and 34°N. The constellation includes the north galactic pole (*v.*

Celestial sphere). This part of the heavens being far from the galactic plane, very many extragalactic nebulae are visible here; the Virgo cluster lies partially in this constellation, as also does the Coma Berenices cluster (v. Pl. 80).

Comet (v. Pl. 23, 24), a small heavenly body belonging to the solar system, which revolves about the Sun in a very elongated elliptical orbit. The appearance of a C. varies greatly according to its distance from the Sun, so that the only clue to a C.'s continued identity is its orbit. The orbits of some 500 C.s have been more or less accurately calculated. Periodic C.s have elongated elliptical orbits and periods of revolution up to several hundred years. Most C.s however, have almost parabolic orbits, with very long periods of revolution. Only a few C.s have nearly circular orbits. Every year some 5 to 10 new C.s are discovered, sometimes by amateur astronomers. Most of them are so small that they are invisible to the naked eye. C.s are designated by the number of the year of their discovery: e.g. 1956h is the eighth C. discovered in 1956 (the bright C. Arend-Roland). When three positions have been plotted, a provisional orbit can be calculated.

The C.s are then given a permanent designation, the year of the perihelion passage, followed by a Roman numeral to indicate the sequence in that year (1957 I, 1957 II, etc.: e.g. the C. Arend-Roland is 1957 III). The orbits of 571 C.s are now known (1959) of which at least 51 are periodic. The shortest period of revolution is that of Encke's comet (3·3 years). Their orbital inclination (to the ecliptic) may be any value between 0° and 180°.

A C. consists of a nucleus of small solid particles and frozen gas, surrounded by a small hazy envelope called the coma. As the C. approaches the Sun, gases are driven off from the nucleus by positively charged solar particles, so that a tail is formed. This slowly disappears into space as the C. recedes again from the Sun. The tail of the Great Comet of 1843 had a length of 200 million miles (320 million km), more than twice the distance from Earth to Sun. The C. Arend-Roland had for a short time a second tail apparently in the opposite direction to the first (end of April, 1957; v. Pl. 24). The spectrum* of a C. consists of bright bands which point to the presence of carbon, cyanogen, hydrogen, methane and several other gaseous materials made incandescent by the Sun. Part of the light emitted by C.s is reflected sunlight, as shown by the Fraunhofer lines* which occur in their spectra (v. Comet cloud).

Comet cloud, a hypothetical cloud containing about 100,000 million comet heads with a combined mass of $^1/_{10}$ to $^1/_{100}$ that of the Earth. The centre of the cloud coincides with the Sun while its outer edges are more than 100,000 A.U. distant from the Sun. This hypothesis was first put forward by Schiaparelli (about 1870) and has since been elaborated by Professor Oort of Leyden, who estimates that only one in 100,000 can be observed.

It explains why there is an apparently endless supply of new comets, and also why their orbits deviate so markedly from those of other bodies in the solar system; the extensiveness of the cloud makes it possible not only for Jupiter but also for the nearest fixed stars to disturb their orbits.

Comet family, v. Jupiter's family of comets.

Comet finder or **comet seeker,** a telescope with a large aperture, weak magnification and a wide field of view. It is particularly suitable for observing heavenly objects which are not points (e.g. comets and nebulae).

Comparison spectrum, the spectrum* of a source of light present at the telescope, which is photographed along with, or immediately after, the stellar spectrum. Every position in a spectrum has its own exact wavelength. It is not usually possible to use the absorption or emission lines of the actual stellar spectrum to determine wavelengths, because these lines may be shifted (e.g. Doppler effect*), or their wavelengths may not be known. Prisms at the top and bottom ends of the spectrograph slit are made to reflect into the spectrograph light from a source whose wavelengths are accurately known, e.g. vaporized iron. Lines of known wavelengths of the C.s. thus appear above and below the star's spectrum whose wavelengths can now be obtained by comparing the stellar spectrum with the C.s. It is also possible to make the star's light, before it enters the spectrograph, pass through a material which absorbs one particular line. In the stellar spectrum we then find one definite dark line from which all the other wavelengths can be measured. The latter method is, in fact, the only one possible if we wish to photograph the spectra of many stars simultaneously with an objective prism.

Compass, v. Pyxis.

Compasses, v. Circinus.

Components, the individual stars of a double star. The main (i.e. brightest) star is given the prefix A, the other component(s) B, C, D, etc.

Conic sections, (→) the figures made by cutting a right circular cone with a plane. If the cutting plane is at right angles to the axis of the cone, the section is a circle (1). If we tilt the plane downwards, we obtain first an ellipse (2); then, when the cutting plane is parallel to the side of the cone, a parabola (3); and finally, when the cutting plane is more nearly parallel to the axis of the cone, a hyperbola (4). The circle and the parabola are limiting cases, i.e. they occur for only one position of the cutting plane. The circle and the

SOME PERIODIC COMETS WHOSE RETURN HAS BEEN OBSERVED

Name	Period in years	Distance of perihelion in A.U.	Distance of aphelion in A.U.	Year of first observation	Eccentricity of orbit	Date of last perihelion passage observed		Next return to perihelion
Encke	3·3	0·34	4·09	1786	0·850	19 Oct.	1957	1961
Giacobini-Zinner	6·3	0·94	5·84	1900	0·720	27 Oct.	1959	1966
Pons-Winnecke	6·3	1·23	5·56	1819	0·640	9 Sept.	1951	1964
Biela	6·6	0·86	6·19	1772	0·760	24 Sept.	1852	1
Faye	7·4	1·65	5·95	1843	0·570	4 March	1955	1962
Arend	7·8	1·83	6·02	1951	0·530	2 Sept.	1959	1967
Westphal	61·7	1·25	30·00	1852	0·920	27 Nov.	1913	1975
Olbers	69·6	1·18	32·70	1815	0·930	21 June	1956	2026
Halley	76·0	0·59	35·30	−466	0·967	20 April	1910	1986
Herschel-Rigollet	156·0	0·75	57·20	1788	0·974	9 Aug.	1939	2095

[1] Biela's comet has not returned since 1852; in 1846, it broke into two parts which have probably disintegrated since then.

ellipse are closed figures, while the parabola and hyperbola extend to infinity.

Kepler was the first to perceive that the orbits of the planets are *C.s.* (*v.* Kepler's laws). The orbits of the larger planets are elliptical, approaching circular form. Those of the smaller planets are elongated ellipses. The comets move in orbits consisting of elongated ellipses (or possibly hyperbolas) which are scarcely distinguishable from parabolas.

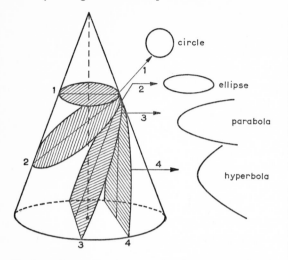

Conjunction, the (apparent) close approach of two heavenly objects on the celestial sphere. When the Moon or one of the planets is in conjunction with the Sun, it does not come above the horizon at night and is therefore invisible. When the Moon is in conjunction with the Sun, it is called the 'new Moon'. Mercury and Venus may both be in conjunction with the Sun twice during one orbit: once when they are between the Sun and the Earth (inferior conjunction) and once when the Sun is between them and the Earth (superior conjunction) (→ Opposition).

Constellations (*v.* Pl. 4), nowadays the areas into which the celestial sphere is divided. The stars are

designated by a serial Greek letter or number, or by one or two Arabic letters, followed by the name of the constellation (*v.* Star atlas). The division into *C.* is a useful means of describing approximate positions in the sky. Almost everyone in the northern hemisphere knows Ursa Major (→ 1–3), from which the north celestial pole can be found, since the line joining the stars β and α points approximately to the Pole Star. The names of most *C.* date back to ancient times. Many are called after animals and, to judge by the species included, might have been so named by shepherds in ancient Mesopotamia. The fact that names such as 'elephant' or 'tiger' are missing, shows that they did not originate in India, for example. Many *C.* were familiar to the Egyptians and the Greeks. They may have been used for position-fixing at sea, and the zodiacal* *C.* in particular were much used in astrology*. Various names of *C.* occur in Homer. The *Almagest* of Claudius Ptolemaeus (*c.* 150 A.D.) contains a description of 21 northern, 15 southern and 12 zodiacal *C.* Among them is the constellation of Argo Navis (the Ship of the Argonauts), which is now divided into Carina, Puppis and Vela. Many names are derived from Greek mythology.

Bayer used a great many of these old names in his star atlas, *Uranometria* (1603). He also gave names to several southern *C.* Hevelius (1611–87) named a few small *C.*, of which Lacerta, Lynx, Leo Minor and Vulpecula are still so called. Various names proposed in that era have since fallen into disuse. It was suggested, for instance, that all *C.* should be given names associated with Christianity, the 12 zodiacal *C.* to be called after the Apostles. The boundaries of the *C.* were originally very irregular. On the initiative of the International Astronomical Union, these boundaries were replaced by arcs of circles parallel or perpendicular to the celestial equator.

There are now 88 *C.* which are given in the adjoining table. The columns give successively the Latin name, the genitive (which is used for the designation of a star: *v.* Star atlas), the standard three-letter abbreviation adopted by the I.A.U., the English name, an indication of position in the sky (N = north, S = south, E = equatorial, Z = zodiacal, P = polar) and the principal stars or objects of interest.

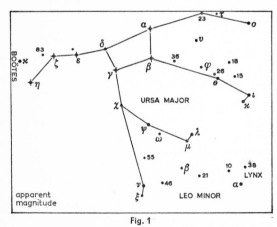

Fig. 1

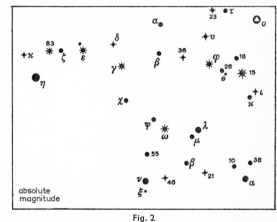

Fig. 2

magnitudes

+5 4 3 2 +1 0 -1 -2 -3 -4

Fig. 1. A constellation is formed by plotting the positions of the apparently brightest stars in relation to each other in a particular area of the sky (that shown is Ursa Major). These apparent magnitudes depend on: (a) the actual magnitudes, and (b) the actual distances of the stars from us. Fig. 2. The same stars plotted according to their actual magnitudes, i.e. as they would appear if each were situated 10 parsecs from the Sun. The original picture has now entirely disappeared

LIST OF 88 CONSTELLATIONS

Latin name	Genitive	Abbreviation	English name	Position	Some stars and other objects
Andromeda	Andromedae	And	Andromeda	N	Mirach, M31
Antlia	Antliae	Ant	Air Pump	S	
Apus	Apodis	Aps	Bird of Paradise	PS	
Aquarius	Aquarii	Aqr	Water-bearer	ZE	
Aquila	Aquilae	Aql	Eagle	E	Altair
Ara	Arae	Ara	Altar	S	
Aries	Arietis	Ari	Ram	ZN	Hamal
Auriga	Aurigae	Aur	Charioteer	N	Capella
Boötes	Boötis	Boö	Herdsman	N	Arcturus
Caelum	Caeli	Cae	Chisel	S	
Camelopardus	Camelopardi	Cam	Giraffe	PN	
Cancer	Cancri	Cnc	Crab	ZN	Praesepe
Canes Venatici	Canum Venaticorum	CVn	Hunting Dogs	N	Cor Caroli, M51
Canis Major	Canis Majoris	CMa	Great Dog	S	Sirius
Canis Minor	Canis Minoris	CMi	Little Dog	E	Procyon
Capricornus	Capricorni	Cap	Sea-goat	ZS	
Carina	Carinae	Car	Keel	S	Canopus
Cassiopeia	Cassiopeiae	Cas	Cassiopeia	N	supernova 1572
Centaurus	Centauri	Cen	Centaur	S	Proxima Centauri
Cepheus	Cephei	Cep	Cepheus	PN	
Cetus	Ceti	Cet	Whale	E	Mira
Chamaeleon	Chamaeleontis	Cha	Chameleon	PS	
Circinus	Circini	Cir	Compasses	S	
Columba	Columbae	Col	Dove	S	
Coma (Berenices)	Comae (Berenices)	Com	Berenice's Hair	N	
Corona Australis	Coronae Australis	CrA	Southern Crown	S	
Corona Borealis	Coronae Borealis	CrB	Northern Crown	N	Gemma
Corvus	Corvi	Crv	Crow	S	
Crater	Crateris	Crt	Cup	S	
Crux	Crucis	Cru	Southern Cross	S	Coal Sack
Cygnus	Cygni	Cyg	Swan	N	Deneb, North American neb.
Delphinus	Delphini	Del	Dolphin	N	
Dorado	Doradus	Dor	Swordfish	S	Large Magel. Cloud
Draco	Draconis	Dra	Dragon	PN	
Equuleus	Equulei	Equ	Little Horse	E	
Eridanus	Eridani	Eri	Eridanus	ES	Achernar
Fornax	Fornacis	For	Furnace	S	
Gemini	Geminorum	Gem	Twins	ZN	Castor, Pollux
Grus	Gruis	Gru	Crane	S	
Hercules	Herculis	Her	Hercules	N	Ras Algheti, M13
Horologium	Horologii	Hor	Clock	S	
Hydra	Hydrae	Hya	Water Serpent	ES	Alphard
Hydrus	Hydri	Hyi	Water Snake	PS	
Indus	Indi	Ind	Indian	S	
Lacerta	Lacertae	Lac	Lizard	N	
Leo	Leonis	Leo	Lion	ZN	Regulus, Denebola
Leo Minor	Leonis Minoris	LMi	Little Lion	N	
Lepus	Leporis	Lep	Hare	S	
Libra	Librae	Lib	Scales	ZS	
Lupus	Lupi	Lup	Wolf	S	
Lynx	Lyncis	Lyn	Lynx	N	
Lyra	Lyrae	Lyr	Lyre	N	Vega, M57
Mensa	Mensae	Men	Table Mountain	PS	
Microscopium	Microscopii	Mic	Microscope	S	
Monoceros	Monocerotis	Mon	Unicorn	E	
Musca	Muscae	Mus	Fly	PS	
Norma	Normae	Nor	Square	S	
Octans	Octantis	Oct	Octant	PS	
Ophiuchus	Ophiuchi	Oph	Serpent-bearer	E	supernova 1604
Orion	Orionis	Ori	Orion	E	Betelgeuse, Rigel, M42
Pavo	Pavonis	Pav	Peacock	S	
Pegasus	Pegasi	Peg	Pegasus	N	
Perseus	Persei	Per	Perseus	N	Algol
Phoenix	Phoenicis	Phe	Phoenix	S	
Pictor	Pictoris	Pic	Painter	S	
Pisces	Piscium	Psc	Fishes	ZE	
Piscis Austrinus	Piscis Austrini	PsA	Southern Fish	S	Fomalhaut
Puppis	Puppis	Pup	Poop	S	
Pyxis	Pyxidis	Pyx	Compass	S	
Reticulum	Reticuli	Ret	Net	S	
Sagitta	Sagittae	Sge	Arrow	N	
Sagittarius	Sagittarii	Sgr	Archer	ZS	Centre of the Galaxy
Scorpius	Scorpii	Sco	Scorpion	ZS	Antares
Sculptor	Sculptoris	Scl	Sculptor	S	
Scutum	Scuti	Sct	Shield (or Sobieski's Shield)	E	M16
Serpens	Serpentis	Ser	Serpent	E	
Sextans	Sextantis	Sex	Sextant	E	
Taurus	Tauri	Tau	Bull	ZN	Aldebaran, Pleiades, M1
Telescopium	Telescopii	Tel	Telescope	S	
Triangulum	Trianguli	Tri	Triangle	N	M33
Triangulum Australe	Trianguli Australis	TrA	Southern Triangle	PS	
Tucana	Tucanae	Tuc	Toucan	S	Small Magel. Cloud
Ursa Major	Ursae Majoris	UMa	Great Bear	N	Dubhe, Mizar
Ursa Minor	Ursae Minoris	UMi	Little Bear	PN	Polaris
Vela	Velorum	Vel	Sails	S	
Virgo	Virginis	Vir	Virgin	ZE	Spica
Volans	Volantis	Vol	Flying Fish	PS	
Vulpecula	Vulpeculae	Vul	Fox	N	

Continuous spectrum, v. Spectrum and Pl. 32.

Convection zone, part of the Sun, or of a star in general, where matter is constantly agitated by rising streams of hot gas, and falling streams of cold gas.

The Sun's convection zone extends from the photosphere to a very great depth. Various stars, not necessarily including the Sun, are thought to have a convective nucleus. This part of a star is, of course, not accessible to direct observation, and views on the subject are hypothetical. They are arrived at by calculations based on a 'stellar model' which has to correspond to an actual star or to the Sun as regards observable physical properties.

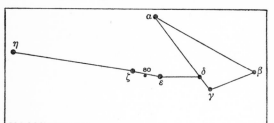

200,000 years ago

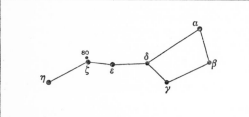

at present

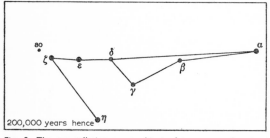

200,000 years hence

Fig. 3. The constellation as an object of temporary duration. Because of the proper motions of the individual stars composing it, the constellation as seen in the sky is slowly changing its shape. Ursa Major is here shown at three stages in its development. Stars β, γ, δ, ε, ξ and 80 belong to the same group and are moving at roughly the same speed and in the same direction. Stars α and η have obviously no connection with this group.

Co-ordinates (orthogonal), the distances of a point from two lines (the axes) which intersect each other at right angles. A system of orthogonal C. can be used to define the position of a point on a plane surface (2 axes) or in space (3 axes), and also to fix the position of a point on the celestial sphere (spherical C.). A system of C. is frequently used to represent the relation between two quantities; this type of representation is called a graph, examples of which are the period–luminosity* relation and the Hertzsprung-Russell diagram*.

Copernican system, the heliocentric theory published in *De Revolutionibus Orbium Coelestium* (1543) by the Polish astronomer, Nikolaus Kopernik or Copernicus (1473–1543). He opposed the ideas of the supporters of the Ptolemaic system* by showing that the celestial phenomena could be more easily explained if rotation of the Earth were assumed (which would at once account for the diurnal motion of the stars) and if the centre of the system were the Sun instead of the Earth. The planets, including the Earth, would then revolve around the Sun. This great break with tradition is usually regarded nowadays as the beginning of modern astronomy.

Cor Caroli, the star α Canum Venaticorum. The name was given by Halley; it means 'the heart of Charles' (Charles II of England).

Corona, the outermost extension of the Sun's atmosphere. Observable visually during a solar eclipse and with a coronagraph. Electromagnetic emission on radio wavelengths from the C. can be picked up on Earth. Temperature close to the Sun is about 1,000,000° K, and the C. has been traced to 10 diameters from the Sun. The C. is divided into two components, the F-corona and the K-corona (v. Sun and Pl. 28).

Corona Australis (the Southern Crown) is a small constellation in the southern hemisphere, situated between 17 h. 55 min. and 19 h. 15 min. R.A. and between —37° and —46° Dec. (→ Telescopium).

Corona Borealis (the Northern Crown), a small constellation in the northern sky, situated between 15 h. 15 min. and 16 h. 25 min. R.A. and between 26° and 40° N. Dec. (→).

Corona condensation, a region of great density in an active area of the solar corona, overlying active sunspots*. The density of a C.c. is 10–20 times greater than that of the surrounding corona.

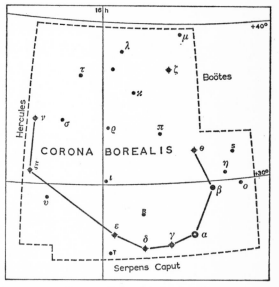

The constellation of Corona Borealis

Coronagraph. Although the Sun's corona can easily be seen during an eclipse when the Moon blots out the sunlight, it is not normally visible through a telescope. There are two reasons. In the first place, the molecules of the Earth's atmosphere scatter the light of the bright solar disk (one million times brighter than the corona) and so blot out the corona.

In the second place, light which is scattered inside the telescope (e.g. from particles of dust on the lens) also produces enough haze to blot out the faint coronal image.

The *C.* is a telescope specially designed to view the corona by ordinary daylight. The first difficulty is overcome by mounting the instrument on a high mountain and viewing the image through a Lyot filter* which passes only the light in one of the emission lines in the corona's spectrum, on the same principle that prominences can be seen in a spectroheliograph*. To overcome the second difficulty, all the optical components are of specially high quality and are kept rigidly free from dust. The lens forms an image of the Sun on a plane mirror whose diameter is very slightly greater than the image and which reflects most of the sunlight out of the tube. Only coronal light should pass the edges of this mirror, but in fact some direct sunlight does get past, due to diffraction at the edge of the lens, and faint images are formed by internal reflections in the lens. Further optical components are needed behind the mirror to allow these to be eliminated before the light is finally passed to the Lyot filter. The telescope must be kept at a uniform temperature to avoid currents inside the tube, which would also pass some light behind the mirror.

Corvus (the Crow) (→ Virgo), a small constellation in the southern hemisphere, situated between R.A. 11 h. 55 min and 12 h. 55 min. and Dec. —11° and —25°.

Cosmic rays (*v.* Pl. 5) are mainly protons of very high energy which originate outside the Earth's atmosphere. They are of great penetrating power. Their intensity increases with height above the Earth's surface, as has been shown by tests on mountains and with balloons and rockets. They can be detected several hundreds of yards beneath the Earth's surface. At very high altitudes *C.r.* seem to consist of very fast protons. Even in our modern laboratories it is still far from possible to impart similar velocities to protons. At sea level we find not only fast protons but also fast electrons and radiation on very short wavelengths (γ-rays). These have been generated by collision between the protons and air molecules. Although some *C.r.* are solar in origin, it is thought that they come mostly from sources outside the Sun. The study of *C.r.* has led to the discovery of various new fundamental particles. Perhaps their origin will be found to be explosions of supernovae, although this probably does not account for those of highest energy. Before man ventures beyond the Earth's atmosphere, he must first have full information about the power of *C.r.*, which are dangerous to living cells.

The artificial satellites have helped to discover a region of intensive cosmic radiation surrounding the Earth up to a distance of about 19,000 miles from the centre of our planet: the Van Allen* radiation belt. This belt contains two areas of particularly strong radiation. The first is about 6,250 miles from the centre of the Earth, and 40,000 particles per sq. cm/sec. have been counted there. At a distance of 10,000 miles this number drops to 1,000 per sq. cm/sec., then it increases again to about 40,000 particles per sq. cm/sec. at a distance of 14,000 miles. When a distance of 31,000 miles from the Earth is reached, the number has dropped to 10 per sq.cm/sec. declining still farther to $2^{1}/_{4}$ in interplanetary space.

Cosmogony (literally, theory of the birth of the universe), theory of the origin and development of the universe. Since the earliest times men have formed views about the origin of the universe. The facts furnished by modern physics, astronomy and chemistry form a good basis for reasonable speculation concerning the origin and history of the universe (*v.* Evolution of the stars and Universe).

Cosmology is used in astronomy in its literal meaning, 'science of the universe as a whole'.

Counterglow, *v.* Gegenschein.

Crab, *v.* Cancer.

Crab nebula, galactic nebula (M1) in the constellation of Taurus. Its distance from the Sun is 3,300 light-years (*v.* Pl. 39). Measurements on photographic plates taken over an interval of about 30 years show that the diameter of the nebula is expanding at an annual rate of about 0·21 seconds of arc (present diameter 1·6′). The nebula is thought to have been produced by the explosion of a supernova. If the rate of expansion (800 m.p.sec.) has remained unchanged, this would mean that the explosion took place about 900 years ago. Old chronicles relate that a new star as bright as Jupiter appeared in this part of the sky in 1054. The *C.n.* is one of the most powerful sources of radio radiation.

The *C.n.* has been the subject of much research in the last few years (since 1950), for it is remarkable in various respects: *a.* its spectrum is continuous, while all known bright nebulosities have line spectra; *b.* small bright spots are moving out from the centre at velocities of 19,000 m.p.sec., as Baade observed as long ago as 1942; *c.* there is no trace of a central star from which the *C.n.* could have originated, or to account for the phenomenon mentioned in *b.* above; *d.* its electromagnetic radiation was a mystery until recently.

When the Russian astronomers, Vashakidze and Dombrovsky, announced that the *C.n.* emits polarized light (i.e. light which vibrates only in one direction or plane), investigations at once took a new turn. The Russian observations were confirmed and supplemented at the Mount Palomar Observatory and at Leiden. Astronomers are now able to account for the peculiarities listed above, by the following explanation: in the innermost part of the *C.n.*, electrons are moving very rapidly in almost circular orbits, as a result of the magnetic fields prevailing there. Consequently polarized light is emitted on all wavelengths. The same mechanism therefore is also responsible for the radio waves emitted by the *C.n.* There is still complete uncertainty as to the origin of the magnetic field.

Crane, *v.* Grus.

Crater (the Cup) is a small constellation in the southern hemisphere. R.A. 10 h. 50 min. to 11 h. 55 min., Dec. —6° to —25°. Its three brightest stars are of the 4th magnitude. (→)

Craters (*v.* Pl. 12, 14), one name for the ring formations on the Moon's surface. The terms 'walled plains' and 'cirques' are preferred nowadays (*v.* Moon).

Crape ring, Saturn's innermost ring. It is much

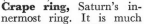

The constellation of Crater

fainter and more difficult to see than the outer two and was first observed in 1850. It is clearly visible with a 6-inch telescope. Inner diameter of *C.r.* 94,000 miles;

width 11,000 miles; distance from Saturn's surface 6,250 miles (*v.* Pl. 21).

Cross, Southern, *v.* Crux.

Crow, *v.* Corvus.

Crown, Northern, *v.* Corona Borealis.

Crown, Southern, *v.* Corona Australis.

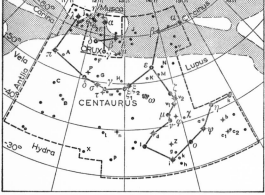

The constellations of Crux and Centaurus

Crux (the Southern Cross) is a small constellation situated in the Milky Way between R.A. 11 h. 55 min. and 12 h. 55 min. and Dec. —55° and —64°.

Culminations of a star are the points where the path of the star in its apparent diurnal motion crosses the meridian*. The upper culmination is the highest point on that path. If the entire path lies above the horizon the point where the star is at its minimum altitude is the lower culmination.

Cup, *v.* Crater.

Curvature of space, a mathematical concept which finds its physical and astronomical application in theories of the universe*. Just as a plane can be curved (e.g. the surface of a sphere), so, too, can space. It is not possible to visualize this idea, but by mathematics the properties of curved space can be determined.

According to the theory of relativity*, rays of light in the vicinity of concentrations of mass (galaxies, star clusters and stars) are slightly curved. This consequence of the theory has been tested with a fair degree of success during solar eclipses*, when the stars near the Sun in the sky are visible. The light rays from them have been found to be deflected through a small angle.

Cusps are the horns of the new or old Moon, or of a planet or satellite showing a similar phase.

Cygnus (the Swan), a northern constellation in the Milky Way between 19 h. 5 min. and 22 h. R.A. and

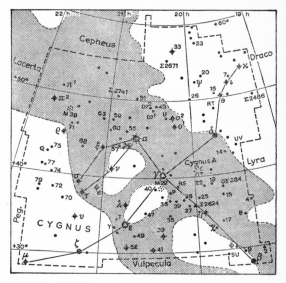

The constellation of Cygnus

+ 28° and + 60° Dec. It is rich in bright and dark nebulae, because here we are gazing in the direction of a spiral arm (*v.* Pl. 47). (→)

D

Dark nebulae, masses of dust in the spiral arms of a galaxy. They are visible in the sky as 'empty' spaces, where few stars can be seen; the light of the stars behind them is obscured by the dust. Two well-known examples are the dark nebulae in the vicinity of α Cygni and the Coal Sack near the Southern Cross (*v.* Interstellar matter). Similar dark nebulae can be seen on photographs of extragalactic nebulae. If a galaxy is so situated in space that it appears edge on to the Earth, we see the dark material in this plane as a dark belt stretching across the whole galaxy (*v.* Pl. 72).

Declination, one of the co-ordinates in the system of co-ordinates based on the celestial equator. The *D.* of a star is measured along the great circle through the star and two celestial poles (and therefore perpendicular to the celestial equator). It is the arc of the *D.* circle, measured from the intersection of this circle and the

celestial equator to the star. It is positive towards the north pole and negative towards the south. (*v.* Celestial sphere).

Deferent, *v.* Ptolemaic system.

Deimos, one of the two small satellites of the planet Mars, discovered by Hall in 1877. It orbits round Mars at a distance of 14,600 miles with a period of 30 h. 18 min. The latter is so nearly the same as the period of rotation of Mars that it remains above the horizon for over 60 hours at a stretch. Its estimated diameter is 5 miles. Observed from Mars, *D.* would be visible merely as a bright star. It can only be seen from Earth with powerful telescopes.

Delphinus (the Dolphin), a small constellation in the northern sky. R.A. 20 h. 10 min. to 21 h. 10 min. Dec. 2°N. to 21°N. (→ facing)

Deneb, the star α Cygni. One of the brightest stars in the sky. Apparent magnitude 1·33, absolute magnitude — 5·2, distance 650 light-years, luminosity 10,000 × Sun's, spectral class A2 (*v.* Pl. 47).

Denebola, the star β Leonis. Apparent magnitude 2·2, spectral type A2.

Descending node, the intersection of the orbit of the Moon or a planet and the plane of the ecliptic; or of the orbit of a double star and a plane at right angles to the line of sight, where the celestial body crosses the plane from north to south (*v.* Orbit).

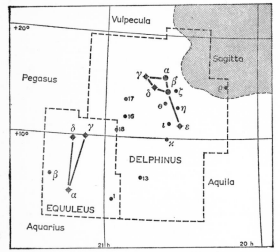

The constellations of Delphinus and Equuleus

Diamond ring effect, a light phenomenon observed at solar eclipses (*v.* Pl. 28).

Dione, one of Saturn's moons, discovered by Cassini in 1864. Distance from the planet 235,000 miles, period 2 d. 17 h. 41 min., diameter 700 miles (?), magnitude at opposition 10·7.

Disappearance, *v.* Immersion.

Discoverer, name of a series of American artificial satellites*.

Distance finding is one of the most important problems in astronomy. Only by knowing the distances of the celestial bodies we see projected on the heavens are we able to say anything about their distribution in space or the spatial structure of the universe as a whole. Astronomy has therefore devised a selection of methods for measuring distances. Some of the most important will be dealt with here.

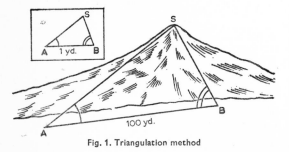

Fig. 1. Triangulation method

The TRIANGULATION METHOD is a method also used by terrestrial surveyors (→ 1). If a mountain peak S is inaccessible but a surveyor wishes to know the distance AS, he proceeds as follows: at A he measures the angular distance between S and a point B. Then he

goes to B (say 100 yards farther) and measures the angular distance between S and A. He now knows three things about triangle ABS: the base AB (100 yards) and angles A and B. He could now draw the triangle to scale (→ 1, inset) and measure AS on it. In actual practice the distance AS is found by trigonometry.

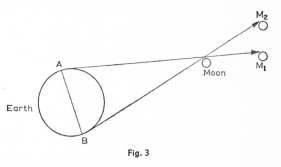

Fig. 2

In much the same way the altitude of a 'falling star' or meteor is determined (→ 2). An observer at A and another at B each measure the elevation and azimuth of M, the end of the meteor trail. The altitude can be calculated from these angles and the distance AB. The distance of the Moon and the nearest planets can be calculated in the same way, but not the distance of the Sun. The direction of the Moon is measured simultaneously from two observatories A and B situated as far from each other as possible. From these two angles and the distance AB, the distance can once more be found (→ 3).

If we wish to apply this method in measuring the distance of a star, we must somehow obtain a much greater base AB than is obtainable on Earth, because the stars are so far away that even the most accurate instruments would give almost the same reading from both A and B. There is, however, one way of extending our base. The Earth describes its orbit around the Sun in one year (→ 4). If we measure the angle at which we see the star S in January and then again six months later in July, we can calculate the star's distance from the triangle ABS, which now has a base of about 186 million miles, i.e. the diameter of the Earth's orbit.

Fig. 3

This is generally done by taking a photograph in, say, January, (→ 5a) and then another in July (→ 5b). The photographs are placed one upon the other (→ 5c). The very remote stars appear to have stayed in the same position, while star S has shifted from its January position. Theoretically, this again appears to be a simple method but it was not until 1838 that it was successfully employed to determine the distance of a 'nearby' star. In the first place the displacement was extremely small; in the second the issue was confused by various other phenomena which also cause displacement of a star, e.g. aberration and the star's proper motion.

Some definitions: (→ 4). Half the angle BSA is called the star's parallax. It is obtained directly from the angles measured at A and B. If it is 1 sec. of arc (i.e. $^1/_{3,600}$°), the star's distance is said to be 1 parsec (→ 6). 1 parsec = 206,265 A.U. = 3·26 light-years. The distance of a star in parsecs is inversely proportional to its angle of parallax. The value in parsecs is derived directly from the observation and the parsec is therefore a unit which astronomers often like to use. In 1836 Bessel at Königsberg was the first to discover the parallax of a star (a small star in Cygnus). This was not the largest stellar parallax, which proved to be that of the star Proxima Centauri, viz. 0·76″, corresponding to a distance of 4·3 light-years. All other stars have a smaller parallax and are therefore farther away. From a distance of about 100 light-years onwards the angle of parallax is too small to measure, so that recourse must be had to indirect methods.

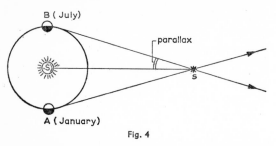

Fig. 4

The following two methods are based on a different principle. If we know how bright a source of light is (e.g. how bright it appears at a distance of 1 yard), we can calculate its distance by its apparent brightness. This is because the brightness of a light-source is inversely proportional to the square of its distance, e.g. a candle appears 9 times fainter at 3 yards than it does at 1 yard. We distinguish between a star's apparent magnitude and its absolute magnitude; the latter is by definition the magnitude it would have at a distance of 10 parsecs (32·6 light-years). The apparent magnitude is that of the star as we see it in the sky; if, somehow or other, we can estimate the absolute magnitude of a star, we can calculate its distance.

The PERIOD-LUMINOSITY LAW is one means of discovering a star's absolute magnitude (v. Cepheid variables). Miss Leavitt showed that in δ Cephei and RR Lyrae type variable stars*, there was a definite relation between the absolute median magnitude of the star and its period. She investigated a number of cepheid variables in the Magellanic Clouds and plotted a graph showing the period of the cepheids on the X-axis and the median luminosity of each cepheid on the Y-axis. As all the stars investigated were roughly the same distance away (belonging to the Magellanic Clouds), the difference in apparent magnitude of the stars was not due to a difference in distance but to one of absolute magnitude.

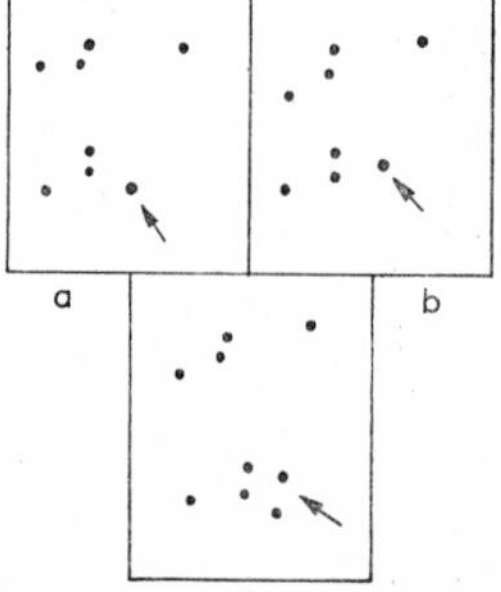

This graph is not yet suitable for determining the absolute magnitude of a cepheid; it has still to be calibrated with the aid of a few cepheids whose absolute magnitude we have determined by another method (→ Period-luminosity law). With these we finally obtain a period-luminosity curve for cepheids, from which we can find the luminosity of any cepheid if its period is known.

The procedure for finding the distance of an obvious

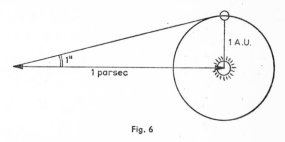

Fig. 5

group of stars with the aid of a cepheid is therefore as follows: *a.* a variable star amongst them has to be discovered photographically: *b.* photographs must be taken daily for about 100 days to establish whether it is a cepheid; *c.* its mean apparent magnitude is determined; *d.* its period is found; *e.* its absolute luminosity is read off from the period–luminosity graph; *f.* the distance is calculated by the formula relating absolute and apparent magnitude (*v.* Distance modulus). With this method and our largest telescope, the Hale telescope on Mount Palomar, it is possible to determine distances up to about 2 million light-years.

Many of the extragalactic nebulae* that have been photographed are so remote that it is impossible to resolve a single star in them (although, in the case of the nearest galaxies outside the Local Group, it is possible to detect the very brightest constituent stars, and their apparent magnitudes enable us to estimate their distances statistically), and the cepheid method of distance finding is therefore inapplicable. It is, however, assumed that extragalactic nebulae of the same type are of approximately the same absolute magnitude. Their distances are thus calculated from their estimated magnitudes and their apparent magnitudes.

This method is obviously not precise, and at best can only be statistically accurate, but so far it is the only method that can be applied to the most distant objects that we are capable of photographing. Distances of several thousand million light-years have been found in this way. The red shift* also provides us with a

Fig. 6

means of establishing the distances of extragalactic nebulae (*v.* Hubble's constant). Other methods of *D.f.* are possible in special cases, e.g. stars for which a detailed spectrum can be obtained (*v.* Spectroscopic parallax).

Distance modulus, a measure of the distance of stars and extragalactic nebulae: the apparent magnitude minus the absolute magnitude (m—M).

If m—M = 5 magnitudes, the distance is 100 parsecs (m—M = 5 $\log_{10}$D—5, where D = distance in parsecs).

D-layer, an ionized part of the Earth's atmosphere between heights of 40 and 50 miles.

Dog, Great, *v.* Canis Major.

Dog, Little, *v.* Canis Minor.

Dog Star, *v.* Sirius.

Dolphin, *v.* Delphinus.

Doppler effect is observed when a radiating source is approaching or receding from the observer. If the radiating source is approaching, we detect more vibrations in one second than are emitted in one second. Thus, when a train is rushing towards us, its whistle has a higher pitch than when the train is stationary. When it is going away from us, we hear a lower pitch. An approaching source of light-waves can be detected from the fact that its spectral lines shift to the

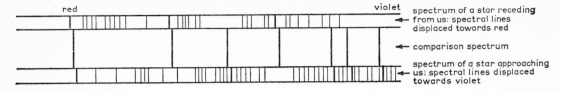

spectrum of a star receding from us: spectral lines displaced towards red

comparison spectrum

spectrum of a star approaching us: spectral lines displaced towards violet

violet end, while in the case of a receding source they are displaced to the red end (*v.* Red shift) (→). The relative velocity of a light source can be calculated from the amount of shift in the spectral lines. If a star has a relative velocity of 62·5 m.p.sec. (100 km/sec.), the spectral lines are displaced 1·67 Å. at a wavelength of 5,000 Å. The *D.e.* not only enables us to find the radial velocity* of a star but can also be used to prove that heavenly bodies are rotating. If a star is rotating on an axis which is not directly in the line of sight, one part of the star approaches us while the other recedes. The spectral lines of that part of the star which is approaching will be slightly shifted towards the blue and, for that part which is receding, towards the red, which results in a typical widening of the spectral lines (→ Rotation and Double stars).

In the case of larger celestial bodies both the velocity and the direction of rotation can be found. For example, if we align the slit of the spectroscope with Saturn's equator, we obtain a spectrum (→ Saturn). In the brighter central part of this the absorption lines slant downwards to the left; this is the spectrum of the actual planet. One half is approaching us, so that the spectral lines are shifted to the violet, while the other is receding, giving a red shift. The result is the slope of the spectral lines. The spectral lines of the ring have a different slope from that of Saturn itself; the ring rotates faster than the planet and its velo-

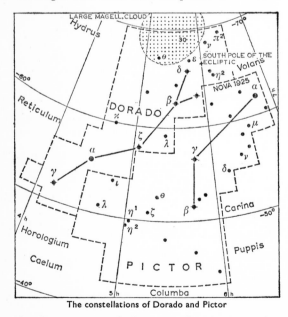

The constellations of Dorado and Pictor

city decreases towards the outer edge. An impressive example of *D.e.* is to be seen in the spectra of distant extragalatic nebulae* (*v.* Pl. 83).

Dorado (the Swordfish), a constellation in the southern hemisphere. It lies between 3 h. 50 min. and 6 h. 35 min. R.A. and —48° and —70° Dec. The most important object in it is probably the Large Magellanic Cloud (*v.* Pl. 64), a galaxy situated close to our Galaxy. This galaxy is clearly visible with the naked eye (*v.* Magellanic Clouds). (→)

Double stars (*v.* Pl. 36), a group of two or more stars which appear close together when viewed by tele-

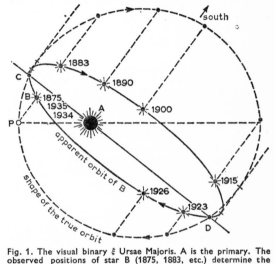

Fig. 1. The visual binary ξ Ursae Majoris. A is the primary. The observed positions of star B (1875, 1883, etc.) determine the apparent orbit, which is the projection of the true orbit on the celestial sphere. Above, the true orbit is the broken ellipse (almost a circle) in the plane of the paper. The correspondence between points in the true and apparent orbits is shown. CD is the line along which the plane of the true orbit intersects the plane of the sky. P = periastron. Stars A and B are both spectroscopic binaries, so that ξ Ursae Majoris is a quadruple system.

scope. Optical doubles are two or more stars which, by accident of position, appear in the sky close to each other but are not physically connected. Binaries are *D.s.* whose components together form a system; as a result of mutual attraction they revolve round each other and move through space as a single whole. Depending on the method required to detect them, binaries are divided into the following categories:

a. visual binaries, which can be resolved with a telescope;

b. spectroscopic binaries, which can only be distinguished with the aid of a spectroscope;

c. eclipsing binaries or variables, whose orbital planes are in line with the Earth, with the result that the components alternately eclipse one another.

As long ago as 1650 Riccioli discovered that **Mizar** consists of two stars. It was thought at that time that stars of this kind merely appear to be together in the celestial sphere.

In 1803 William Herschel first succeeded in observing the orbit of the components of Castor. Then

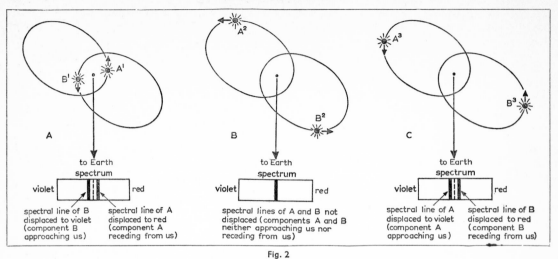

Fig. 2

astronomers started to distinguish between apparent and true binary systems. The first catalogues of these objects were compiled by William Herschel (1782–84) and Wilhelm Struve (1827). Binaries are designated by the initial or name of the discoverer and the number of the star in his catalogue: W. Struve = Σ, Otto Struve = $O\Sigma$, Burnham is β, Hussey = Hu, Aitken = A. The brightest component is called A, the next brightest B, and so on, e.g. Krueger 60B.

It appears that a large proportion of all stars are multiple systems. Investigation of the stars in the vicinity of the Sun (all stars within 5 parsecs), which were thus readily observable, showed that of the 42 'stars' in that area 11 are composite systems, or that the 42 objects, in fact, consist of 55 stars. Kuiper thinks that 80% of all stars belong to multiple systems. The view is generally held nowadays that the evolution of multiple systems is a normal development. It is assumed that they evolve from nebular masses. After a star has formed, the remaining nebular mass is supposed either to have developed into yet another star or possibly to have condensed into a planetary system. If insufficient nebular matter is left over, a cloud of comet heads may be formed (v. Solar system). In the first case the star formed is a binary.

Visual binaries (→ 1). The instrument used for measurement is a double-image micrometer. The values found are the angular distance between the components in seconds of arc and the position angle, which is the angle that the line joining the brighter component to the fainter component makes with a circle of right ascension, measured from the north in an easterly direction. The possibility of observing binaries which are very close depends on the resolving power of the telescope, and this in turn is determined by the diameter of the lens or mirror (v. Telescope). Pairs whose members differ greatly in magnitude are more difficult to resolve than pairs in which the members are equally bright. The star Sirius B, though of the 7th magnitude, is very difficult to observe directly, even with a powerful telescope, because it is outshone by Sirius A (magnitude −1·6). If the components are too close to each other for the resolving power of a large telescope, an interferometer may be used.

Recourse may also be had to photography for the measurement of binaries, in which case a Muller micro-

meter (double-image) is employed. The actual orbit of the lighter component around the heavier is not obtained directly; for the orbit observed is merely the apparent projection of the actual orbit on the celestial sphere. The elements of the orbits correspond to those of planetary orbits (v. Orbit). If the orbit is known from a number of observations and from calculations, the spectroscope can be used to determine in which part of the orbit the star is moving towards or away from us. We then know which part of the orbit is directed towards us (v. Doppler effect).

Spectroscopic binaries (→ 2). The first spectroscopic pairs were discovered in 1889. Telescopes cannot resolve the components of such pairs because the distances between them are too small. The spectral lines shift periodically to the left and right of their normal position. From the amount of this shift, to the violet end of the spectrum if the component is approaching us, to the red if it is receding (v. Doppler effect), we can calculate the change in velocity and find out the period. For the latter a velocity curve is drawn by plotting direction and speed against the time of the observation. Most orbital elements can then be calculated. If the two components are about equally bright, the lines will be seen to double periodically, i.e. one line shifts to the red while the other shifts at the same rate towards the violet: one component is moving towards us, while the other is moving away from us.

If the orbital plane of a close double star is perpendicular to our line of sight, there are no motions towards or away from us, and the double stars cannot be identified as such. The lower limit for observed periods of spectroscopic binaries is very short, viz. a few hours for a binary in which the two stars are almost touching. There is really no upper limit to the periods, which eventually merge with those of visual binaries. In fact there are some border-line stars which can be observed both ways—with the telescope and with the spectroscope.

Eclipsing variables (→ 3) are *D.s.* whose orbital plane is edgewise to the earth, so that the components are able to occult each other in turn. All *D.s.* would therefore be eclipsing variables if observed from a particular direction. Consequently, eclipsing variables form a special group only with regard to the method of observation.

As long ago as 1670 Montanari observed that Algol varied in brightness. In 1782 Goodricke discovered that this variation is periodic in character (2 d. 20 h. 49

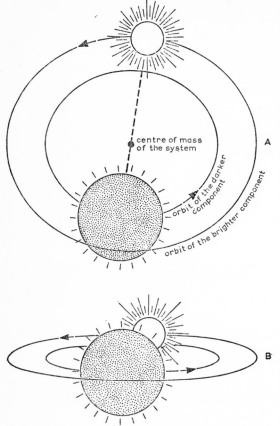

Fig. 3. A. A double star. The dark star is the larger component, the bright star the smaller. B. The same star as seen from a point close to the orbital plane. The double star is now an eclipsing variable

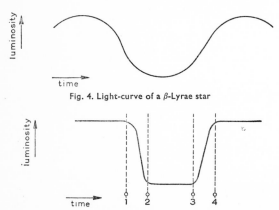

Fig. 4. Light-curve of a β-Lyrae star

Fig. 5. Light-curve of a central eclipse. 1–2: the eclipsed star disappears; 2–3: the eclipsed star moves behind the disk of the eclipsing star; 3–4: the eclipsed star re-appears

min.). For about 60 hours the luminosity remains nearly constant, during the next 5 hours it decreases

to $^1/_3$, then returns to normal in another 5 hours. During the eclipse (lasting 10 hours) a darker star passes in front of a brighter star, decreasing the luminosity of the system as a whole (→ 6). It was later discovered that 25 hours after the end of the eclipse another, but slight, decrease in light occurs: the brighter star is then occulting the darker. The latter attenuation of the light is called the 'secondary minimum', the former the 'primary minimum'. The form of the light-curves reveals various items of information about the actual stars and their orbits. If one star is brighter than the other, we see a curve similar to Algol's, with a deep primary minimum and a shallow secondary minimum. If the minima are equal, the stars are equally bright. Usually, the orbital plane of the component will not be exactly edgewise to the Earth. The transit of one star by the other is therefore not central, and the eclipse is only partial. The light from the system lessens, then quickly becomes brighter again. If the transit is central, then the loss of light, which increases steadily while the one star is disap-

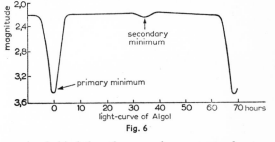

Fig. 6

pearing behind the other, remains constant as long as that star is fully occulted (→5). If the stars are equally bright and describe an orbit so tight that they nearly touch, the transit from one eclipse to the other takes place without a definite interruption (→ 4). Double stars of spectral types A–F are almost always practically touching. The light variations of some eclipsing variables are observable with the naked eye, as follows:

Star	Magnitude		Period
	Maximum	Minimum	
β Persei (Algol)	2.2	3.5	2 d. 20 h. 49 min.
β Lyrae	3.4	4.3	12 d. 21 h. 48 min.
λ Tauri	3.8	4.2	3 d. 22 h. 52 min.
V Puppis	4.1	4.8	1 d. 10 h. 55 min.
δ Librae	4.8	5.9	2 d. 7 h. 51 min.
u Herculis	4.8	5.3	2 d. 1 h. 14 min.

Although it was formerly thought that *D.s.* could be created by fission of a single star (e.g. by fast rotation), it is thought nowadays that a multiple star originates from separate condensations in a single globule.

Slight perturbations observed in the orbits of some stars in the vicinity of the Sun have led to the conclusion that these stars have invisible companions. One example is 61 Cygni (*v.* Star, Table 11). 61 Cygni is a double star whose components rotate round each other once per 720 years. In 1942, a third dark companion was found by K. A. Strand. The orbit of this body occupies only 0·02″ in the sky. As its mass is 0·008 of a solar mass (8 times the mass of Jupiter), it is not clear whether this body is to be regarded as a small dark star or as an exceptionally heavy planet. The following stars are thought to have dark companions of this kind: Barnard's Star (distance from Sun 6

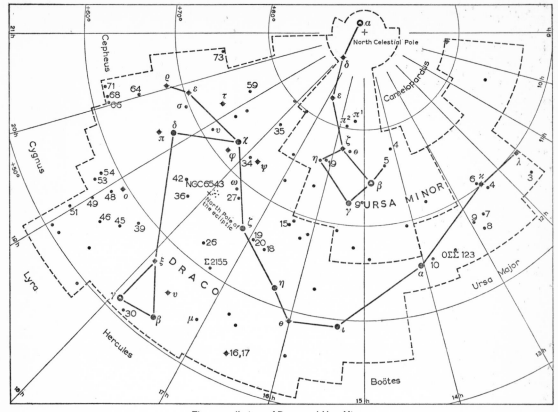

The constellations of Draco and Ursa Minor

light-years), Lallelande 21185 (8·2 l.y.), 61 Cygni (11·1 l.y.), Ross 614 (13·1 l.y.: dark companion observed with the 200-inch telescope, magnitude 14·8(?)), and BD + 20° 2465 (15·4 l.y.).

Double star cluster in Perseus, example of an open star cluster (*v.* Pl. 41).

Dove, *v.* Columba.

Draco (the Dragon), a constellation in the vicinity of the north celestial pole, between 9 h. 20 min. and 20 h. 40 min. R.A., and 47° and 86°N. Dec. (→)

Draconids, name of two meteor showers* whose radiants are situated in the constellation of Draco: *a.* also called the Giacobinids, observable about 9th October. Period 6·6 years, associated with the comet 1900 III; *b.* name of a meteor shower, observable about 28th June, associated with Pons-Winnecke's comet.

Dragon, *v.* Draco.

Draper Classification, a special arrangement of stars into spectral types (*v.* Spectral types). The photographic study of stellar spectra was initiated by Pickering in 1885. This work was continued at Harvard Observatory under the direction of Miss Cannon, who gave the *D.C.* its present form. The result is the Henry Draper Catalogue, which gives the positions, magnitudes and spectral classes of 225,300 stars in 9 volumes (completed in 1924). The name Draper was given to the catalogue and the classification used in it as a tribute to Henry Draper, who was the first man in America to photograph a stellar spectrum.

Dubhe, the star α Ursae Majoris, apparent magnitude 1·9, spectral class K0.

Durchmusterung, a star catalogue in which the properties of all stars down to a certain magnitude in a particular part of the sky or the whole sky, are described. The Bonner *D.* (BD) lists the positions of 450,000 objects down to a magnitude of 9·5. The Harvard *D.* and the Potsdamer *D.* list stars of photographic magnitudes down to 6·5 and 7·5 respectively. A well-known spectral *D.* is the Henry Draper Catalogue (*v.* Star catalogue and Draper Classification).

Dust in the spiral arms of galaxies, *v.* Pl. 66, 70, 72, 74, 77, 79, 86.

Dust, volcanic, *v.* Moon.

Dwarf stars are relatively faint stars which are to be found in two places in the Hertzsprung-Russell diagram*. Red dwarfs are all stars at the lower end of the main sequence while white dwarfs occur on the left below the main sequence (→ Hertzsprung-Russell diagram). Because of their faintness, they have to be fairly near to be observable and only a few hundreds have been positively identified. It may be that over half the stars in the universe are red dwarfs.

The white dwarfs, which must also be relatively common, have an exceptionally high density. A well-known white dwarf is the small companion of Sirius (Sirius B). Its mass is nearly equal to the Sun's, but its dimensions are those of a large planet (4 × the Earth's diameter). Its density is about 30,000 times that of water. This is possible because the material of which the star is made has been broken down into loose nuclei and electrons and these have recombined in a new compact formation unknown in other types of star.

Eagle, *v.* Aquila.

Earth (*v.* Pl. 7), one of the planets of our solar system, on which life originated and where man is now the most highly developed form of life. It was thought in antiquity that the *E.* was at the centre of the universe (*v.* Ptolemaic system), but it is now known that the *E.* does not even occupy a special place in the solar system, nor does the Sun in our Galaxy, nor our Galaxy in the universe. All that can be said is that the *E.*, by its position in relation to the Sun, is well placed, with regard to temperature, for the development of life as we know it: planets closer to the Sun are too hot, and planets farther from it are too cold. And while it is naturally not beyond the bounds of possibility that life in some form or another can exist under different circumstances, development similar to that which has taken place on *E.* is unlikely elsewhere in the solar system (*v.* Life in the solar system, under Solar system).

The *E.* has an atmosphere which shields life from: *a.* particles (meteorites) and *b.* harmful ultra-violet rays and X-rays, and prevents excessive heat radiation and hence excessive cooling at night. The possession of an atmosphere by a planet depends, *inter alia*, on the planet's mass; smaller bodies exert a lesser power of attraction, making it possible for molecules of gas, by their high velocity, to escape beyond the planet's zone of influence and disappear into space (*v.* Atmosphere and Pl. 5).

The *E.* consists of the lithosphere, or solid portion; the hydrosphere, or water on its surface; and the atmosphere, or gaseous envelope. The lithosphere is

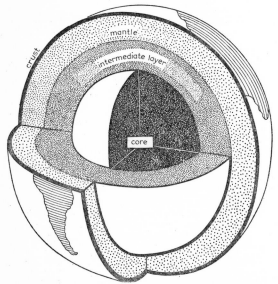

Fig. 1. Diagram to illustrate the Earth's structure: crust (granite, basalt), mantle (plateau basalts, sialsima or sialma), intermediate layer (silicates, oxides, sulphides, metals), core (nickel-iron)

thought to comprise a 'core'—composed, most geologists believe, of nickel iron—a 'mantle' and a 'crust' (→ 1). Some scientists think that the number of shells

is larger and opinions, therefore, also vary as to the chemical composition and physical properties of the layers. The outer layer, or crust, is very thin (22 miles) and consists mainly of granite and basalt. The structure of the inner *E.* is investigated in various ways, including the measurement of the direction and speed of propagation of seismic waves.

The investigation of the lithosphere is the task of geologists; that of the hydrosphere is conducted by, *inter alios*, meteorologists and geologists, the latter being concerned, for example, with the effect of water and ice on the form of the *E.*'s surface.

The atmosphere is a mixture of various gases, and at sea level consists on the average of:

nitrogen	77·6 %
oxygen	20·7 %
water vapour from	2·6 % at the equator to
	0·0 % at the poles
argon	0·9 %
carbon dioxide	0·03 %,

with traces of several other gases and solid particles of ash, soot, salt and sand, etc.

This mixture of gases becomes less dense with height but its chemical composition (except for the water-vapour content) remains constant up to an altitude of $12^1/_2$ miles. Ozone occurs in the layer from $12^1/_2$ to 25 miles above the *E.*, and then the composition is the same as at ground level, except for water-vapour.

The atmosphere (*v.* Pl. 5) is divided into various layers, the most important of which are the troposphere (0–5 miles at the poles, 0–11 miles at the equator), where weather is formed; the stratosphere (up to 50 miles); the ionosphere (up to 250–300 miles); and finally, the exosphere, which gradually merges into interplanetary space. Physical phenomena in the atmosphere are studied by meteorologists.

THE EARTH'S MOTION. In 395 B.C. Heraclides of Pontus maintained that the *E.* rotated about an axis, but until the time of Copernicus (sixteenth century) the diurnal rotation of the celestial sphere was usually interpreted as actual motion of the Sun, stars and planets (*v.* Ptolemaic system). In 1851 Foucault demonstrated the *E.*'s rotation with his famous pendulum experiment. The pendulum consisted of a heavy iron ball suspended on a steel wire in the dome of the Panthéon at Paris. When the pendulum was set in motion it was found that the vertical plane of the pendulum's motion started to rotate in relation to the floor. It was not the pendulum that was changing its direction but the building itself: because of the *E.*'s rotation, the south side was moving eastwards faster than the north. If the experiment had been conducted at the pole, the pendulum's plane would have completed one revolution per 24 hours; at the equator no deviation would have been noticeable.

At present several proofs of the *E.*'s axial rotation are known, e.g. deviations in the direction of winds and sea currents, resulting from the fact that the linear speed of the *E.*'s rotation is greatest at the equator and decreases towards the poles.

In 1956 and again in 1959 Professor Danjon observed that the Earth rotated more slowly after a powerful eruption on the Sun. In other words, the Earth is

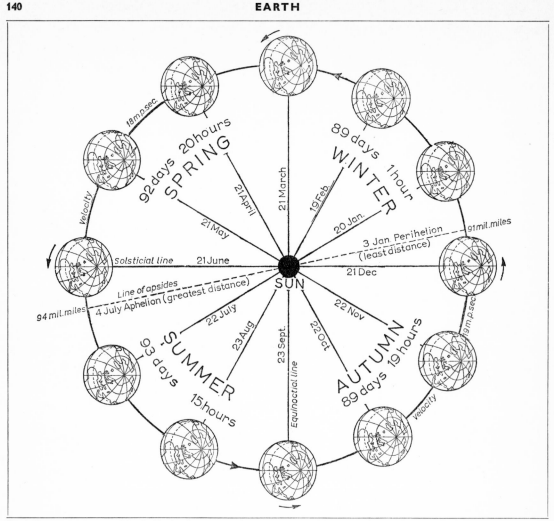

Fig. 2. The positions occupied by the Earth relative to the Sun in the course of a year, and the resultant seasons. Spring and summer are about 5 days longer than autumn and winter because Earth's orbit is slightly elliptical

being slowed down by the Sun, the difference after the 1959 explosion being 1/1000 sec. per day. From this we must conclude that the day is gradually becoming longer.

The E. also moves in an orbit around the Sun. The time necessary for one complete revolution of this kind is called a year (365¼ days). The shape of the orbit is an almost circular ellipse, with the Sun at one of its two foci (v. Orbit). As the inclination of the E.'s axis does not change, the northern and southern hemispheres are alternately presented more or less directly to the Sun's rays (→ 2). In June the north pole is presented more to the Sun, the Sun shines more strongly on the northern hemisphere and it is summer there. In December, after half a revolution by the E., the south pole is presented more to the Sun and it is summer in the southern hemisphere (winter in the northern).

THE SHAPE OF THE EARTH. Owing to its rotation on its axis and the centrifugal forces consequently set up, the E. is not perfectly spherical but is approximately a spheroid*. As the linear speed of rotation is greatest

at the equator and decreases towards the poles, where it is zero, the parts of the E.'s surface nearest the equator have swung out from the E.'s axis more than have those parts at higher latitudes. Its elasticity, however, has prevented the sphere from being torn asunder, although it is slightly flattened at the poles.

This flattening amounts to 13 miles. Observations of the orbit of the artificial satellite Vanguard 1 (launched on 17 March, 1958) have led to the conclusion that the Earth's shape displays yet another irregularity, viz. that the North Polar region lies 10 miles higher and the South Polar region 10 miles lower than the flattening.

THE AGE OF THE EARTH. Formerly, it was thought that the planets were originally part of the Sun and that they had been cast off and then cooled down to form solid bodies. It is now believed by many that the planets were formed cold, about the same time as the Sun (v. Planetary system and Pl. 93); attempts to compute the age of the E. appear to show that it is of the same order as that of the Sun and stars. Various methods can be used to assess the E.'s age:

a. By determining the age of the atoms of which all matter is composed. Radio-active isotopes occurring in nature are used for this purpose. Such substances decay at a particular rate which is independent of external influences. This rate is expressed in terms of 'half-life', i.e. the length of time required for the substance to decay to a half of its original quantity. It has been found that isotopes with a half-life greater than 5,000 million years are still encountered in fairly large quantities, while those with a half-life smaller than that occur less often. 5,000 million years is now accepted as the most probable estimate of the age of these atoms.

b. By determining the age of the E.'s crust. For this, various methods are used which are also based on radio-active processes, e.g. the uranium-lead method. When uranium and thorium decay, lead isotopes are formed which differ from normal lead. By determining the ratio between these lead isotopes and the surviving uranium and thorium in different samples of earth, it is possible to work out, on the basis of the half-life, the time at which these radio-active elements must have originated. The conclusion reached is that the matter forming the E.'s crust existed at least 3,500 million years ago. The rubidium-strontium method is somewhat similar.

c. On the basis of gases in the E.'s atmosphere which may have originated from the decay of substances in the E.'s crust, an age of 5,000 million years is arrived at for the E.'s atmosphere.

During the International Geophysical Year (1 July, 1957 to 1 Jan. 1959) the atmosphere and the oceans in particular were the objects of international investigation. This period was chosen because of the maximum sunspot activity expected then (*v.* Sun). During solar activity the Sun's radiation has a pronounced effect on the Earth's magnetism and on the outer layers of the Earth's atmosphere, and consequently on the propagation of radio waves and on radio communication. Artificial satellites were also used in the investigation.

Data:

E.'s radius at the equator (a)
                    3,963·347 miles (6,378·388 km)
E.'s radius at the poles (b)
                    3,950·002 miles (6,356·912 km)
Oblateness* $= \text{a-b}/\text{a} = \frac{1}{297}$ a–b = 13·3 miles
Equatorial circumference   24,902·4 miles
Surface area   196,951,000 sq. m. (510,100,900 km²)
Mass   5,977 × 10²⁷ g = 5,883 × 10¹⁸ tons
Mean density   5·52 × that of water
Axial rotation   23 h. 56 min. 4 sec. = 1 sidereal day
Distance from Sun (= 1 A.U.)   92·96 million miles
Period* (sidereal year*)   365 d. 6 h. 9 min. 9 sec.
Eccentricity   0·017
Orbital velocity   18·5 m.p. sec. (29·8 km/sec.)
Albedo*   0·39
Velocity of escape (surface) 7·0 m.p.sec. (11·2 km/sec.)

Eccentricity is one of the elements of an orbit. It defines the shape of the elliptical orbit and is the ratio *e* of the distance between the centre and one of the foci to the semi-axis major (*v.* Orbit; in the figure *e* = MS/a). In the case of a circle, *e* = 0; of an ellipse, *e* is between 0 and 1; of a parabola, *e* = 1; and of a hyperbola, *e* exceeds 1.

ECCENTRICITY OF PLANETARY ORBITS

Mercury	0·21	Saturn	0·06
Venus	0·01	Uranus	0·05
Earth	0·02	Neptune	0·01
Mars	0·09	Pluto	0·25
Jupiter	0·05		

The orbits of the comets are generally much more eccentric (Halley's comet is 0·967).

Echo is the name for a series of American Earth satellites of which one (launched on 12 August, 1960) has so far been successful. This satellite consists of a large spherical balloon (100 feet in diameter), and two radio transmitters (*v.* Artificial satellite).

Eclipse, *v.* Lunar eclipse and Solar eclipse.

Eclipsing variables, or eclipsing binaries, *v.* Double stars.

Ecliptic (→ 11 Celestial sphere), the path followed by the Sun on its apparent yearly journey, in relation to the stars, on the celestial sphere. The plane of the E., therefore. passes through the centre of the Sun as well as through that of the Earth. As seen from the Sun, the E. is the Earth's annual orbit round the Sun. The E. is a great circle inclined at $23\frac{1}{2}°$ to the celestial equator. It cuts the latter at the vernal equinox (R.A. 0 h.; Dec. 0°) which the Sun reaches on 20th or 21st March and at the autumnal equinox (R.A. 12 h.; Dec. 0°), which it reaches on 23rd September. At the vernal equinox, it moves from the southern to the northern half of the celestial sphere; at the autumnal, from the northern to the southern half. The Sun attains its greatest declination north and south respectively on 21st or 22nd June (summer solstice, R.A. 6 h., Dec. $23\frac{1}{2}°$ N.) and 21st or 22nd December (winter solstice, R.A. 18 h., Dec. $23\frac{1}{2}°$ S.). The direction of the Sun's motion in the E. is opposite to that of the diurnal revolution of the celestial sphere.

The belt round the celestial sphere in which the E. lies is called the Zodiac*. The E. is used as the basis of a system of co-ordinates enabling points on the celestial sphere to be defined, viz. longitude (λ) and latitude (β). Because the orbits of all the planets, except Pluto and Mercury, are on approximately the same plane as the Earth, the planets are always found in the sky near the E.

E-layer, a highly ionized part of the Earth's atmosphere at a height of about 60 miles (*v.* Pl 5).

Electron, a negatively charged elementary particle with a mass equal to $\frac{1}{1840}$ of a proton.

Elevation is astronomically synonymous with altitude* (*v.* Celestial sphere).

Ellipse has two foci F_1 and F_2, such that whatever the position of a point A on the E., $AF_1 + AF_2$ is constant (→) (*v.* Conic sections and Orbit).

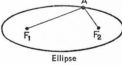
Ellipse

Ellipsoid is a solid figure having three mutually perpendicular axes XOX', YOY', ZOZ' such that any plane through one of the axes or perpendicular to one of the axes cuts the figure in an ellipse (→). When two of the axes are equal in length, the ellipsoid is known as a spheroid*: when all three axes are equal, it is a sphere.

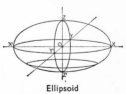
Ellipsoid

Elliptical galaxy, a particular type of extragalactic nebula*. It is shaped like a globe or an ellipsoid and has no spiral arms. The nearest examples are the two satellite galaxies of the Andromeda nebula, i.e. NGC205 and M32 (*v.* Pl. 66, 67, 71, 75).

Elongation is the difference between the celestial longitude of the Sun and that of a planet or the Moon (*v.* Celestial sphere). When the *E.* is small, the planet cannot be observed.

Emergence, the re-appearance of a celestial body after being eclipsed by the Moon, or of a satellite after being eclipsed by the planet (*v.* Jupiter and Pl. 19).

Emission lines are the bright lines which occur in the spectrum* of an incandescent gas. Their number and position are characteristic of the gas. They are generated when the electrons of an atom fall to lower energy levels. The energy thus released is emitted in the form of light of definite wavelengths (*v.* Light and Pl. 32).

Emission nebulae, *v.* Interstellar matter and Nebulae (*v.* Pl. 52, 54).

Emission spectrum is a spectrum consisting of emission lines* (*v.* Pl. 32).

Enceladus, one of Saturn's moons, discovered by Herschel (1789). Distance fr m Saturn 148,000 miles, period 1 d. 8 h. 53 min., magnitude at opposition 11·6, diameter about 300 miles.

Ephemeris, a table giving the computed positions of a celestial body for a series of future dates. From the orbital positions of the body and the Earth, the distance between the two and their situation in relation to one another are calculated. The R.A. and the Dec. of the object, for example, are then known. These positions are computed annually and those of the Sun, Moon and planets, and certain other bodies, are published in the various almanacs.*

Ephemeris time (E.T. or T.E.), a method of reckoning time used in astronomical almanacs which has replaced universal time* since 1960. Because the Earth's rotation is not completely regular, universal time is not uniform. The difference between *E.t.* and U.T. has been as follows: 1900, —4 sec.; 1910, +10 sec.; 1920, +20 sec.; 1930, +23 sec.; 1940, +24 sec.; 1950, +29 sec.; 1960, +34 sec. *E.t.* is based not on the axial rotation of the Earth but on the Earth's revolution round the Sun; a second is thus 1/31556925·9747 of the tropical year 1960.

Epicycle, *v.* Ptolemaic system.

Equation of time. Because the Earth moves in an elliptical orbit about the Sun, its velocity is not always the same. Consequently, the seasons are not of uniform length, spring being 92·8 days, summer 93·6, autumn 89·8 and winter 89·0. Because of the irregular motion of the Earth* the apparent velocity of the Sun along the ecliptic* is naturally not uniform. The length of a true solar day, i.e. the interval between two successive meridian passages of the Sun, is continually changing throughout the year. In practice we use the mean solar day, i.e. the mean of all true solar days in a year. The mean Sun is an imaginary point which moves eastwards at a uniform rate along the celestial equator and completes a single revolution in the same time taken by the Sun to complete a revolution on the ecliptic. The time difference between the Sun's meridian passage and the middle of the mean solar day is called the equation of time, which is therefore the difference in hour angle between the true and the mean Sun.

Equator, the imaginary great circle drawn on the surface of a celestial body at right angles to the axis of rotation. The celestial *E.* (or equinoctial) is the line along which the plane of the terrestrial *E.* intersects the celestial sphere. The celestial *E.* is a great circle; it divides the rotating celestial sphere into a northern and a southern hemisphere, and serves as the basis for a system of co-ordinates used to define the positions of points in the sky. These co-ordinates are right ascension* and declination*. (*v.* also Celestial sphere).

Equatorial mounting is the usual one for any astronomical telescope, other than a small telescope or a transit instrument. The telescope is made to rotate about two perpendicular axes, one of which (the polar axis) is parallel to the Earth's axis (pointing to the pole star in the northern hemisphere). Consequently, in order to prevent the Earth's rotation from moving any heavenly body out of the field of view, it is only necessary to rotate the telescope once per day about the *single* polar axis. In this way, the telescope will remain pointing at a star. (*v.* Hale telescope and Telescope).

Equinoctial, *v.* Equator.

Equuleus (the Little Horse) (→ Delphinus), a small constellation in the northern hemisphere, situated between R.A. 20 h. 55 min. and 21 h. 25 min. and Dec. 2° and 13° N.

Eridanus, an extensive constellation in the southern hemisphere, lying between 1 h. 25 min. and 5 h. 10 min. R.A. and 0° and —58° Dec. (→)

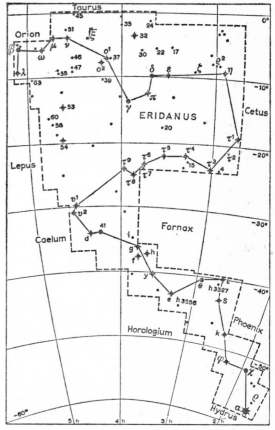

The constellation of Eridanus

Eros, one of the asteroids which can come close to the Earth. In 1931 the distance between *E.* and the Earth was about 15½ million miles. The fact that it is sometimes near the Earth, its consequently large geocentric parallax*, and its small dimensions, which make *E.*

almost a mathematical point in the heavens, enable its distance from the Earth in miles to be determined very accurately. This distance can also be obtained in astronomical units* from the elements of the orbit (v. Orbit). By comparing the two results, it is possible to determine the length of the astronomical unit very

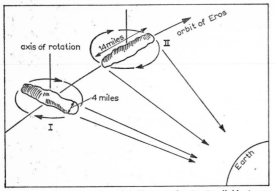

Eros, a rotating 'lump of rock'. I. Minimum luminosity. II. Maximum luminosity. Eros is illuminated by the Sun which here lies in the direction of Earth as seen from Eros. One complete cycle of light variation (up to 1½ magnitudes) takes 5 h. 16 min.

accurately. *E.* varies in luminosity, a fact which can be accounted for by assuming that the asteroid is not spherical, but consists of an elongated piece of rock which rotates round its axis in 5 hours. *E.* is brightest when the longer side reflects the sunlight in our direction; when the shorter side and smaller surface are exposed, less light is reflected (→). Average distance from Sun 136 million miles, period 1·76 years, maximum diameter 14 miles, axial rotation 5 h. 16 m., magnitude at opposition 9·7.

Eruption, a solar flare (v. Sun and Solar flare).

Eunomia, a small asteroid with a periodic variation of brightness (3 h. 2 min.) (v. Eros).

Europa (Jupiter II), one of Jupiter's four brightest satellites, discovered by Galileo* in 1610. Distance from Jupiter 417,000 miles, diameter 1,960 miles, magnitude at opposition 5·7 (→ 3 Solar system).

Evening star, v. Venus.

Evolution of the solar system, v. Solar system (v. also Pl. 93).

Evolution of the stars (v. Pl. 90) is the development of the stars from their origin to the present day, and their possible future development. It is thought that several thousand million years ago the Galaxy consisted of gas and dust unequally distributed. This dust and gas contracted to form local condensations from which, as the result of further contraction, the older stars of Population type II were produced. Rotation of the system as a whole caused the remaining gas and dust to form a flat disk within the system. This disk rotated about the centre of the Galaxy, and the matter comprising it arranged itself in an unknown way in the form of spiral arms. It is from this matter that stars of Population type I were formed and are still being formed. These stars, like the Sun, revolve around the centre (v. Population types and Pl. 60).

When compacted clouds of gas and dust (diameter about 1 light-year, density 1.000 hydrogen atoms per c.c., temperature several hundred degrees above absolute zero), i.e. proto-stars, condense still further under the influence of gravitation, the internal temperature increases, until the central temperature becomes

sufficiently high (about 5,000,000°) for nuclear reactions* to occur. The energy thus released escapes from the star as radiation.

The various types of star in the main sequence of the Hertzsprung-Russell diagram* are thought to have originated in this way. These stars belong to spectral classes O to M and are grouped diagonally in a narrow band across the diagram. The less massive stars, such as the Sun and those from the Sun to the M-class stars, evolve slowly. Stars of larger mass than the Sun evolve more rapidly. In particular O- and B-class stars have a relatively short life as such. New stars are believed to be in process of formation in globules, small compact masses of dark material which are visible on photographs projected on bright nebular aggregations (v. Pl. 43). It is believed that stars are still being formed at present, for blue supergiants radiate their supply of energy so lavishly that they cannot have been formed very long ago. Equally, considerable radiation would long since have exhausted the energy stored in an older star, so that it would no longer be visible. The expectation of life of the star S Doradus, for example, is only 100,000 years.

When the internal temperature has reached several million degrees, the hydrogen of which the stars mainly consist begins to be transformed into helium by nuclear reactions. When the hydrogen supply threatens to become exhausted, the radiation increases. The star will then perhaps leave the main sequence in the Hertzsprung-Russell diagram and move to the right;

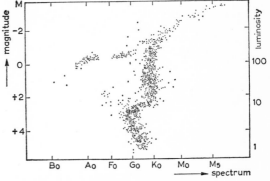

Fig. 1. Hertzsprung-Russell diagram of a group of older stars: the globular star cluster M3

it then becomes a giant. This conclusion has been reached from the study of Hertzsprung-Russell diagrams of groups of older stars, e.g. globular star clusters (v. Pl. 59). A diagram of this kind certainly suggests an evolutionary process (→ 1). Although this diagram does not, in fact, include any stars less bright than the Sun, this does not mean that there are no such stars in the cluster but only that their small magnitude and the cluster's great distance make them impossible to observe. The O- and B-class stars of the main sequence are also missing, but in their case it is thought that, having long ago exhausted all their hydrogen stocks, they have evolved towards another position in the diagram. All that remains of the main sequence is a small stump at the bottom, consisting of stars of luminosity fairly close to that of the Sun, and also fainter stars which still have plenty of hydrogen and take even longer than the lifetime of a globular cluster to show any visible signs of evolution. Stars near point (a) (→ 2) are about to recede from the main sequence because they have already used up a great deal of their hydrogen supplies. Stars which were higher than (*a*) on the main sequence, and therefore radiated more energy, have moved off even farther from the main sequence. The evolution of these stars is proceeding much faster.

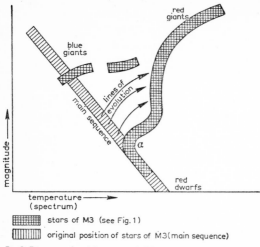

stars of M3 (see Fig. 1)

original position of stars of M3 (main sequence)

Fig. 2. Diagram of positions occupied by stars in the course of their evolution

When a star moves away from the main sequence, it will increase in magnitude until its hydrogen disappears. After that, it may keep its radiation up to the former level for some time (*v.* the horizontal section of Fig. 3) by other nuclear reactions (e.g. the transformation of helium to carbon, oxygen and neon). Possibly the star will then drop below and to the left of the main sequence in the Hertzsprung-Russell diagram, as its brightness and temperature decrease. It will thus perhaps reach the region of the white dwarfs (→3). This evolutionary path is, however, generally considered to be highly speculative. As far as brighter stars are concerned—those which have passed through the stages of evolution rapidly—it is now generally accepted that they are at the end of their existence as white dwarfs (*v.* Dwarf stars). Nuclear processes are then of no account and the star will probably die out slowly. Hence, whereas a Hertzsprung-Russell diagram of the stars in the neighbourhood of the Sun (Population type I) shows stars of all ages, created at different times, the

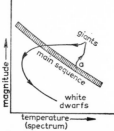

Fig. 3. Possible evolutionary path followed by an individual star. It leaves the main sequence at *a*

diagram of a cluster shows stars which are all of the same age. They evolve at different speeds, depending on their mass, and are situated at different points along the path of evolution.

Evolution of the universe, *v.* Universe and Pl. 83, 94.
Exobiology is the branch of science concerned with the possibilities of life outside the Earth. Its chief preoccupations are with the theory of living matter in different environments, with studying such evidence as there is for extra-terrestial life and with the develop-

ment of instruments which, in space probes, will best detect any life they may encounter.

Exosphere, the outermost layer of the Earth's atmosphere (*v.* Earth and Pl. 5).

Expanding universe, a theory according to which the scale of the universe as a whole is changing. From the red shift, in spectral lines (Doppler effect*), of the light from distant galaxies, it has been generally agreed that the latter are all receding from us at velocities which are greater the farther the galaxies are from us. It can also be said that distances in the universe are increasing in the course of time. Some regard the *E.u.* as a temporary phenomenon; upon reaching a maximum size it will again contract, i.e. the universe is pulsating (*v.* also Extragalactic nebulae and Pl. 83, 94).

Explorer, name of a series of American artificial satellites.*

External galaxies, *v.* Extragalactic nebulae.

Extragalactic nebulae, external galaxies or galactic systems are stellar systems situated far beyond our own Galaxy. In the northern hemisphere only one of these is visible with the naked eye, which sees it as a hazy spot; it is the Andromeda nebula* (*v.* Pl. 66) in the constellation of the same name. In the southern hemisphere the two Magellanic Clouds* (*v.* Pl. 63) in the constellations of Dorado, Mensa and Tucana can be seen without a telescope. With even a small telescope it is possible to see several more as hazy spots, although the latter cannot be resolved into stars. For the study of these galactic systems it is necessary to use photographs made with the aid of large telescopes. Long exposures, sometimes lasting several hours, show enough detail on the plates to permit investigation of these objects. Views on the true nature of these 'nebulae' have undergone striking modification in the past. The oldest literature on the subject reflects the view that these spots, in which no stars could be distinguished, were stellar systems at very great distances from the Earth. This view was not based on observations, which were then impossible, but was the result of logical deduction (Thomas Wright, 1750, and Kant, 1755). Even William Herschel, working with a large reflecting telescope at the end of the eighteenth century, thought that the spots were stellar systems so remote that the individual stars could not possibly be visible with his telescope. These ideas keep recurring in literature in the eighteenth century. When, in the second half of the nineteenth century, the spectroscope* was invented and used to analyse the light from stars and nebulae, it soon became apparent that at least a proportion of the nebular spots consisted of luminous clouds of gas and had to be accorded a place in our own Galaxy (Huggins, 1864, and Keeler, 1900).

A peculiar development now followed: for various reasons doubts again grew as to the existence of stellar systems outside our Galaxy. Thus, it was thought that these nebulae show a regular and symmetrical distribution round the plane of our Milky Way. Hardly a single one of them is found in the vicinity of the Milky Way in the heavens, whereas their number grows steadily in the direction of the galactic poles, i.e. in the direction at right angles to the plane of the Milky Way. This was considered a strong argument for the thesis that the nebulae are related to our Milky Way and therefore part of it. The idea of very large distances was therefore dismissed. It is now known that the concentration of nebulae in the direction of the galactic poles is only apparent and is mainly due to the presence of clouds of gas and dust in the plane of our Galaxy (v. Pl. 45, 60). Gas and dust decrease in the direction of the galactic poles. In the galactic plane they prevent us from seeing distant galaxies, but towards the galactic poles there is less absorption and countless numbers of galaxies can be photographed there. At the beginning of the twentieth century doubts as to the nearness of these galaxies began to revive; velocity measurements and the discovery of novae, cepheid variables*, B-type stars and globular star clusters* in the nebulae made much larger distances more probable. Owing to their relative proximity, the Magellanic Clouds were soon resolved into stars, but they were assumed to be large star clouds, or to form a kind of satellite system of the Galaxy (→ Magellanic Clouds). When Hubble announced in 1926 that he had resolved about a hundred of these 'nebulae' partly into stars (v. Pl. 68, 70) all doubts vanished; they are comparable with our Galaxy.

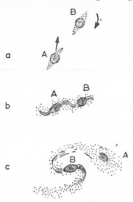

Fig. 1. Possible course of events in the formation of a bridge of intergalactic material between two galaxies (after Zwicky). (a) galaxies A and B pass close to each other; (b) streams of material are pulled from both galaxies by tidal effect; (c) A and B revolve round each other, with a connecting bridge of material between them

Even nowadays, with the most modern aids, it is impossible to see individual stars in the millions of galaxies that can be photographed, so great are the distances involved. Only systems that are relatively near are known in greater detail. For the vast majority all that can be done is to study their general properties and compare those with the few systems which are known more accurately.

The following classification (Hubble's) is in use (v. Pl. 75, 76):

A. Regular galaxies:
1. Elliptical galaxies (symbol E),
2. Spiral galaxies, subdivided into:
   a. Normal spirals (symbol S),
   b. S-shaped or barred spirals (symbol SB).
B. Irregular galaxies (symbol Ir).

That this classification is not the final word on the subject is clearly shown by the fact that, according to Mayall and Zwicky, the spiral nebula NGC 5194, which is classified among the normal spirals, shows a normal spiral shape in the light of the blue stars but appears as a barred spiral in that of the yellow-green stars. Also in recent years a number of peculiar galaxies, which defy general classification, have been discovered.

A1. Elliptical galaxies (E) (v. Pl. 67, 71) possess no clear-cut limits and show no visible structural details. Their external shapes vary from spherical to lenticular (v. Pl. 75). On recent photographs even elliptical nebulae have been resolved into stars, and dark areas discovered in them (v. Andromeda nebula, NGC205, class E2, and Pl. 71). Their shape is indicated by one of the digits 0–7 placed after the letter E: 0 = spherical, 7 = lenticular. (If a = major axis, and b = minor axis, this number is $10\,(a-b)/a$ to the nearest whole unit. The extreme case is when the ratio of b to a is as 1 to 3, i.e. E7). Elliptical galaxies are strongly con-

centrated and generally have a greater percentage of red stars than do the spiral nebulae, whose spectra show a preponderance of white and blue stars. If it is true that blue and white giants are younger than red giants (v. Evolution of the stars), the inference would be that these blue and white giants have disappeared from the elliptical galaxies, which would therefore be older and represent a later stage than the spirals in the evolution of extragalactic nebulae. This would be the opposite of Hubble's views, according to which evolution was from elliptical systems to spiral galaxies.

Some elliptical systems are also known which have no concentrated central region and are much less compact in structure. Examples are the galaxies in Sculptor and Fornax.

A2a. Normal spiral galaxies (S) (v. Pl. 70). Their visible shape depends on the angle between the line of sight and the plane of the galaxy. Spiral galaxies usually possess definite and very bright central regions. Depending on the appearance of the central portion and of the arms, normal spiral nebulae are subdivided into:

Class Sa: Distinct central region and closely coiled arms (v. Pl. 72).

Class Sb: Central region smaller and arms open wider. Examples are the Andromeda nebula* and probably our Galaxy* (v. Pl. 60).

Class Sc: Small central portion, arms wide apart and of less definite shape. Example: M33 in Triangulum (v. Pl. 70, 77). From Sa to Sc, therefore, the central region is progressively less pronounced and the arms progressively more prominent; the latter also become more complicated in structure, while the occurrence of separate condensations becomes more marked. It is for this reason that the course of spiral arms in class Sc is sometimes difficult to follow (v. Pl. 70).

The intricate patterns of bright clouds and dark patches of dust which cut across the spiral arms are typical of this class. The dust clouds are very clearly

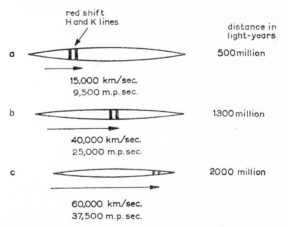

Fig. 2. Red shift of absorption lines in the spectra of extragalactic nebulae. Cases (a), (b) and (c) refer respectively to the spectra of galaxies in Ursa Major, Boötes and Hydra, with the H and K lines of calcium drawn in. The relative displacement of these lines towards the red end of the spectrum is indicated by the length of the arrows. The red shift is related to the distances of the galaxies: the farther a galaxy is from us, the greater its red shift. It can therefore be used as a measure of distance (v. Hubble's constant)

seen in galaxies which present the edge of the spiral plane to our line of sight; they then form a dark band dividing the galaxy in two (v. Pl. 72).

A2b. S-shaped or barred spirals (SB). The spiral arms do not emerge from the edge of the central region but start at the end of a bright bar or beam projecting from both sides of the central region (v. Pl. 79). The Large Magellanic Cloud* (v. Pl. 64) is thought to be an SB spiral, though not very distinct in shape, partly because of the relatively short distance from which we observe it. The following subdivisions are distinguished:

Class SBa: Extremely pronounced central portion, with less well-developed spiral arms which bend round the central part and end where the next arm emerges. The shape is not unlike the Greek letter theta: θ (v. Pl. 76, 79).

Class SBb: The central region is not so pronounced but the arms are more developed (v. Pl. 76).

Class SBc: Small central portion with distinctly S-shaped spirals far removed from each other (v. Pl. 76, 79).

Barred spirals thus have only two spiral arms which first emerge radially from the central region, then bend more or less sharply into circular or spiral coils.

B. Irregular galaxies (Ir) (v. Pl. 75).

These show no definite symmetrical shape. Only 2–3 % of all known galaxies are irregular, but this figure could be misleading because they are smaller and fainter than other classes of galaxies and only the nearer irregular galaxies can be observed. In recent times a large number of dwarf galaxies have been found, most of which are irregular.

The diameters of the irregular systems are the smallest. Then comes class E, while the S and SB types are, as a rule, the largest. Our Galaxy (v. Pl. 45, 46, 60) is a medium-sized spiral (diameter about 100,000 light-years). Of the systems in our vicinity, only the Andromeda nebula M31 (v. Pl. 66) is considerably larger (diameter 200,000 light-years); the Large Magellanic Cloud (v. Pl. 64) is comparable in size (but not in mass) with our Galaxy, while all other near-by galaxies are much smaller.

Distribution in Space. Examination of the distribution of galaxies reveals a great number of distinct groupings which are not merely apparent and due to observation in depth, but are in actual fact concentrations in space. It is agreed nowadays that most galaxies belong to groups and clusters. Photography, in particular, has made us familiar with a great number of these larger groups. The positions of more than 2,700 have been fixed.

Astronomers distinguish between: *a. groups* consisting of up to 100 galaxies each. A group has no definite condensation towards the centre. *b. clusters* (v. Pl. 80, 82) which may each contain hundreds or even thousands of galaxies. In this category counts have revealed a distinct concentration towards one or more centres. *c. clouds of galaxies* which are irregular large groups without observable structure, comprising several hundreds or thousands of galaxies. *d. clouds of groups*, consisting of a large number of groups of galaxies, loosely associated. *e. clouds of clusters*, which are the largest groupings of matter known in the universe and may consist of as many as 100,000 galaxies.

The Local Group of galaxies (v. Pl. 69). Our Milky Way galaxy is a member of this group, which extends coil-shaped over a distance of several million light-years. Our Galaxy lies near one end. This concentration of galaxies in our vicinity is fortunate; the relatively short distances enable us to view the members in greater detail and thus to form a clearer idea of the universe as a whole. B-type stars, variable stars such as the cepheids* and novae*, and also globular star clusters*, can be resolved in galaxies of the Local Group, allowing their distances and approximate diameters to be calculated (v. Distance finding).

The Local Group consists of the following members:

Galaxy	Constellation	Class	Distance in light-years	Absolute magnitude	
Milky Way		Sb		— 18 ·0	triple system
L. Mag. Cloud	Dorado	Ir, SB	146,000	— 17 ·5	triple system
S. Mag. Cloud	Tucana	Ir	146,000	— 16 ·0	
Sculptor Gal.	Sculptor	E	460,000	— 13 ·2	
Fornax Gal.	Fornax	E	920,000	— 13 ·2	
NGC6822	Sagittarius	Ir	1,040,000	— 12 ·5	
NGC147	Andromeda	E	1,320,000	— 11 ·8	double system
NGC185	Andromeda	E	1,320,000	— 12 ·1	double system
M31	Andromeda	Sb	2,200,000	— 19 ·0	triple system
M32	Andromeda	E2	2,200,000	— 14 ·5	triple system
NGC205	Andromeda	E5	2,200,000	— 13 ·0	
IC1613	Cetus	Ir	1,800,000	— 12 ·5	
M33	Triangulum	Sc	1,800,000	— 16 ·5	
IC10	Cassiopeia	Sc	2,000,000	— 11 ·5	
IC342	Camelopardus	Sc	2,000,000		
NGC3946	Cepheus		2,000,000	— 10 ·5	
NGC2419	Gemini			— 10 ·5	

On photographs taken with the 48-inch Schmidt telescope* on Mount Palomar (v. Pl. 81), dwarf galaxies belonging to the Local Group were recently discovered, viz. 2 in Sextans, 2 in Leo, in Ursa Major, Ursa Minor, Serpens, Draco, Capricornus and Pegasus. It is possible that yet other members are hidden behind the dust of our own Galaxy.

Clusters and clouds of extragalactic nebulae. The best known are:

Name of cluster or cloud	Apparent magnitude	Distance in millions of light-years[1]
Virgo	12 ·5	33
Pegasus	15 ·5	100
Pisces	15 ·4	140
Cancer	16 ·0	140
Perseus	16 ·4	150
Coma Berenices	17 ·0	240
Ursa Major 1	18 ·0	500
Leo	19 ·0	650
Corona Borealis	19 ·0	700
Gemini	19 ·5	750
Boötes	21 ·0	1,300
Ursa Major 11	21 ·0	1,400

[1] The distances are given according to a recent distance scale (1958).

Some clusters were discovered in the course of visual observations last century, e.g. the Coma Berenices cluster (v. Pl. 80) in 1865 (d'Arrest). Later discoveries involved the use of photography. In 1901 M. Wolf investigated the Coma cluster and raised the number of known members from 25 to over 100. In the last few years with the aid of the 48-inch Schmidt telescope, 30,000 galaxies have been counted within a radius of 6° from the centre. It has been calculated that 10,000 of these belong to the Coma cluster.

The Pegasus cluster has at least 400 galaxies within a circle of 1° radius round it. Three hundred galaxies of photographic magnitude from 13·8 to 18·2 have been counted in the Cancer cluster. The Coma cluster is thought to occupy a volume of 440 million million million cubic light-years. The Virgo cluster is elliptical in shape and is a cloud of galaxies rather than a cluster. The term 'cloud' is also applicable to the irregularly shaped Ursa Major I.

In the central part of the Coma cluster the average distance between galaxies is 200,000 light-years or less. The average velocity is 1,250 m.p.sec. (2,000 km/sec.) This makes it possible for galaxies in clusters to collide (in the Coma cluster the average rate is once in 3,000 million years for any one galaxy). The stars in colliding systems are far from each other and pass unhindered but the gases collide, setting up shock waves which are perceived as intense emissions on radio wavelengths (e.g. radio sources Cygnus A, NGC 1275, and NGC 4038–4039) (*v.* Collision of extragalactic nebulae and Pl. 84).

The number of *E.n* is very large. As viewed by the 48-inch Schmidt telescope, about 100 galaxies per square degree have been counted in the clear parts of the sky. The number of galactic clusters is about 1–2 per 100 square degrees. The latest photographs taken with the 48-inch Schmidt telescope have revealed 2,500 galaxies per square degree and an average of 150 clusters per 100 square degrees. The existence of intergalactic matter, i.e. matter in the space between galaxies, has not yet been established. If it does exist, it must be extremely tenuous, although Zwicky found that some galaxies are connected by strands of matter consisting at least partly of stars and extending sometimes over very large distances (→ 1) (*v.* Magellanic clouds). He discovered a great many of these luminous formations linking not only galaxies which were close to each other, but some which were very far apart. He believes that intergalactic space is everywhere inhabited by individual stars and groups of stars (*v.* Pl. 85).

The radial velocities of extragalactic nebulae and the shape of the universe. The spectra of the *E.n.* are the averages of all the stars and gases in them and are somewhat similar to those of G-class stars, such as the Sun, except that their absorption lines are considerably displaced in relation to their normal positions.

This shift may be due to the Doppler effect*, i.e. to the motion of the galaxy relative to the observer (→ 2). If allowance is made for the Sun's motion, the shift is always found to be towards the red end of the spectrum, and can be interpreted in terms of velocities in directions away from us. As these velocities increase regularly with the distances of the objects from us, the amount of red shift can be correlated with distance. The velocities of recession of the galaxies increase at the rate of roughly 50 m.p.sec. (80 km/sec.) per megaparsec (1 megaparsec = about 3 million light-years). The largest red shift so far noted (1956) corresponds to a velocity of $^2/_5$ of the velocity of light (*v.* Hubble's constant).

The theory most commonly held at present is that all galaxies are in fact receding from each other at relative velocities which are greater the farther the galaxies are apart, and hence, since the distances

separating all galaxies are constantly increasing, the universe as a whole is expanding. It is believed that at some time in the past all matter must have been concentrated in a single 'atom', and that an explosion in this primeval atom gave rise to an expanding universe as we know it (Lemaître, Louvain, 1927, and Gamow). This event is supposed to have taken place at least 10,000 million years ago (*v.* Pl. 94).

Eyepiece, a lens system, e.g. of a telescope, through which the image formed by the objective* is viewed. A single lens gives a sharp picture only in the centre of the field and is therefore not used (*v.* Optics). A system of two or more lenses gives a wider field and a sharp picture right to the edges of that field. The lens nearest the eye is called the eye lens, and the lens at the objective side of the *E.* the field lens. With a positive *E.* the image from the objective falls in front of the field lens and therefore outside the lens system, and it is viewed as through a magnifying glass. In a negative *E.* the image from the objective falls between the lenses composing the *E.* The advantage of the positive *E.* is that it allows wire systems of graticules, for instance, to be used for measurements on the image. These must coincide with the image from the objective, so that the wires or lines, and the image, are seen sharply and simultaneously. In a positive *E.* such wire systems or graticules are easily fitted because they occur outside the lens system, which is not the case with a negative *E*

The magnifying power of a telescope is the focal length of the objective divided by the focal length of the *E.* The *E.s* most used by astronomers are: *a.* Huygenian *E.,* consisting of two plano-convex lenses of the same kind of glass, both with their plane surface towards the viewer. It is a negative system and is used for medium magnifications (e.g. with a focal length of $1^1/_2$–3 cm). *b.* Ramsden *E.,* comprising two plano-convex lenses with the convex sides facing each other. It gives less distortion than the Huygenian *E.* It is a positive system. *c.* Kellner *E.,* a modified Ramsden *E.,* in which the eye lens is a double lens designed to correct chromatic aberration (*v.* Optics). It is a positive system. This *E.* is used to obtain more powerful magnification (focal length 7–12 mm). *d.* Orthoscopic *E.,* comprising a triple field lens and a single eye lens. Even for very large magnifications (focal length 3–10 mm) the image is free from distortion right to the edges of the field. This is a positive system. *e.* Monocentric *E.,* consisting of a triple cemented lens. Excellent for observation of lunar and planetary details, but not used otherwise, on account of its very small field. It is a positive *E.* Also in use is a solar *E.,* the only purpose of which is to protect the eye in observation of the Sun; this it does by eliminating the excess light which would otherwise damage the vision.

Faculae, bright areas in the Sun's* inner chromophere, associated with an active region. Sunspots and other phenomena develop in areas of *F.* An area of *F.* always coincides with a magnetic field (*v.* Pl. 30).

Family of comets, *v.* Jupiter's family of comets.

F-corona, the outermost part of the Sun's atmosphere. It extends to farther than 10 solar diameters from the Sun's surface and has a very high temperature (1,000,000°K.). It can be seen as a result of the radiation (light) reflected from the particles there. The

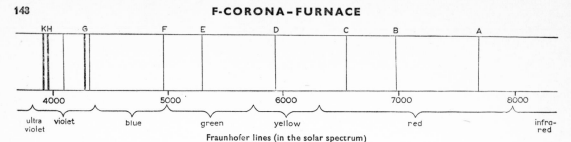

Fraunhofer lines (in the solar spectrum)

radio waves from the corona are mainly emitted by the K-corona. The *F-c.* merges into interplanetary dust (*v.* Sun).

Fechner's law states that the intensity of a stimulus is proportional to the logarithm of the stimulus. This law is the basis of the system whereby stars are classified according to magnitude (*v.* Star).

If we illuminate a screen in turn with $1 = 2^0, 2 = 2^1, 4 = 2^2, 8 = 2^3, 16 = 2^4, 32 = 2^5 \ldots$ lamps, the effect on the eye of these different degrees of illumination will be equivalent to intensities of 1, 2, 3, 4, 5, 6, etc.

The same applies to the impression made on our eye by stars. This will be clear from the following table.

Magnitude of star	6	5	4	3	2	1
Intensity of light we perceive from star	1	2·5	2·5²	2·5³	2·5⁴	2·5⁵

Filters are used in photographing celestial objects. A series of photographs taken with different colour *F.* gives a picture of the composition of the light received. They also help to show which details of a planet, for instance, are situated on the surface (orange, red or infra-red *F.*), and which in the atmosphere (blue or ultra-violet *F.*) (*v.* Astrophotography, Monochromatic filter and Mars, Pl. 17, 18).

Finder, a small telescope with weak magnification and a wide field, the eyepiece of which is generally fitted with cross-wires. The *F.* is attached to a larger telescope in such a way that when a star is observed at the intersection of the cross-wires of the *F.*, it is also in the centre of the field of the larger telescope. It is therefore used to aim the latter.

Fireball is a very bright meteor* or shooting star.

Fishes, *v.* Pisces.

Fish, Southern, *v.* Piscis Austrinus.

Flare, a sudden bright explosion in the Sun's chromosphere or K-corona, invariably associated with an active region. *F.s* are brighter than other parts of the Sun. They form very quickly (about 5 min.) and have a short life (20–30 min. on an average). The temperature of a *F.* is 10,000–20,000°K. The density of the material composing a *F.* is about 1,000 times greater than that of the upper chromosphere or K-corona*. *F.s* can sometimes be clearly seen projecting from the edge of the Sun's disk. They are frequently accompanied by outbursts of radio noise on various wavelengths (called flare bursts) and by the emission of particles at velocities ranging from 30 m.p.sec. (50 km./sec.) to almost the speed of light (*v.* Sun and Pl. 31).

F-layer, an ionized part of the Earth's atmosphere at a height of about 130 miles. The layer is sometimes considered as being subdivided into F_1 and F_2 (*v.* Pl. 5).

Fly, *v.* Musca.

Flying Fish, *v.* Volans.

Focus of a telescope, *v.* Telescope.

Fomalhaut, the star α Piscis Austrini. Its comparative nearness to the Sun makes it one of the brightest stars in the sky. Apparent magnitude 1·29, absolute magnitude 2, distance 24 light-years, luminosity 13 × Sun's, spectral type A3.

Fornax (the Furnace), an inconspicuous constellation in the southern hemisphere. R.A. from 1 h. 40 min. to 3 h. 50 min., Dec. from — 24° to — 40°. (→)

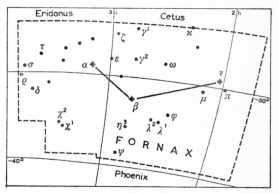

The constellation of Fornax

Fox, *v.* Vulpecula.

Fraunhofer lines (→), are absorption lines in the solar spectrum (*v.* Spectrum and Atlas, *Photometric Atlas of the Solar Spectrum,* also Pl. 32). They were first studied in 1814 by Fraunhofer, who mapped several hundreds of them, and named several of the most conspicuous by letters which are still used today. Not until 1859 was it discovered that these dark lines were caused by the absorption of certain wavelengths from the continuous spectrum by the gases in the Sun's or the Earth's atmosphere. The principal *F.l.* are:

Letter	Wavelength	Colour		Absorbed by
A	7594 Å	red	oxygen	(Earth's atm., a band)
B	6867	red	oxygen	(Earth's atm., a band)
C	6563	red	hydrogen	(Sun's atmosphere)
D1 and D2	5896 and 5890	yellow	sodium	(Sun's atmosphere)
E	5270	green	iron	(Sun's atmosphere)
F	4861	blue	hydrogen	(Sun's atmosphere)
H	3968	violet	calcium	(Sun's atmosphere)
K	3934	violet	calcium	(Sun's atmosphere)

About 22,000 *F.l.* have now been listed of which about 60% have been identified as due to particular atoms or molecules.

Furnace, *v.* Fornax.

Galactic, pertaining to the Milky Way (*v.* Extragalactic nebulae).

Galactic latitude and longitude, co-ordinates in the system based on the galactic equator (*v.* Celestial sphere).

Galactic nebulae, clouds of gas and dust in the plane of the spiral arms of the Milky Way (*v.* Pl. 45, 46). They are local concentrations of interstellar matter which are thought to be a continuing source of new stars (*v.* Evolution of the stars). *G.n.* are divided into emission nebulae and dark nebulae, some of which can be observed through a small telescope. *G.n.* of a third type, consisting of neutral hydrogen, are perceptible only because of their radiation on radio wavelengths. A well-known example of an emission nebula which is visible even to the naked eye as a hazy spot, is the Orion nebula (*v.* Pl. 53) in the constellation of the same name (*v.* also Interstellar matter and Nebulae).

Galactic poles, the two points where a line through the observer's position at right angles to the plane of the spiral arms (i.e. to the galactic equator) intersects the celestial sphere.*

Galactic rotation (*v.* Pl. 60), rotation of the Galaxy. This does not rotate as a solid body: the parts closer to the centre have a greater angular velocity than the parts situated farther away. As a result of *G.r.* the form of the spiral arms is not permanent, but is slowly being altered. In the neighbourhood of the Sun, the velocity of revolution is 134 m.p. sec. (216 km/sec.) and the period of revolution 220 million years.

Galaxies or **galactic systems,** *v.* Extragalactic nebulae.

Galaxy, *v.* Milky Way and Pl. 45, 46, 60, 62.

Galilei, Galileo (1564–1642), Italian physicist and supporter of the Copernican system* (heliocentric theory), according to which the planets revolve about the Sun. In 1609 *G.* heard of the invention of the telescope. Understanding the principle, he constructed one for himself and exhibited it the same year in Venice. The observations he made with it revolutionized astronomy. His first discoveries were the mountains on the surface of the Moon, and Jupiter's four brightest satellites (1610).

He also observed the motion of these moons around the planet, which thus provided him with an excellent example of a solar system on a small scale. He published his discoveries in the *Siderius Nuncius* or 'Star Messenger' (1610). Most philosophers of his time refused to accept his observations as true, maintaining that the telescope was good enough for terrestrial observations but could not be used for the heavens, of which it gave false representations. Some, in fact, refused to look through a telescope and be convinced by the evidence of their own eyes. The controversy was based not on physical but on religious principles. The new theories were regarded as heretical and contrary to the doctrine of the Church. In 1633 *G.* was compelled formally to abjure the heliocentric theory.

G. was also the first to observe the phases of Venus and the ring of Saturn. His small telescope gave him an imperfect image of the ring's structure and he thought he saw two smaller planets, one on either side of the main planet.

Two of *G.'s* telescopes are preserved in Florence. They have lenses with diameters of 4 and 4·4 cm, and focal lengths of 95 and 125 cm (*v.* Pl. 1).

Ganymede (Jupiter III), one of Jupiter's four brightest moons, discovered by Galileo* in 1610. Distance from the planet 665,000 miles, diameter 3,200 miles, magnitude at opposition 5·1, period of revolution 1 d. 3 h. 43 min. (→ 3, Solar system).

Gegenschein or counterglow is a very faint glow, difficult to observe, in a position exactly opposite to that of the Sun (*v.* Zodiacal light).

Gemini (the Twins) is a zodiacal constellation and therefore on the ecliptic. It lies in the northern hemisphere between R.A. 5 h. 55 min. and 8 h. 5 min. and between Dec. 10° and 35° N. (→)

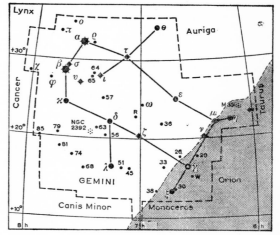

The constellation of Gemini

Gemma, the star α Coronae Borealis, apparent magnitude 2·3, spectral class Ao.

Giacobinids, *v.* Draconids.

Giant, star of great absolute magnitude and of great superficial area (e.g. Capella, Arcturus). Stars of even greater absolute magnitude are called supergiants (e.g. Rigel, Betelgeuse, Antares). Hertzsprung first observed that the red stars (spectral classes G, K and M) clearly fall into two groups: faint stars with absolute magnitudes of + 5 to + 10, and very bright stars with absolute magnitudes of + 2 to − 2. The latter are now known as giants and supergiants. The difference is clearly shown in the Hertzsprung-Russell diagram*. Measurements taken with the interferometer* have further shown that these bright, red stars have large diameters (*v.* Star).

Many giants and supergiants of spectral class M and some of class K are surrounded by expanding gas envelopes. One component of the visual double α Herculis, an M-type star, has a gas envelope with a thickness of about 1,000 astronomical units*, which is expanding with a speed of 6 m. p. sec. The rate of expansion (between 4 and 15 m. p. sec. for stars of this kind) is the same for parts of the gas at different distances from the star. It is thought that hydrogen atoms in the vicinity of the surface are repelled by powerful radiation. If the velocity of an atom increases, the Doppler effect will cause the amount of radiation absorbed by the atom to decrease and the motion will not be accelerated any further. Equilibrium is thus automatically set up between the force of the repellent radiation and the force of attraction of the star, and the atom moves away at a constant velocity. In small hot stars such as the Sun, the hydrogen atoms will not be driven off because the gravitation of the star is more powerful there.

Giraffe, *v.* Camelopardus.

Globular star cluster (*v.* Pl. 59), group consisting of numerous individual stars; usually spherical in shape and very compact. All globular clusters are at very great distances from the Sun and only two of them, both in the southern hemisphere, are clearly visible with the naked eye: Omega Centauri (NGC 5139) and 47 Tucanae (NGC 104). One cluster in the northern skies, M13 (NGC 6205) in the constellation of Hercules, discovered in 1714 by Halley, is visible as a hazy speck to a strong pair of eyes unassisted by a telescope.

G.s.c.s are situated far from the plane formed by the spiral arms of the Milky Way. As a group they occupy a spherical portion of space, whose centre coincides with that of the Milky Way. The radius of this spherical space is of the order of 50,000 light-years. The stars in *G.s.c.s* belong to Population type II (*v.* Population types). Not a single *G.s.c.*, so far as can be seen, lies within 4,000 light-years of the spiral plane of the Galaxy. This is not conclusive proof, however, that they do not exist there, for they may be hidden behind nebulae and dust in the spiral arms (*v.* Pl. 58). An average *G.s.c.* contains at least 100,000 stars, which are so close to each other towards the centre that they cannot be resolved even by the largest telescopes. The fact that these clusters are rich in variable stars of the RR Lyrae type enables their distances to be determined (*v.* Distance finding). The shortest distances are those of Omega Centauri and 47 Tucanae (22,000 light-years). M13 in Hercules is 34,000 light-years away, and NGC 2419 no less than 250,000 light-years away.

Even at the distances at which Omega Centauri and 47 Tucanae lie, only supergiants, giants and the brighter main sequence stars are visible to us. Stars with a luminosity equal to that of the Sun cannot be observed. Roughly 100 *G.s.c.s* are known. In the last few years 13 more, very weak, have been found on plates of the National Geographic Palomar Sky Survey. One of these lies far beyond the limits of our Galaxy, viz. 475,000 light-years from the Sun.

The diameter of an average globular cluster is more than 100 light-years. The cluster is very dense at its centre, where the average distance between stars is of the order of 10 A.U. This is large enough to accommodate the movements of the stars without risk of collision. M13 in Hercules has a diameter of 160 light-years and is estimated to contain at least 500,000 stars. The spherical shape of *G.s.c.s* is sometimes slightly flattened, but not more so than in the case of the planet Jupiter. Their rotation is probably very slow and has not yet been observed. It is assumed that the *G.s.c.s* move in elongated elliptical orbits about the centre of the galactic system, with periods of the order of 1,000 million years. If this is so, they have passed several times through the spiral plane of the Galaxy since their formation, and it is possible that any diffuse matter originally contained in clusters has been filtered out during these passages by collision with the

diffuse matter in the spiral arms. This would make it impossible for young stars to be created in the *G.s.c.s*; the stars in these clusters are, in fact, older stars and all belong to Population type II.

Globules, small compact clouds of dark matter which stand out locally against bright galactic nebulae*. The formation of new stars is thought to take place in them (*v.* Evolution of the stars). They vary in diameter from $^1/_{100}$ to $^1/_{10}$ of a light-year (*v.* Pl. 43 and Evolution of the stars.).

Gnomon, an instrument used in antiquity to measure the elevation of the Sun. In its simplest form it consists of an upright rod (or a pillar). The Sun's elevation is easily found from the length of the rod and the length of its shadow. The arm of a sun-dial is still known as a gnomon.

Granules or **granulation.** Under exceptional observing conditions, it is possible to see that the solar disk is not uniform but has a granular texture of brighter and fainter patches. These *G.* have an average diameter of 600 miles and are short-lived, the whole pattern being unrecognizable after ten minutes. They are the result of a seething movement in the Sun's unstable upper layer.

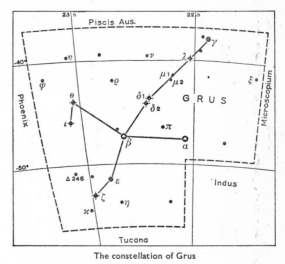

The constellation of Grus

G. are difficult to observe because of their small size and the shimmering caused by the Earth's atmosphere. Sharp photographs of *G.* were made in 1957 with the aid of a telescope mounted in a balloon which climbed to an altitude of $15\frac{1}{2}$ miles above the Earth's surface where it was beyond 98% of the terrestial atmosphere (*v.* Pl. 30).

Gravitation, *v.* Kepler's laws and Space travel.

Great Bear, *v.* Ursa Major.

Great Dog, *v.* Canis Major.

Greek alphabet is used in the nomenclature of stars. The brightest star in each constellation is called α, the next brightest β, and so on, followed by the Latin name of the constellation in the genitive case.

α Alpha	η Eta	ν Nu	τ Tau
β Beta	θ Theta	ξ Xi	υ Upsilon
γ Gamma	ι Iota	ο Omicron	φ Phi
δ Delta	ϰ Kappa	π Pi	χ Chi
ε Epsilon	λ Lambda	ϱ Rho	ψ Psi
ζ Zeta	μ Mu	σ Sigma	ω Omega

Green flash. When the Sun is setting, the last remaining segment is sometimes seen to turn green and afterwards, a flash of green light shoots up for a few seconds. This is the *G.f.* It is best seen over a sea horizon when the atmosphere is very clear, but can sometimes be seen under other conditions. The flash is caused by atmospheric refraction* of sunlight and its green colour arises because the blue light is removed by the usual atmospheric scattering while the red light is removed by the absorption of water vapour when there is a very long path close to the water surface.

Grus (the Crane), a constellation in the southern hemisphere, extending from 21 h. 25 min. to 23 h. 25 min. R.A. and from — 37° to — 56° Dec. (→ facing)

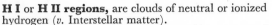

H I or **H II regions,** are clouds of neutral or ionized hydrogen (*v.* Interstellar matter).

Halation ring is the ring sometimes to be seen around star images on a photograph (*v.* Pl. 57). It is caused by light which has penetrated the photographic emulsion and has been critically reflected by the rear glass surface of the plate.

Hale telescope (*v.* Pl. 1), is the world's largest optical telescope. It is a reflector or reflecting telescope* with a 200-inch mirror, sited at an altitude of 5,600 feet on Mount Palomar in California, north of San Diego. The site is much more suitable than Mount Wilson, where the 100-inch telescope is, and where photography is hampered by the lights of Pasadena and Los Angeles. The *H.t.* is the largest telescope in the world and can photograph celestial objects up to 4,000 million light-years away. In 1928 $ 6 million were set aside for a large reflector. The task of designing it was entrusted to the California Institute of Technology. It was to be a photographic, not a visual, telescope and was intended primarily for the study of remote extragalactic nebulae and for more detailed analysis of astral and nebular light. The design was fixed in 1932, and towards the end of 1934, after one failure, the circular block of Pyrex glass for the mirror was cast. This disk, which weighed 20 tons, took 8 months to cool and did not reach Pasadena, where it was to be ground and polished, until the spring of 1936. In these two processes 31 tons of powder were used. The telescope was completed on 3rd October, 1947 (over 5 tons of glass having been removed by grinding in the space of 11½ years), and the sky was first viewed through it in December of the same year.

The instrument was named after the astronomer,

George Ellery Hale, who had helped to plan the Mount Wilson and Mount Palomar observatories. The telescope weighs 530 tons. The weight of the mirror is 14½ tons. Optical system (→ 1): A. prime

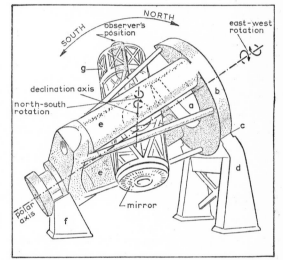

Fig. 2. Sketch to illustrate the construction of the Hale telescope
The position of the observer when using the prime focus, is shown.

focus (of large mirror): focal length 55 ft., focal ratio f/3·3; B. Cassegrain focus: focal length 266½ ft., focal ratio f/16; C. and D. Coudé focus: focal length 500 ft., focal ratio f/30. The telescope tube (g), (→2),

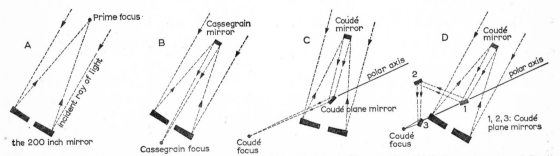

Fig. 1. There are several possible optical arrangements with the Hale telescope. A. The prime focus of the large mirror is used. Focal length 55 ft. The Moon's disk has a diameter of 6 in. B. The insertion of the convex Cassegrain mirror causes the light-rays to pass through the hole in the large mirror to the Cassegrain focus. Focal length 226½ ft. Diameter of Moon 28 in. C. If a larger image is required, the Coudé mirror is inserted. The light is reflected along the polar axis by a plane mirror. Focal length 500 ft. Diameter of Moon 53 in. D. When directed at certain positions in the northern hemisphere, arrangement C is impracticable. Three plane mirrors are then used as shown

is mounted in a massive yoke (e) so that it can turn in declination (i.e. north–south rotation). The yoke has a large horseshoe-shaped bearing (b) at the north end and a hemispherical bearing at the south end. These are held on piers (d and f) and the weight floats on a thin layer of oil (c) forced in at high pressure. The whole telescope moves on these bearings for sidereal movement and right ascension setting (east–west rotation). The friction is so small that a ½ h. p. motor can turn the whole instrument. The mirror is fitted at the lower end of the tube, and at the top, near the focus of the main mirror, is a cubicle containing photographic equipment and a space for the observer.

The dome is 134 ft. high and 137 ft. in diameter, and weighs 1,000 tons. It rests on 32 four-wheeled trucks running on circular rails. The dome is driven by four 5 h.p. motors.

Halley's comet (v. Pl. 23), is the best known of the comets* and also the first which was shown to be periodic. Halley worked out the orbit of the bright comet of 1682 and noticed that it was very similar to those of 1531 and 1607. He predicted, correctly, that it would return in 1758. The next two returns took place in 1835 and 1910 and it is expected to appear again in 1986. It has a period of about 76 years and takes nearly half that time to cover the part of its orbit which lies beyond the orbit of Neptune (→).

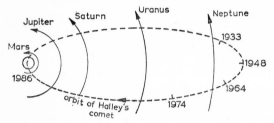

Halo, the spherical star cloud round the main body of the Milky Way galaxy, containing stars of Population type II (v. Milky Way and Population types). Its diameter is of the order of 100,000 light-years. The H. is concentrated towards the galactic centre, outwards from which it becomes more and more thinly populated (v. Pl. 60).

Hamal, the star α Arietis, apparent magnitude 2·2, spectral class K2.

H- and K-lines, v. Fraunhofer lines.

Hare, v. Lepus.

Harvest Moon is the full Moon that occurs nearest to the time of the autumnal equinox. At this particular date, as a result of the Moon's orbit being at an acute angle to the horizon, the Moon rises only 20–30 minutes or so later for several consecutive nights. Consequently, there is bright moonlight in the evening for several days in succession.

Heliocentric is the term applied to a system of co-ordinates based on the Sun as centre.

Helium, the second most abundant element in the universe (v. Hydrogen). The H.-atom consists of a nucleus containing two protons and four neutrons with two electrons in orbital motion about it. This arrangement is so stable that its spectrum is difficult to excite so that, in spite of the great abundance of H., the spectrum is only seen in the hottest stars, or in other special conditions.

Most of the energy of stars is produced by a process which converts hydrogen into H. (v. Nuclear reactions).

Hercules, a constellation in the northern hemisphere, situated between R.A. 15 h. 45 min. and 18 h. 55 min. and Dec. 4° and 51° N. This constellation contains the

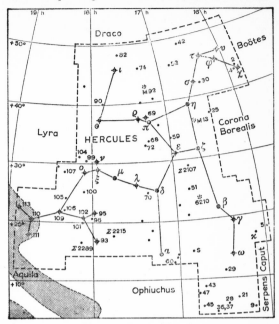

The constellation of Hercules

nearest globular star cluster* in the northern hemisphere, M13, whose stars can be clearly resolved with a 6-inch telescope. (→)

Herdsman, v. Boötes.

Hermes, a small asteroid* which sometimes comes very close to Earth. The smallest distance between the orbit of Hermes and that of Earth is 219,000 miles, which means that this asteroid is on occasion closer to the Earth than the Moon is.

Hertzsprung-Russell diagram (H.R.), a graph in which the absolute magnitudes of stars are plotted along the vertical axis and their spectral classes* along the horizontal axis. Each star is represented by a dot.

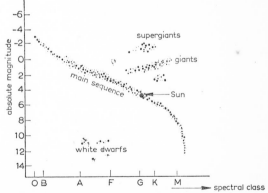

Fig. 1. H.R. diagram of stars belonging mainly to Population type I

Most stars are found to be grouped along a band stretching from the top left to the lower right of the diagram; this band is called the main sequence*. The

Sun occurs about halfway along the main sequence. The most striking feature of the diagram is that the hottest stars (white) also have the greatest absolute magnitudes and the coldest stars (red)the least absolute magnitudes. Hertzsprung showed that there were also red stars (spectral classes G and M) of very great absolute magnitude. These stars are called 'giants' (e.g. Capella and Arcturus) and 'supergiants' (e.g. Rigel, Betelgeuse and Antares). They form a separate branch at an angle to the main sequence. Apart from these, there are other white stars with very small absolute magnitudes, called white dwarfs (e.g. the companion of Sirius). The *H.R.d.* shown (→ 1) for stars of known absolute magnitudes gives a distorted impression of the distribution of the various types, for giant stars can be observed at great distances from us, while only the nearest dwarfs can be detected. Within a radius of 30 light-years round the Sun we find 246 main-sequence stars, 7 white dwarfs, a single giant (Pollux) and not one supergiant. An *H.R.d.* confined to the stars in the vicinity of the Sun thus gives a truer picture of the actual distribution of types.

The physical properties of a star can mostly be found from its position in the main sequence. The radii, masses and temperatures of stars have been included in Fig. 2. The *H.R.d.* is extremely important in various kinds of statistical research, in the study of the evolution of the stars* and for finding the distances of groups of stars. Thus, to find distances, we draw an *H.R.d.* of the stars in the group, plotting their *apparent* magnitudes along the vertical axis. The stars in the group being all at approximately the same distance, it follows that there is a constant difference between their absolute magnitudes and their apparent magnitudes. This constant can be found by displacing the *H.R.d.* in a vertical direction until it coincides with

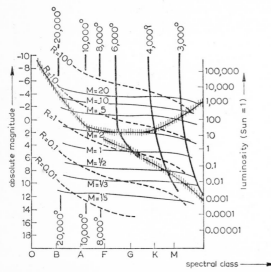

Fig. 2. The lines of equal temperature are almost vertical, those of equal mass almost horizontal. The Sun's mass is taken as 1. The lines of equal radius are the broken lines running from upper left to lower right. The Sun's radius is taken as 1

a standard *H.R.d.* The distance can then be calculated from this displacement. A considerable proportion of main-sequence stars (→ 1) belong to stellar Population type* 1. The *H.R.d.* for Population type II (the older stars) looks quite different (→ 1 Evolution of the stars)

and includes relatively few main-sequence stars. White and blue stars are completely absent. Almost all type II stars are found either in the remaining part of the main sequence; or in an almost horizontal branch; or among the giants and supergiants. The differences

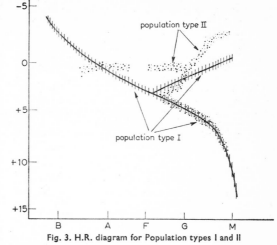

Fig. 3. H.R. diagram for Population types I and II

between the *H.R.d.s* for the two stellar populations are due to the effects of evolution, which has proceeded further in the case of Population type II than in that of type I. A combined *H.R.d.* of the two types is shown schematically in Fig. 3. The diagram, (which is sometimes plotted with colour index instead of spectral type, when it is called the colour–magnitude diagram), is usually referred to as the Hertzsprung-Russell diagram, after the two astronomers who first introduced it. Ejnar Hertzsprung is a Dane who was attached to the Leiden Observatory from 1919 to 1945. Henry N. Russell, an American astronomer, was Director of the Princeton Observatory.

Hidalgo, one of the smaller asteroids, with its aphelion* near the orbit of Saturn and its perihelion* near the orbit of Mars. The inclination of its orbit to the ecliptic is 43°, its eccentricity 0·63.

High-velocity stars are stars in the halo* of the Galaxy, and situated in the neighbourhood of the Sun. They do not share in the motion of the Sun (and other stars embedded in the spiral arms) about the central region of the Galaxy. Their 'high velocity' relative to the Sun is due to the fact that the Sun, by its own orbital velocity (about 125 m. p. sec. or 200 km/sec.), is rapidly leaving them behind. The *H-v.s.* are also revolving round the centre of the Galaxy, but their orbital planes are as a rule steeply inclined to the plane of the spiral arms. They belong to stellar Population type II (*v.* Population types and Pl. 60) and are older than the stars in the spiral arms. The 'subdwarfs' belong to this category.

History of astronomy, *v.* Astronomy.

Hooker telescope at the Mount Wilson Observatory has a 100-inch mirror and is named after John D. Hooker, who provided the funds for its purchase. From 1918 to 1948 it was the largest telescope in the world. The American astronomer, George Ellery Hale, took the initiative with regard to this telescope in 1903; it came into use in 1918. The 100-inch mirror weighs 4½ tons. The dome has a height and diameter of 100 feet, and weighs 600 tons. The weight of the telescope is 100 tons. Its optical system can be used in various ways (→ 1 Hale telescope): at the prime focus, or focus of the large mirror: focal length 41$\frac{1}{3}$ ft., focal ratio f/5; at the Cassegrain focus: focal length 133$\frac{1}{3}$ ft., focal ratio f/16; at the Coudé focus: focal length 250 ft., focal ratio f/30. The *H.t.* made some very important discoveries possible; for instance, it provided proof that: *a.* many faint objects in the sky (e.g. the Andromeda nebula*) lie far beyond our Galaxy; *b.* these objects are themselves galactic systems containing thousands of millions of stars; *c.* there are millions of such nebulae in the universe; *d.* these galaxies or extragalactic nebulae* are receding from us at high velocities (*v.* Red shift).

Horizon, in astronomy, is the line along which the plane through the observer's position at right angles to the vertical cuts the celestial sphere*.

Horizontal telescope comprises a coelostat* which directs sunlight horizontally to a fixed telescope. This, and the solar tower* are the usual instruments for observing and studying the Sun.

Horologium (the Clock), inconspicuous constellation in the southern hemisphere, situated between R.A. 2 h. 15 min. and 4 h. 20 min. and between Dec. — 40° and — 67°. (→)

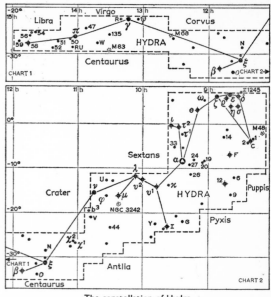

Horse-head nebula (Barnard 33), a dark nebula south of the star ζ Orionis, which completely obscures stars behind it. In shape it resembles a horse's head and it is about 5′ of arc in width. The edge of the nebula is bright

The constellation of Horologium

as if illuminated by bright stars hidden behind it. The area round Barnard 33 is rich in dark and bright nebulae. Like B33 these cannot be observed visually, even through the largest telescope, but only on photographs taken with long exposures (*v.* also Interstellar matter and Pl. 55, 56).

Horse, Little, *v.* Equuleus.

Hour angle of a celestial body is the arc measured along the celestial equator from the celestial meridian to the hour circle* of the body. The *H.a.* changes constantly with the diurnal motion. Together with declination, the *H.a.* forms a system of co-ordinates used for defining positions in the sky (*v.* Celestial sphere).

Hour circle, a great circle passing through the north and south poles of the 'static' celestial sphere. In the course of a sidereal day a star passes through every *H.c.* between 0 and 24 hours. The 0-hour circle coincides with the observer's meridian. A star on the 2-hour circle is therefore one which crossed the meridian two sidereal hours previously. The *H.c.* determines the hour angle, one of the co-ordinates—the other is declination—used to define positions in the sky (*v.* Celestial sphere).

Hubble's constant relates the velocities at which galaxies appear to be receding, and their distances from us (*v.* Extragalactic nebulae and Red shift). The value given to it nowadays is roughly 50 m.p.sec. (80 km/sec.) per million parsecs* (*v.* Pl. 83).

Hunter, *v.* Orion.

Hunting Dogs, *v.* Canes Venatici.

Hyades, an open star cluster in the constellation of Taurus, near the star Aldebaran (a Tauri).

Hydra (the Water-serpent), a very long constellation in the southern sky, situated between R.A. 8 h. 10 min. and 15 h. and extending from 7° N. to 35° S. Dec. (→)

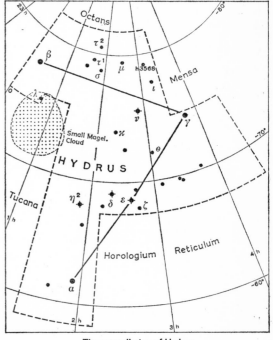

The constellation of Hydra

Hydrogen, the most abundant element in the universe. The only other element which exists in comparable abundance is helium. There are four *H.* atoms

The constellation of Hydrus

to every one of helium. All other elements are comparatively so rare that it is fair to say that the universe consists of a mixture of four parts of *H.* to one of helium with trace impurities (*v.* Sun, table of relative abundances).

The *H.* atom is the simplest of all, consisting of a single proton as nucleus and a single electron. Its spectrum is also simple. In the visible region of the spectrum it shows a single series of lines called Hα, Hβ, Hγ etc., which appear in the spectra of most astronomical sources.

Hydrus (the Water-snake), a southern constellation extending from o h. to 4 h. 35 min. R.A. and from —58° to —82° Dec. (→ facing)

Hyperbolic orbit is followed by a body entering the solar system from a great distance. It will first move along an almost straight line, will then curve round under the Sun's gravitational attraction and will eventually leave the system along another straight line.

Hyperion, one of Saturn's moons, discovered by Bond in 1848. Mean distance from Saturn 922,000 miles, period 21 d. 6 h. 38 min., diameter 250 miles (?), magnitude at opposition 13·0. Visible only with large telescopes.

I

Iapetus, one of the moons of Saturn, discovered by Cassini in 1671. Its mean distance from the planet is 2,215,000 miles, period of revolution 79 d. 7 h. 56 min., diameter 800 miles (?), magnitude at opposition 10·1–11·9.

I.A.U., *v.* International Astronomical Union.

Icarus, one of the smaller asteroids*; perihelion* within the orbit of Mercury.

Immersion, the disappearance of a star on being eclipsed by the Moon, or of a satellite on being eclipsed by a planet (*v.* Jupiter).

Inclination of an orbit*, the angle between the plane of the orbit and a given plane. In the case of planets, the latter is the plane of the ecliptic*; in the case of binary stars*, it is the plane of the sky, i.e. the plane at right angles to a line joining the observer and the binary stars.

Indian, *v.* Indus.

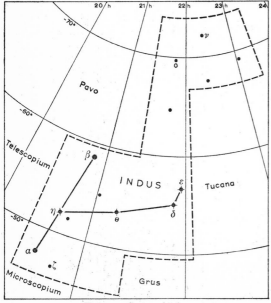

The constellation of Indus

Indus (the Indian), an inconspicuous constellation in the southern hemisphere, extending from 20 h. 25 min. to 23 h. 25 min. R.A. and from —45° to —75° Dec. (→)

Inferior planet is nearer to the Sun than is the Earth. There are two – Mercury and Venus.

Infra-red is the invisible radiation beyond the red end of the spectrum. It is a large band of wavelengths and extends to link up with short-wave radio radiation at about 1 cm. wavelength.

Interferometer, in observational astronomy, an instrument for measuring the diameter of large and not too distant stars. The largest stars are points of light in even large telescopes, so that direct measurement of their diameters is impossible. Nevertheless, the rays from two diametrically opposite points on a star form a small angle. By using an *I.,* to make these rays interfere with each other, it is possible to measure this angle and hence to determine the distance and diameter of the star. The diameters of 7 stars have been measured by this method. Nowadays the principle is used more in radio-telescopes than in optical astronomy.

Intergalactic matter is matter in the spaces between extragalactic nebulae*. It is sometimes visible on photographs as hazy luminous veils linking two or more galaxies (*v.* Pl. 85 and → Magellanic Clouds). It probably consists mainly of individual stars and of star clusters.

International Astronomical Union (I.A.U.), an organization for promoting contact between astronomers all over the world and one of the earliest international scientific unions, the first meeting in its present form having been held in 1922. Its chief aim is to hold conferences at which important subjects, prepared in advance by various special committees, are discussed. Problems that have arisen are dealt with from every angle, and lines along which research into such problems should develop are tentatively laid down. Particular emphasis is always placed on co-ordinating the work done and still to be done by the various member observatories and institutions. The special committees, of which there are now more than 40, may also hold symposia to compare results in their particular fields and to make further plans. The deliberations of the Union as a whole are published in the *Transactions of the I.A.U.* and those of the committees under the titles of the individual symposia. Recent conferences of the *I.A.U.* have been: Zürich 1948, Rome 1952, Dublin 1955, Moscow 1958. The next will be held in Berkeley (California) in 1961.

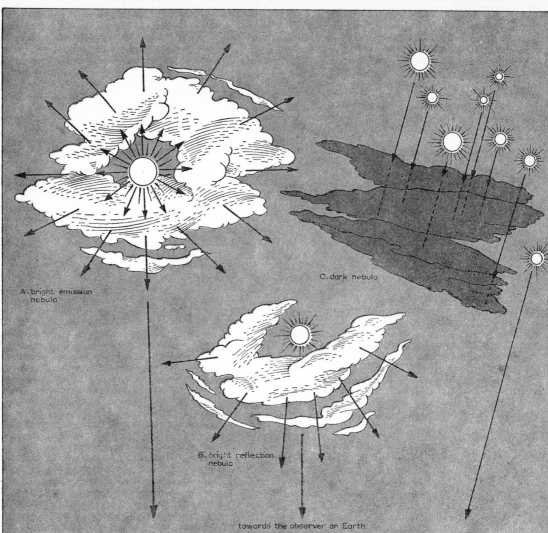

Galactic nebulae. A. Bright emission nebula. Radiation from one or more very hot stars (O- or B-class stars, temperature 30,000–50,000°) ionizes the hydrogen atoms in the nebula. The ionized nuclei capture substitute electrons and the reconstituted hydrogen atoms emit light. B. Bright reflection nebula. The nebula reflects light from one or more bright stars in its vicinity. C. Dark nebula. This nebula dims the light of stars behind it

The International Geophysical Year (I. G. Y.), (1st July 1957, to 1st Jan. 1959) coincided with the period of greatest sunspot activity for the last few centuries. International co-operation enabled the Sun to be kept under continual observation by astronomers and radio-astronomers throughout the period. In addition to the Lyot filter used hitherto, which gives a monochromatic picture of the Sun in the α-line of hydrogen, spectrographs were also used. Further observations were made with the aid of rockets and several artificial satellites*.

Interstellar absorption (v. Pl. 58) attenuates the light from most stars. Interstellar matter may completely obscure stars behind it, or may make them appear redder than they are, because it tends to scatter violet light more than red. This difference in colour indicates the presence of interstellar dust (v. Colour index) and assumes importance when the apparent magnitudes are compared with absolute magnitudes for the purpose of determining distances. Allowance must then be made for the fact that the extra attenuation of the light is due, not to greater distance, but to *I.a.* Correct distances are important because they give a truer picture of how stars are distributed in space. On the whole, *I.a.* is least in the direction of the galactic poles and greatest in that of the galactic equator (v. Interstellar matter).

Interstellar matter exists in the spaces between stars in our Galaxy and consists mainly of hydrogen. It occurs chiefly in the spiral arms (v. Pl. 45, 46). The thickness of this layer perpendicular to the plane of the spiral arms is about 1,000 light-years. *I.m.*, consisting of gas and dust and concentrated locally into clouds, is visible to us as bright and dark galactic nebulae. Its presence is also revealed by the absorption of starlight shining through it, i.e. it makes stars appear fainter and redder than they really are and than their spectral class would suggest (*v.* Pl. 58) (by the emission of radiation on a wavelength of 21 cm), by certain nebulae (*v.* Radio astronomy and Pl. 62), and by absorption lines sometimes to be found superimposed on the spectra of distant stars. The luminous appearance of some clouds is due to reflection and scattering of starlight; these are known as reflection nebulae (e.g. the nebula surrounding the Pleiades) and contain dust. In other cases, hot radiation from nearby stars ionizes the nebula and light is radiated; these are known as emission nebulae and consist of gas (*v.* Ionization). Reflection nebulae (*v.* Pl. 40) have continuous spectra, and emission nebulae, line spectra.

I.m. sometimes forms globules (*v.* Pl. 43) of dust, with diameters between $^1/_{100}$ and $^1/_{10}$ of a light-year, but more usually exists as rarefied clouds with diameters ranging up to several hundred light-years but with an average of 30 light-years. Their average density is about 10 atoms per c.c. The density in the neighbourhood of the Sun is one hydrogen atom per c.c. Yet this very tenuous gas amounts to 10^{30} gm per cubic light-year. The mass of this interstellar gas and dust in the spiral arms of the Milky Way is roughly equal to the constituent masses of all stars in them. Its principal component is hydrogen; other gases are rarer. Several chemical combinations occur, the molecules of which may unite to form small grains of dust. Only 1–2% of the entire mass of *I.m.* consists of dust.

Emission Nebulae or H II Regions (→ A, facing). These are clouds of ionized hydrogen. Hydrogen is ionized in the vicinity of hot stars (O and B stars); the ions and electrons move about independently of each other. The range of influence of a star depends on its temperature and in the case of a very hot star may extend to a sphere with a radius of 300–500 light-years. The temperature of these hot gases is of the order of 10,000°. The recombination of the ions with free electrons to form neutral atoms causes the hydrogen to radiate light (emission), and this is what enables us to perceive emission clouds. Example of an emission nebula: the Orion nebula* (*v.* Pl. 53, 54, 55).

Clouds of Neutral Hydrogen or H I Regions (*v.* Pl. 62). This gas is not ionized and is not situated near hot stars. The existence of such clouds is known to us by the 21 cm electromagnetic radiation (*v.* Radio astronomy) which the neutral hydrogen can emit. Their temperature is of the order of 100°K. Occasional clouds of hot gas (emission nebulae) occur among the more normal neutral hydrogen. The hot gas expands under radiation pressure from the hot stars and pushes cool gas ahead of it, which therefore becomes more concentrated on the edge of the hot gas. It is perhaps possible that the conditions thus created are favourable for the formation of very compact dust clouds where future stars will be born.

Dark Nebulae (→ C). The atoms in the cold gas may combine to form very simple chemical substances such as water, methane and ammonia, etc., which may combine further to make particles of dust. The dust absorbs starlight and forms dark clouds which sometimes completely obscure the stars behind them from our view (*v.* Coal Sack and Pl. 42, 43, 49, 55, 56, 57). As these very fine particles of dust scatter mainly blue light and absorb more violet light than red, they make starlight which passes through them on its way to us appear redder than it is. If the spectral class of the star is known, and hence the luminosity appropriate to a star of that class, the amount of light attenuation can be found, and this enables deductions to be made concerning the amount of dust between the Sun and the star in that direction.

Knowledge of the quantity of interstellar dust is in turn linked up with knowledge of the number and distribution in space of the external galaxies*, for it has been found that the number of visible galaxies increases in the direction of the galactic poles, where there is less dust. This is because the observer is then looking in a direction perpendicular to the galactic plane and therefore along the least diameter of the dust disk.

The dark clouds probably consist of particles the size of a molecule and larger. The obscuration, however, is due to the very fine dust. The particles possibly consist, to a large extent, of ice. The least rarefied dust clouds have a density of 1,000 to 10,000 atoms per c.c. As they move at different speeds (up to about 60 m.p.sec.) in different directions, collisions will occur. Heat will therefore be generated which can evaporate the particles. It is thus impossible for the particles to increase indefinitely in size, and they are mainly of the same size, viz. 10–50 Å (or 10^{-6} to 5×10^{-6} mm).

Dark clouds occasionally have bright edges (*v.* Pl. 55, 57). These are thought to be the limits to which the atoms in the dark nebula are ionized and made to glow by the light from a hot star. The transformation of a dark nebula into a bright nebula has been observed on occasion. This was caused by a variable star* increasing in brightness, or by the occurrence of a nova in or near the nebula. As a rule nebular masses expand. It has been discovered that most clouds are elongated in shape and lie more or less parallel to the galactic equator. This is believed to be due, not to galactic rotation, but to the fact that expansion is arrested in a direction perpendicular to the lines of force of the interstellar magnetic field. The clouds therefore expand mainly in the direction of these lines of force, i.e. roughly parallel to the galactic equator.

Similar clouds of gas and dust have been found in other galaxies (*v.* Pl. 66, 70, 74, 77, 86). Bright and dark clouds are very clearly visible in the spiral arms of the Andromeda nebula* M31, for instance.

Io, one of Jupiter's four brightest moons, discovered by Galileo* in 1610. Mean distance from Jupiter 262,000 miles, period 1 d. 18 h. 28 min., diameter 2,310 miles, magnitude at opposition 5·5 (→ 3 Solar system).

Ionization is the removal of electrons from an atom*. The matter composing stars and nebulae is ionized to varying degrees. The degree of ionization partly determines the pattern of lines in the spectra of stars or nebulae. Ionization plays a considerable part in theoretical speculation on the interior of stars. The matter of which white dwarfs* (*v.* Dwarfs) are composed is probably completely ionized and consists solely of separate nuclei and electrons not combined to form atoms.

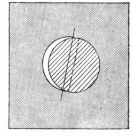

Irradiation

Ionosphere, part of the Earth's atmosphere, extending from the stratosphere to the exosphere, i.e. from 50 to

250–300 miles above the Earth's surface (*v.* Earth and Pl. 5).

Iris, a small asteroid with a periodical change of brightness (6 h. 12 min.) (*v.* Eros).

Irradiation is the phenomenon whereby brightly illuminated or self-illuminating bodies appear bigger than they in fact are. The Moon's crescent, for instance, appears to be part of a larger circle than the shaded part of the disk (→ p. 157). The effect is also very noticeable in photography due to the scattering of light in the photographic emulsion. In particular, since bright stars produce more scattered light than faint stars, photographs of star fields show the images of bright stars larger than those of faint stars (*v.* Pl. 33, 34).

Irregular variables, *v.* Variable stars.

J

Jacob's staff, a simple astronomical measuring instrument much used at the time of the Renaissance. It consisted of a long, graduated staff and a short cross-head. The staff was held in the hand and aimed visually at the sky. The cross-head was moved along the staff until the extremities coincided with two stars. The graduation on the staff then showed the angular distance between the two stars. Thus the instrument could also be used to measure the elevation of a celestial body above the horizon.

Julian calendar, a method of reckoning time, introduced in 46 B.C. by Julius Caesar to put an end to the variety of calendars in use at that time. He decreed a solar year of 365·25 days. By inserting a year of 366 days (leap year) after three years of 365 days, it proved possible for the civil calendar to keep pace approximately with the course of the Sun. The tropical year (*v.* Year) which governs the seasons is, however, slightly shorter, viz. 365·2422 days. By the middle of the sixteenth century the calendar was thus more than 10 days behind the course of the Sun. By a papal decree of Gregory XIII, 10 days in October, 1582, were annulled, Thursday, 4th October of that year being followed by Friday, 15th October. To ensure that such drastic corrections would not be necessary in the future it was also decreed that centurial years would not be leap years unless they were divisible by 400. Thus, 1700, 1800 and 1900 were not leap years, but 2000 will be a leap year. Not until 3,000 years from now will our calendar be as much as a whole day out.

Julian day, a day-count independent of months and years. Introduced by Scaliger in 1582 and named by him after his father, Julius Scaliger (and therefore not related to the Julian calendar*). When phenomena extend over a considerable period of time, it is easier to calculate, not in months and years, but in days, if the latter are consecutively numbered. The date arbitrarily chosen as zero day for this system was the 1st January, 4713 B.C. As observations were made mainly at night and the midnight change was considered undesirable, the *J.d.* begins at 12 noon. The *J.d.* numbering is used in records dealing with the luminosity of variable stars. The time at which a variable star reaches its maximum brightness, for instance, may be stated as 2,414,827·15 + 7·1767 × *n*. The first term is expressed in *J.d.* and the second is the period of variation in days. The times of future maxima can then be predicted by substituting 1, 2, 3, etc. for *n*.

1st January, 1962 = Julian day 2,437,666
1st January, 1963 = Julian day 2,438,031

Juno, one of the four largest asteroids*, discovered by Harding in 1804. Diameter 150 miles, albedo 0·12.

Jupiter (*v.* Pl. 19), largest planet in the solar system and one of the brightest objects in the sky. Its mass is greater than that of all the other planets together. With its four brightest moons, *J.* is one of the objects most favoured by amateur astronomers. Even with a very small telescope it is possible to see the planet as a disk and to follow the four satellites in their orbits. If *J.* were less bright, the moons, which it outshines, would be visible with the naked eye.

What we see of *J.* is not its solid surface but the outer layers of its atmosphere. It is not even known whether the planet has in fact a solid nucleus; opinions on this point vary. On its disk we see dark and light belts running parallel to its equator. The bright central equatorial zone is bounded by darker stripes, the northern and southern equatorial belts; while both hemispheres exhibit a series of less distinct bands. These belts are currents in the atmosphere, set up by the fast rotation of the planet. This rotation is betrayed by the displacement of details on the disk which can be seen to take place even in a single evening.

Various spots remain visible in the atmosphere for longer or shorter periods. Two of the most conspicuous are the 'great red spot' (*v.* Pl. 19) and the 'southern tropical veil'. The red spot is located on the surface of *J.*'s atmosphere, in the southern hemisphere. It varies irregularly in brightness and size. It was visible

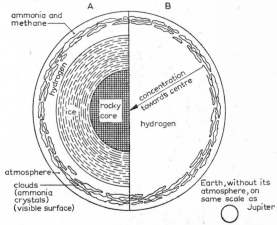

Fig. 1. Cross-section through Jupiter: two hypotheses (A and B)

by 1835 and from 1879 to 1882 was about 25,000 miles long and 8,000 miles across. From 1882 onwards it started to become less conspicuous. At the beginning

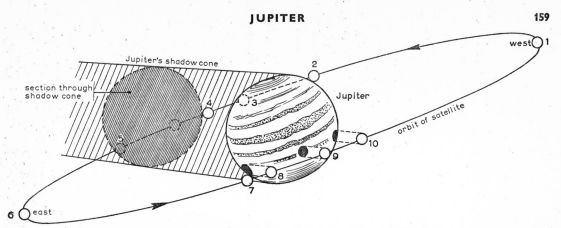

Fig. 2. Observable phenomena as a satellite of Jupiter revolves around the planet

of the nineteen-twenties and in 1936–7 it was again a striking sight. The latitude of the red spot varies by 2° to 3°. The spot also moves to and fro in longitude to some extent, so that its period of revolution is irregular. From this it can be assumed that the spot is not directly connected with a fixed point on the planet's surface (e.g. a volcano). Wildt supposes that the spot is a solid mass floating in an ocean of greatly condensed gases. The varying degree of conspicuousness is due to the fact that the depth of this mass in the atmosphere is subject to variation. Solid helium, among other things, is suggested as the substance of which the mass consists. Its colour is far from being as red as the name suggests.

It is thought that the outermost layers of the atmosphere consist of hydrogen with some ammonia and methane (marsh gas) and clouds of crystallized ammonia. The temperature there is 135–150° K. As a result of the high pressure it is probable that the atmosphere rapidly becomes more liquid towards the planet's surface. The red spot can be regarded as a solid island floating in a liquid atmosphere and covered with clouds. According to one theory (→ 1, A) the layer of hydrogen overlies a thick layer of ice (39 % of the radius of $\mathcal{J}$.), beneath which the actual surface of the planet is hidden. Another theory is that there is no rocky nucleus, but that the planet consists of more than 80 % of hydrogen forced towards the centre under ever-growing pressure (→ 1, B). The nucleus would therefore consist of solid hydrogen in metallic form. The speed of rotation varies for the different parts of the atmosphere's surface, being fastest at the equatorial zone and decreasing towards the poles. It is therefore believed that the various lightly coloured belts pass each other at a speed of the order of 60 m. p. sec., setting up great turbulence in the border areas of the atmosphere. These atmospheric eddies or cyclones are visible as the darker belts. The different colours observed (red in the red spot, brown and greenish hues in the zones and belts) are believed to be caused by the solution of light metals such as sodium and calcium in liquid ammonia. The high-speed rotation period (less than 10 hours) has caused so great a degree of flattening at the poles that this is immediately visible through the telescope and on photographs (v. Pl. 19).

Since 1955, by observing $\mathcal{J}$. with radio-telescopes, it has been found that the radio radiation from $\mathcal{J}$. is polarized, which may mean that the planet has an ionosphere and a magnetic field. It also appears that the parts of its surface with maximum and minimum activity revolve in 9 h. 55 min. 28·8 sec. It is further thought that $\mathcal{J}$. like the Earth, has Van Allen belts*, containing one millionth as many charged particles as the terrestrial Van Allen belts.

$\mathcal{J}$.'s average distance from the Sun is 843,600,000 miles, period of revolution 11·862 years, orbital speed 8·1 m. p. sec., average diameter 86,800 miles or 10·97 × the Earth's, density 0·241 that of the Earth, period of rotation 9 h. 50 min. to 9 h. 56 min., albedo 0·51.

Jupiter's Satellite System. The system consists of twelve moons. The four brightest and largest were discovered as early as 1610 by Galileo. These were given the names of Io, Europa, Ganymede and Callisto by Simon Marius. They are observable with a small telescope. The others are not named but are numbered according to the order of discovery, viz. $\mathcal{J}$.v to $\mathcal{J}$.xii. Axial rotation has been established for the four brightest satellites only, in the case of Ganymede and Callisto from the movement of surface details and in that of the other two by the variability of the reflected light.

All four appear always to turn the same side of their surface to $\mathcal{J}$., as the Moon does to the Earth, which means that their periods of rotation are the same as their periods of revolution. The remaining satellites are very small and most of them would not be visible with the naked eye from $\mathcal{J}$.

$\mathcal{J}$. vi to $\mathcal{J}$. xii were all discovered photographically. The smallest of them may be asteroids* which have been captured by $\mathcal{J}$. According to recent research Europa and Ganymede may be covered with snow (G. P. Kuiper, 1957). In the case of Europa this theory is the more acceptable because of the high reflecting power of the satellite's surface (v. Albedo). Ganymede, however, is darker in colour and may be covered with snow which has been polluted with dust.

The satellite system may be divided into three groups:

a. The four largest moons and $\mathcal{J}$. v. They are nearest to the planet and move from west to east.

b. $\mathcal{J}$. vi, $\mathcal{J}$. vii and $\mathcal{J}$. x. These revolve from west to east with periods of about 260 days and at an average distance of 7,000,000 miles from $\mathcal{J}$.

c. $\mathcal{J}$. viii, $\mathcal{J}$. ix, $\mathcal{J}$. xi and $\mathcal{J}$. xii. These move from east to west at an average distance of 14,000,000 miles and with an average period of 700 days.

Observations of the four brightest moons. Because the planes of the orbits are approximately in line with the Earth, the moons appear to us to move to and fro on a straight line and we can see them at regular times in front of or behind the disk of *J.* The following phenomena may occur (→ 2): (1) The moon has reached its greatest western elongation, i.e. it appears to us to be at its greatest distance to the west of *J.*; (2) the moon disappears behind *J.* and occultation begins; (3) it reappears and occultation ceases; (4) it disappears in the shadow cone of the planet and the eclipse begins; (5) it reappears and the eclipse is ended; (6) it reaches its greatest eastern elongation; (7) it moves in front of *J.*'s disk and the transit begins; (8) the shadow of the moon starts moving over *J.*'s disk, i.e. the shadow transit begins; (9) the moon leaves the disk, and the transit is ended; (10) the shadow of the moon leaves the disk, and the shadow transit is ended.

Because of *J.*'s position in relation to the Sun, its shadow cone may occupy various positions in which the sequences 2–5 and 7–10 differ from those stated above. When *J.* is in opposition*, the shadow cone as seen from Earth is behind the planet's disk, and eclipses and shadow transits are not observable. The exact times of the various phenomena numbered 1–10 are given for each day in the *Astronomical Ephemeris*.

Jupiter's family of comets is a group of about 25 comets with an orbit similar in many respects to that of Jupiter. Encke's comet, which has a period of only $3^1/_2$ years, is one of them. It is thought that Jupiter, with its great power of gravitational attraction, has forced these comets into their present short orbit. It was formerly believed that comets were not original members of the solar system but had all been captured by the Sun. The most widely accepted view nowadays is that comets originated at the same time as the planets and the Sun.

PARTICULARS OF JUPITER'S MOONS

Name	Discovered in	Av. dist. from planet in miles	Period	Diameter in miles	Magn. at oppos.
Jupiter (v)	1892	112,700	11 h. 57 min.	100 (?)	13
Io (i)	1610	262,000	1 d. 18 h. 28 min.	2310	5
Europa (ii)	1610	417,000	3 d. 13 h. 14 min.	1960	6
Ganymede (iii)	1610	665,000	7 d. 3 h. 43 min.	3200	5
Callisto (iv)	1610	1,170,000	16 d. 16 h. 32 min.	3220	6
Jupiter (vi)	1904	7,100,000	251 d.	75 (?)	14
Jupiter (vii)	1905	7,300,000	260 d.	30 (?)	17
Jupiter (x)	1938	7,300,000	260 d.	12 (?)	19
Jupiter (xii)	1951	13,000,000	625 d.	(?)	18
Jupiter (xi)	1938	14,000,000	696 d.	15 (?)	18
Jupiter (viii)	1908	14,700,000	739 d.	30 (?)	16
Jupiter (ix)	1914	14,800,000	755 d.	14 (?)	18

K

K-corona, the inner part of the Sun's corona* (*v.* Sun).

K-line, *v.* Fraunhofer lines.

Keel, *v.* Carina.

Kepler's laws relate to the motions of the planets around the Sun (and also of satellites around the planets, and of double stars around each other).

1. The orbits of the planets are ellipses with the Sun at one of the foci.

2. The line joining a planet and the Sun sweeps out equal areas in equal times. It follows that the planet travels faster the closer it is to the Sun (→).

3. The square of the sidereal period of revolution of a planet bears a constant relation to the cube of its distance from the Sun.

This law enables us to calculate any planet's distance from the Sun from its period, provided that the distance of any one planet from the Sun and its period of revolution are known.

The following is a rough calculation to show how the distance of Uranus can be found from its period of revolution.

Pe = the period of the Earth = 1 year.
Pu = the period of Uranus = 84 years.
De = the distance from Earth to the Sun = 1 A.U.
Required to find Du, the distance of Uranus from the Sun.

From Kepler's third law:

$$\frac{Pe^2}{Pu^2} = \frac{De^3}{Du^3}, \text{ i.e. } \frac{1^2}{84^2} = \frac{1^3}{Du^3},$$

from which it follows that $Du^3 = 84^2$. Hence $Du = 19\cdot2$ A.U. These laws were deduced by Kepler (in 1609) from careful observations of the motions of the planets, made by Tycho Brahe (1546–1601) over a long period. In his *Principia* (1687) Newton showed how *K.l.* could be derived from his law of universal gravitation.

Later on, Newton's theory was further expanded to cover the motions of all celestial bodies (*v.* Three-body problem). In our own time Einstein has studied the mechanics of celestial bodies from a much more general point of view (*v.* also Double stars).

Kiloparsec is 1,000 parsecs (*v.* Parsec).

Krueger 60, a double star in the constellation of Cepheus which is only 13·1 light-years from the Sun. On photographs taken in different years the displacement of the two components in relation to each other is very clearly visible. Its period is 44·5 years (*v.* Pl. 36).

Details: Krueger 60A: apparent magnitude, 9·9; absolute magnitude, 11·9; spectral class, M4; luminosity 0·0013 × Sun's; Krueger 60B: apparent magnitude, 11·3; absolute magnitude, 13·3; spectral class, M5; luminosity, 0·00033 × Sun's.

Lacerta (the Lizard), an inconspicuous constellation in the northern hemisphere between Cygnus and Andromeda. Situated between 21 h. 55 min. and 22 h. 55 min. R.A., and between 35° and 56° N. Dec. (→).

Latitude and Longitude are the co-ordinates of the ecliptic system (v. Ecliptic and Celestial sphere).

Latitude and Longitude, galactic, the co-ordinates in the system used to define the position of a celestial object in relation to the plane of the spiral arms of the Galaxy, i.e. its position on the celestial sphere* in relation to the 'galactic equator'. The galactic latitude is measured along the great circle passing

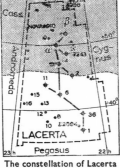

The constellation of Lacerta

through the object and the galactic poles, at right angles to the galactic equator. It is the angular distance between the galactic equator and the object, and is positive in the direction of the north galactic pole and negative in that of the south galactic pole.

Leo (the Lion), constellation (→) in the northern hemisphere, situated between 9 h. 20 min. and 11 h. 55 min. R.A. and between 6° S. and 33° N. Dec. It is

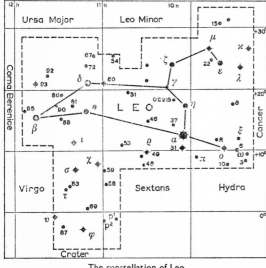

The constellation of Leo

on the ecliptic and is therefore one of the constellations of the zodiac*.

Leo Minor (the Little Lion), a small northern constellation, situated between R.A. 9 h. 20 min. and 11 h. 5 min. and between Dec. 23° and 42° N. (→)

Leonids, name of a meteor shower*, the radiant of which lies in the constellation of Leo. Observed on or about 16th November, associated with the comet 1866 I. There were extremely heavy meteor showers in

1833 and 1866. The shower disappeared in the nineteen-thirties.

Lepus (the Hare), a constellation in the southern hemisphere below Orion. It lies between 4 h. 55 min. and 6 h. 10 min. R.A. and —11° and —27° Dec. (→)

Libra (the Scales), one of the constellations of the zodiac* and therefore astride the ecliptic. It lies between 14 h. 20 min. and 16 h. R.A. and between 0° and —30° Dec. (→ p. 162)

Libration, a small oscillatory, 'nodding and shaking' movement of the Moon. The

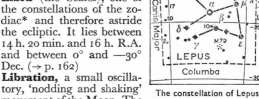

The constellation of Lepus

Moon revolves round its axis in such a way that the same side of the sphere is always shown to the Earth. According to its source, L. is divided into optical and physical L.

OPTICAL LIBRATION. a. L. in latitude. Because the Moon's equator is inclined at an angle to its orbital plane, we see in the course of a month first more of its northern hemisphere, then more of its southern hemisphere. A similar cause accounts for the Earth's seasons, for in the course of a year the Sun first shines more on the Earth's southern hemisphere, then more on its northern.

b. L. in longitude (→ 1), a monthly L. due to the fact that the Moon's rotation is almost uniform in speed while its motion around the Earth is not. In the neighbourhood of the perigee, when its distance from the Earth is least, the Moon's orbital velocity is greater than in the neighbourhood of the apogee, where its distance from the Earth is greatest. Suppose the Moon to be in perigee. M. is the point at the centre of the lunar disk as seen from the Earth, O. After a quarter of a period of revolution the Moon will have rotated exactly 90°. In its orbit around the Earth, however, it has described an angle of 96°, so that point M on the Moon appears to have shifted to the east. In the

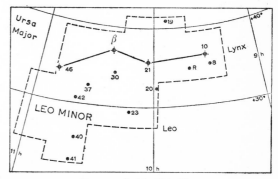

The constellation of Leo Minor

west of the disk we see slightly farther than the average limit of visibility. Half a month after being in perigee the Moon is at apogee and has turned through 180°

relative to the Earth. It has also rotated 180°, so that point M is again at the centre of the disk. A quarter of a period of revolution after apogee, the Moon has

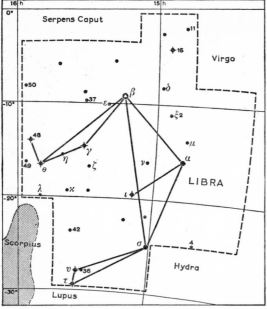

The constellation of Libra

again turned 90° on its axis, but only 84° in relation to the Earth because the velocity of revolution is less than average in the vicinity of the apogee. We now see

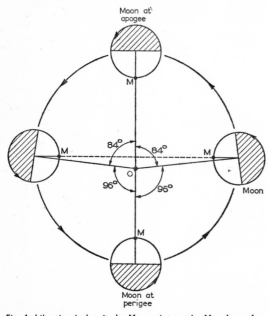

Fig. 1. Libration in longitude. M = point on the Moon's surface. O = observer on Earth. The hatching does not represent shadow but only indicates the half of the Moon that is invisible at O

slightly more of the east side of the Moon's sphere and point M is now west of the centre of the disk. After

another quarter of a period of revolution, the Moon has reached the perigee at a slightly greater velocity and M is back at the centre of the disk seen from the Earth.

c. L. in longitude, a daily *L.* (→ 2). The observer moves with the Earth's surface round the centre of the Earth. If the Moon is on the horizon, the line from the observer to the Moon makes an angle of 1° with the line connecting the Earth's centre and the Moon's. The observer thus sees slightly farther round the Moon.

PHYSICAL LIBRATION. This is an actual lunar oscillation and is an irregularity in the Moon's rotation, due to the fact that the Moon's diameter is slightly larger in the direction of the Earth. This slight 'hump' is attracted by the Earth, causing the Moon to rock to

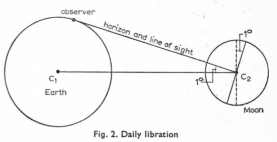

Fig. 2. Daily libration

and fro. Physical *L.* can also be resolved into a *L.* in longitude and a *L.* in latitude.

Life on other worlds, *v.* Life in the solar system, under Solar system.

Light. According to the wave theory first elaborated by Huygens and later modified by Maxwell and Lorentz, *L.* is an electromagnetic wave radiation which is propagated with a velocity of 186,000 m.p.sec. (300,000 km/sec.) in a vacuum. The colour of light depends on its wavelength; red. *L.*, for example, has a wavelength of 0·00007 cm and violet *L.* a wavelength of 0·00004 cm. The wavelength of *L.* is usually expressed in Ångström units: 1 Å = $^1/_{100\cdot000\cdot000}$ cm. The visible part of the spectrum is only a small part (a single octave) of the range of electromagnetic radiation.

Type of radiation	Wavelength		Number of octaves
Gamma rays	0·006 Å –	0·05 Å	3
X-rays	0·05 Å –	200 Å	12
Ultra-violet light	200 Å –	4,000 Å	4·5
Visible light	4,000 Å –	7,600 Å	1
Infra-red light	7,600 Å – 3,000,000 Å		8·5
Radio waves	0·3 mm – over 30 km		—

Until recently knowledge of celestial objects depended on visible *L.* and the adjacent parts of the ultra-violet and infra-red. Nowadays they are also studied by means of radio waves (*v.* Radio astronomy). Although the wave theory of light could account for many optical phenomena, there were others, such as the photo-electric effect or energy distribution over the spectrum of an incandescent body, which it failed to explain. These can be accounted for by the corpuscular theory, which states that *L.* consists of small particles (called photons by Einstein) possessing definite amounts of energy. These contradictory descriptions of *L.*, as a wave phenomenon and as discrete bundles of energy can be reconciled by recognizing that its essence is neither of these, but when it is in free space it behaves *as though* it were a wave motion and when it is in interaction with matter, it behaves *as though* it consisted of discrete quanta of energy.

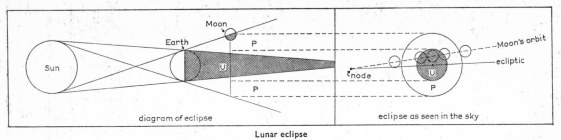

Lunar eclipse

Electromagnetic waves, which include L.-waves, are created when an electron in an atom jumps from one orbit to another. The orbits which an electron can traverse are very strictly defined, and so, too, are the amounts of energy released in the form of radiation. In the spectrum of an incandescent gas, therefore, we also see emission lines of definite wavelengths. Thus, the single electron which moves round the nucleus of an atom of hydrogen can produce a series of lines in the spectrum (hydrogen lines), which are characteristic of hydrogen. Each element has its own characteristic spectrum, so that elements occurring in distant celestial objects can be identified from their spectra. A gas under high pressure, e.g. in the interior of a star, produces radiation on practically all wavelengths. The spectrum is then continuous (v. Radiation laws and Pl. 32). If an atom in the cooler and more tenuous atmosphere of a star is hit by a ray of a particular wavelength (i.e. by a photon of a particular energy), the ray (or photon) may be absorbed: an electron then jumps into an orbit of higher energy. The spectrum is no longer continuous but contains a dark absorption line.

Light-curve, a graph formed by plotting the magnitude of an eclipsing binary or variable star as one co-ordinate, and the time of observation as the other (v. Double stars and Variable stars).

Light-year, the distance travelled by light in a year. 1 L.-y. = 5,880,000,000,000 miles = 0·3068 parsec.

Limb is the visible 'edge' of the Sun, Moon or a planet.

Line spectrum, v. Spectrum and Pl. 32.

Lion, v. Leo.

Lion, Little, v. Leo Minor.

Little Bear, v. Ursa Minor.

Little Dog, v. Canis Minor.

Little Horse, v. Equuleus.

Little Lion, v. Leo Minor.

Lizard, v. Lacerta.

Local group of galaxies, v. Extragalactic nebulae and Pl. 69.

Long-period variables, v. Variable stars.

Loop nebula in Cygnus (v. Pl. 47, 48), luminous nebular mass, south of the star ε Cygni, consisting of a large number of hazy wreaths, the most striking of which (NGC6960 and NGC6992) are arcs with their concave sides facing each other. Recent measurements show that the nebula is not expanding (the braking effect of interstellar matter is too great; see below) but is in turbulent motion. The nebula is about 1,000 light-years from us and has a diameter of about 50 light-years. These gaseous nebulosities are believed to be the remnants of a supernova explosion which must have occurred a very long time ago. The gas has an estimated mass of 5 solar masses but it is probable that gases ejected by the star have mingled with existing matter in space and that the original mass was accordingly not much more than 1 solar mass. Expansion was probably slowed down by interstellar matter* already present in the area (v. Pl. 48, top, on which fewer stars are to be seen to the right than to the left of the nebula, suggesting the presence of interstellar matter to the right of the nebula).

Lowell, Percival, v. Mars and Pluto.

Luminous nebula (emission nebula), v. Interstellar matter, Nebulae and Pl. 43, 54.

Lunar eclipse takes place when the Moon comes within the shadow thrown by the Earth in the light from the Sun; it can thus occur only during a period of full Moon. Since the Moon's orbit makes an angle

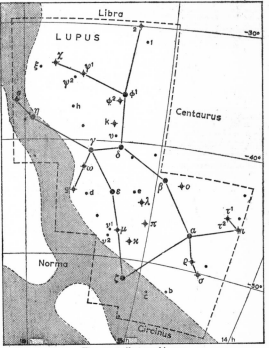

The constellation of Lupus

of 5° 9′·0 with the ecliptic, a L.e. occurs only when the full Moon has reached a node or is at most 10° distant from one (→ 2a, 2b Moon).

Eclipses of the Moon (and Sun) occur in the same sequence after a period of 18 years and 11 days (v. Saros). On the average, one or two L.e.s occur each year. Unlike solar eclipses, L.e.s can be seen from every point on Earth from which the Moon is visible in the sky. The part of the shadow where no sunlight can penetrate is called the inner shadow or umbra (U) (→); that where only part of the sunlight is intercepted is the half shadow or penumbra (P). When the Moon comes

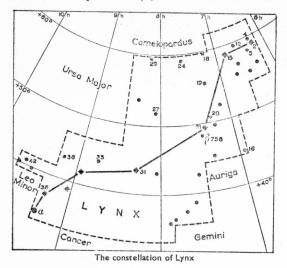

The constellation of Lynx

only partly within the Earth's shadow we speak of a partial *L.e.* The maximum length of a total eclipse is 1·75 h. Here the Moon passes through the Earth's shadow from west to east, while at the same time the Moon and the shadow follow the daily movement towards the west.

In the geometrical inner shadow, the Moon is still visible as a result of sunlight's being refracted into the shadow region by the Earth's atmosphere. As a result of the atmosphere's absorbing and scattering blue light more than red (the reason for the setting sun's being red), the moon is visibly red in colour at this phase of the eclipse. This breaking-up of light by the Earth's atmosphere also gives the shadow a blurred outline (*v.* also Umbra). The observation of *L.e.* is of little importance to modern astronomy.

Lunation is the period elapsing between two similar phases of the Moon, e.g. between two successive new Moons, and is the same as the synodic period* (29·53059 days, *v.* Moon). Owing to the eccentricity* of the Moon's orbit and other factors, *L.* may vary between 29·72 and 29·83 days.

Lunik, the name for a series of Russian Moon rockets (*v.* Space travel and Artificial satellite).
Lupus (the Wolf), a constellation in the southern hemisphere, containing numerous bright stars; situated between 14 h. 15 min. and 16 h. 5 min. R.A. and —30° to —55° Dec. (→ p. 163)
Lynx, an inconspicuous constellation in the northern hemisphere between 6 h. 10 min. and 9 h. 40 min. R.A. and 33° and 62° N. Dec. (→)
Lyot filter, *v.* Monochromatic filter.
Lyra (the Lyre), a constellation in the northern hemisphere, situated between 18 h. 10 min. and 19 h. 30 min. R.A. and 25° and 47° N. Dec. (→)

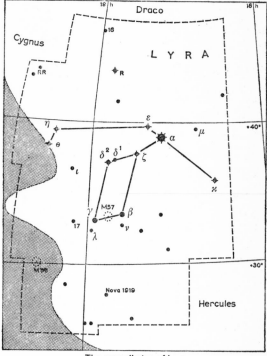

The constellation of Lyra

Lyre, *v.* Lyra.
Lyrids, name of a meteor shower (*v.* Meteor) whose radiant is in the constellation of Lyra.

M

Macrocosm, the whole universe, *v.* Universe and Pl. 92.
Magellanic Clouds (*v.* Pl. 63, 64), two galactic systems in the southern celestial hemisphere, in the constellations of Dorado, Mensa and Tucana. They are known in much greater detail than any other galaxy. They are named after the Portuguese navigator, Magellan. The nearest of all the galaxies, they are quite clearly visible with the naked eye, and have visual diameters of 7° and 4° respectively. Until recently they were considered to be much smaller than

our own Milky Way system, but it is now thought that the Large Cloud is comparable in size although much less massive. The *M.C.* and the Galaxy together form a triple system (→). A 5-inch telescope reveals just as much detail in the *M.C.* as the 200-inch reflector at Mount Wilson does in the Great Nebula in Andromeda! Larger telescopes in the southern hemisphere can distinguish details with a dimension of 1 light-year in the *M.C.* The Large Cloud is possibly connected to the Galaxy by a long arm consisting of stars, bright gaseous clouds and dust. This bridge is of the type

Zwicky discovered between various extragalactic nebulae (v. Pl. 85). A complicated structure in the arm of the Galaxy in the vicinity of the Sun is thought to be possibly due to a 'root' of the Magellanic arm. A similar arm leading off in the opposite direction is found on the far side of the Large Cloud from us (v. also Pl. 89).

Both systems are presented to us at an angle; the Large Cloud's galactic plane is inclined at 65° to the line of sight, the Small Cloud's at 30°. In actual fact both are roughly circular in shape. Photographs suggest a spiral structure, which may be more clearly demonstrated by star counts. Star counts give an apparent diameter of 20° for the Large Cloud and 9° for the Small. As the distance of both nebulae is 150,000 light-years, the linear diameters are therefore: Large Cloud 50,000 light-years, Small Cloud 22,500 light-years.

The Small Cloud is bluer in the central region and redder in the outer regions, while the Large Cloud is uniformly reddish.

COMPOSITION OF THE CLOUDS. At least half of the mass of the M.C. is accounted for by neutral hydrogen. The Small Cloud is much more transparent than the

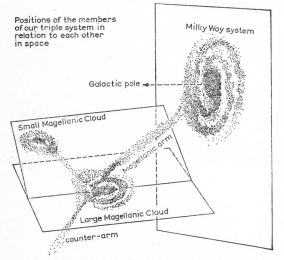

Positions of the members of our triple system in relation to each other in space

Milky Way system

Galactic pole

Small Magellanic Cloud

Magellanic arm

Large Magellanic Cloud

counter-arm

Situation of the Magellanic Clouds in space in relation to the Galaxy. The connecting arms are shown

Large and a great number of more remote galaxies can be seen through it; hardly any such galaxies are observable through the Large Cloud. This shows that there is dust in the Large Cloud but not in the Small Cloud. The Large Cloud probably consists mainly of stars of Population type I and is similar in structure to the spiral arms of the Galaxy.

Emission nebulae (v. Galactic nebulae and Pl. 64). Dreyer's *New General Catalogue* lists 301 star clusters and nebulae in the Large Cloud alone. The average diameter of 160 nebulae in the Small Cloud is about 25 light-years. Just off the axis of symmetry of the Large Cloud lies the Rosette Nebula (30 Doradus), with a diameter of some 1,300 light-years.

Open star clusters. There are many of these, with diameters up to 300 light-years. They consist of blue and red supergiants*, bright nebulae and dust.

Globular star clusters. 31 of these have been found in the Large Cloud and 14 in the Small. In view of the

normal composition of these clusters we may say that the M.C. consist at least partly of star Population type II. The M.C. also have a type of globular cluster not known in the Galaxy; this consists of blue giants which appear to belong to Population type I.

Cepheids.* Many of these variables have been observed in the M.C. and it was from the cepheids in the Small Cloud that astronomers derived the relation which enables the distances of stars of this type to be calculated from their apparent magnitudes (v. Distance finding). Nowadays, however, it is thought that the absolute luminosities of the cepheids in the M.C. may not be the same as those in the Galaxy, so that distances found in this way must be used with caution.

Eclipsing variables. About 50 of these have been found in the M.C. All these systems consist of blue giants, and in most of them the components are close to each other, as in the case of β Lyrae stars*.

One of these binaries, S Doradus, is the brightest star we know. It has an absolute magnitude of at least —10, or perhaps even —11 if we allow for the interstellar absorption* in these regions. In brightness, therefore, it is equivalent to roughly a million Suns. The components of this eclipsing variable are of approximately equal magnitude and revolve round each other once in 40 years. Their respective masses are 160 and 145 solar masses, their radii being 2,100 and 1,900 times that of the Sun. They are radiating energy on such a vast scale that they are expected to exhaust it in only 100,000 years. Several novae have been observed in the M.C. (6 in the Large and 4 in the Small Cloud over the last 50 years).

Magnifying power of a telescope is the focal length of the objective divided by the focal length of the eyepiece. The diameters of details which are only just visible on the surface of a planet, however, depend not only on the *M.p.* but also on the resolving power* (v. also Telescope).

Magnitude, v. Star.

Magnitude at opposition is the magnitude of a superior planet or asteroid when most fully illuminated by the Sun (i.e. at opposition*), as seen from the Earth. As a planet has no fixed magnitude because its distance from the Earth is constantly changing, the magnitude at opposition is taken as one of the characteristics of a superior planet or asteroid. The distance from the Earth at successive oppositions, however, is not always the same (e.g. Mars), and the *M.a.o.* of a planet or asteroid is actually its magnitude at mean opposition.

Main sequence, a series of stars in the Hertzsprung-Russell diagram*; 90% of all stars belong to it.

Maksutov telescope, v. Meniscus-mirror system.

Mare, name for the dark patches on the Moon which can be seen with the naked eye. The name *mare* (Lat. for 'sea') was given during the time when the Moon was regarded as a second Earth. This inaccurate name continues to be used. A *M.* is a plain, probably covered with ash (v. Moon and Pl. 10, 13).

Mars (v. Pl. 17, 18), the planet which follows the Earth in order of distance from the Sun. Because of its great brilliance at opposition*, this planet was not only well known in antiquity but its red colour led to its being named after the god of war.

Of all the planets of our solar system *M.* is the one which most closely resembles the Earth. We perceive a vast surface which shows practically unvarying details. Unfortunately, even when viewed through a medium-sized telescope under the most favourable circumstances, the picture offered by *M*. is disappointing. At the most favourable opposition, in 1956 for example, the planet could be seen only as a small disk 25″ in diameter, that is, smaller than a sixpence viewed from a distance of about 135 yards! From the extremely detailed sketches of surface features we have formed a composite picture of *M*. which is more elaborate than that revealed by observation. We can see only a small, orange-coloured disk with small and barely perceptible darker markings and an occasional lighter patch at the rim indicating the presence of a polar cap or a mist bank. This apparent contrast between the visual image and the detailed maps of *M*. is due to the fact that the latter represent, not what can be seen at a given moment, but the accumulation of many observations. On a few rare occasions certain features of the planet appear much more clearly than usual, and the results of all these observations are combined on a detailed map.

The earliest sketch of *M*. (Christiaan Huygens, 1659) already shows one of these darker patches which can still be seen on *M*. today (the Syrtis Major). Huygens observed that this patch moved in the course of the evening and returned to the same place at roughly the same time on successive nights. From this he concluded that *M*., like the Earth, has a rotation period of about 24 hours.

Since *M*. takes longer than the Earth to revolve around the Sun, oppositions occur every two years and two months (→ 1 and 5). It is only at these times that this planet can be satisfactorily observed, for, following an opposition it rapidly begins to appear smaller and in the neighbourhood of conjunction* even becomes completely invisible.

Owing to the eccentricity* of its orbit, not all oppositions of *M*. are equally favourable (→ 1). When

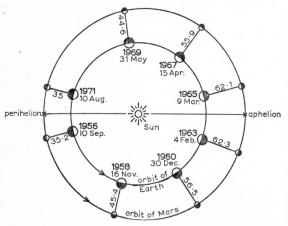

Fig. 1. Oppositions of Mars from 1956 to 1971. As Mars' orbit is closest to Earth's at perihelion, oppositions of Mars occurring near the perihelion are the most favourable for observation. Observations are good in August and September, but very unfavourable in February and March. The planet's disk will attain an apparent diameter of 25″ in 1971, as compared with 14″ in 1965. Favourable oppositions will occur in 1971, 1973, 1986 and 1988. The distances shown above are in millions of miles

they occur where the orbits of *M*. and the Earth lie close together, that is, near the perihelion*, the disk of *M*. attains its greatest apparent diameter and many details of the planet can be seen. Oppositions in the vicinity of the perihelion always occur in August or September. The opposition of September 1956

was particularly favourable, the distance between the Earth and *M*. on 7th September being only 35 million miles. The next favourable oppositions will take place on 10th August 1971 and 28th September 1988. The distance between the Earth and *M*. will also be fairly small at the oppositions of 5th October 1973 and 10th

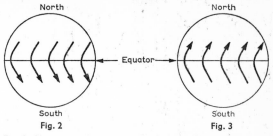

Fig. 2. Summer in the southern hemisphere. The air above the southern hemisphere is heated and rises, bringing cold air from the northern hemisphere. Winds therefore blow from north to south. Because of the planet's axial rotation, winds on Mars, as on Earth, (Buys Ballot's law), are deflected in opposite directions in the two hemispheres; upon crossing the equator they change their direction. Fig. 3 shows summer in the northern hemisphere: the winds blow from south to north

July 1986. At extremely unfavourable oppositions (for example in 1963, 1980 and 1995) the distance separating the Earth and *M*. will be over 60 million miles.

The surface of *M*. displays greyish-green or brown markings and reddish patches. The red has been taken to indicate the presence of deserts. If this is indeed true they must be very extensive, but this is not improbable since *M*. possesses very little water. The polar caps probably consist merely of a layer of hoar frost only a few millimetres thick. The atmosphere too contains very little vapour (*v*. Pl. 17).

The greyish-green patches may perhaps indicate some form of vegetation, e.g. lichen (*v*. Life in the solar system, under Solar system). Another theory is that these regions are darker in colour because they are formed by volcanic ash blown here by the wind (→ 2, 3, 4). It seems more likely, however, that this colouring is due to some form of vegetation, since it changes with the seasons, being greener in spring and early summer and shading from brown to lilac in late summer and autumn. Moreover, recent spectroscopic evidence in the infra-red, obtained with the aid of the 200-inch Hale reflector, by Sinton, strongly suggests that these regions contain some form of plant life.

During the opposition of 1959, Dr Sinton repeated a 1956 investigation with the 200-inch telescope. Proceeding on the assumption that organic molecules absorb infra-red light with a wavelength of about 3·5 microns, he found on *M*. absorption at 3·43, 3·56 and 3·67 microns, and this in the light from the darker regions (e.g. Syrtis Major, Mare Sirenum and Mare Cimmerium). This absorption was found to be absent from or weak in the light from brighter areas (e.g. Arabia and Amazonis). The absorption is close enough to 3·5 microns to originate in organic molecules. The simplest explanation is to assume that vegetation is present on the darker regions of *M*.

The polar caps can be seen growing in autumn and winter for the appropriate hemisphere. In spring they become smaller again and by summer are either extremely small or have disappeared altogether (*v*. Pl. 17). It is evidently colder in the southern hemisphere than in the northern, since the cap at the north pole disappears completely in summer while that at the south pole remains. Upon the surface of *M*. we can sometimes make out rather indistinct long, straight, grey stripes or lines, the so-called 'canals' (*v.* Pl. 18).

Schiaparelli, who made his observations during the oppositions from 1877 to 1888, was the first to see these lines, which he called 'canali', with the warning that this should not lead people to draw firm conclusions concerning the true nature of these features. Unfortunately, he reckoned without the vivid imagination of the press and general public, and the *M*. canals were considered the most enthralling discovery of the nineteenth century. These canals intersected each other at darker patches, the 'oases'. A few years later Schiaparelli made the astounding announcement that the canals doubled themselves every now and then! In place of one thin line two could sometimes be noticed running completely parallel for hundreds of miles. The American, P. Lowell, had an observatory built (called the Lowell Observatory, in Flagstaff, Arizona), especially to study *M*. More than 400 canals were charted, some of them more than 3,000 miles long! These canals gave rise to the idea of irrigation systems, which led people to suppose that *M*. was inhabited. When someone offered a reward to the first person to communicate with the inhabitants of another planet, contact with the inhabitants of *M*. was excluded as being too easy!

Nevertheless, doubt was expressed as to whether all these canals and oases really existed. Indeed, some extremely practised observers were unable to see them at all. It also happened that on a particular evening some observers saw the canals double while Schiaparelli saw them single. This led many people to conclude that the so-called canals were an optical illusion. Photography provided no solution, since the length of exposure required rendered the details insufficiently clear, but it has since been shown by experiment that rows of small spots lying at the verge of visibility appear to merge into more or less straight lines. It is therefore probable that isolated microscopic details which cannot yet be properly observed appear to us as continuous 'canals', which may also be borders

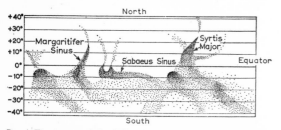

Fig. 4. The apexes of the darker fan-shaped areas are thought to be the sites of volcanoes which scatter ash. These areas are mainly oriented in the direction of the prevailing summer winds in the southern hemisphere. This may be due to the fact that summers in the southern hemisphere are far warmer than those in the northern because the planet is nearer the Sun. The winds from north to south would therefore be much stronger than in the opposite direction. Weak spurs running from the hypothetical volcanoes in a northerly direction can also be seen. These could be caused by the lighter winds which blow during the colder summers in the northern hemisphere

between areas of slightly differing brightness. Some of those which can be seen most distinctly are probably broader lines of specks which stand out clearly against the red of the desert.

The climate of *M*. is cold and dry. Surface temperatures at the equator (according to G. de Vaucouleurs):

3 a.m.	—40° to —25°C.	
noon	—5° to +25°C.	
50° N. latitude		
3 a.m.	—50° to —25°C.	
noon	—30° to +15°C.	

There is, moreover, a great difference between the air temperature just above the ground and that of the surface itself: the air is about 30° colder than the ground. The average temperature makes it unlikely

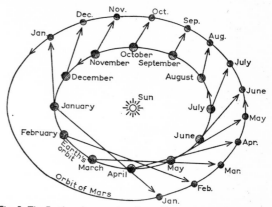

Fig. 5. The Earth and a superior planet. The position of Earth and Mars during a single revolution by the Earth. During this time Mars covers only part of its orbit. The illuminated side of Mars is always more or less presented to Earth. Note the change in the distance between Earth and Mars from January to September and then from September to January of the following year

that there exists on *M*. any highly developed form of animal life comparable to that on the Earth, but microorganisms and some lower forms of plant-life could exist there.

Probable composition of the atmosphere: nitrogen 98·5%, argon 1·2%, carbonic acid 0·25%, very little or no oxygen, very little water vapour. The atmospheric pressure at the surface is equivalent to about 65 mm (2·6 in.) of mercury, compared with about 760 mm (29·9 in.) of mercury on Earth.

By photographing with different colour filters (*v.* Pl. 18) the atmospheric details can be distinguished from those of the surface. Photographs in ultra-violet and blue light show the polar caps, mist banks and clouds. Photographs in yellow light show clouds probably composed of dust. Surface details are shown on photographs taken in red or infra-red light.

To give an idea of what can be seen on *M*. with modern telescopes, it may be stated that with the 24-inch refractor at Pic-du-Midi, it is just possible visually to see as separate, points which are 55 km (34·5 miles) apart. The polarization of various areas has also been determined visually. For the lighter parts, it accords with the view that these are covered with iron oxide powder. The darker spots show a variation in polarization which is related to the change of seasons on *M*. The polarization of the atmosphere has also helped to reveal the presence of thin layers of ice crystals.

Since the axis of rotation of *M*., like that of the Earth, is not at right angles to the plane of its orbit, a change of seasons occurs (*v.* Earth). The seasons are the same as on Earth except that, since *M*. takes longer to revolve around the Sun, they last about twice as long.

M. has two small moons, Phobos* and Deimos*.

Data: mean distance from the Sun, 142 million

miles; time taken to complete its orbit, 1·8809 years; eccentricity 0·09; apparent diameter in the sky, 3·5″ to 25·1″; mass, 0·108 × the Earth's; rotation, 24 h. 37 min. 23 sec.; albedo, 0·15; brightness at average opposition, —1·85; shortest distance from the Earth during opposition, 0·373 A.U. (34,650,000 miles); length of spring, summer, autumn and winter in the southern hemisphere (thus autumn, winter, spring and summer in the northern hemisphere), 146, 159, 199 and 183 days respectively.

Megaparsec, 1,000,000 parsecs (v. Parsec).

Megrez, the star δ Ursae Majoris, apparent magnitude 3·4, spectrum A2.

Meniscus-mirror system, also called the Bouwers or Maksutov system, is an image-forming system consisting of a concave spherical mirror whose spherical aberration (v. Optics) is corrected by a meniscus lens of relatively small negative strength placed in front of it (invented by a Dutchman, Professor A. Bouwers; first Dutch patent granted on 14th October, 1940). Working independently of Bouwers, and at a later date, the Russian, Maksutov, applied the *M-m.s.* to astronomical telescopes and published his work in May 1944; Bouwers first published his system in 1946 in *Achievements in Optics.* In most of its applications the meniscus lens is arranged so that its concave and convex surfaces have the same centre of curvature, and that this coincides with the centre of curvature of the concave mirror (concentric mirror system). A diaphragm is fitted at the centre of the system. Two arrangements of the meniscus lens are then possible (→ 1 and 2).

The advantage of the Bouwers system is that every

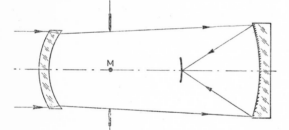

Fig. 1. Meniscus lens arranged so that the centre of curvature lies between the mirror and the meniscus lens

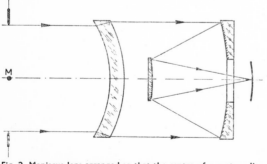

Fig. 2. Meniscus lens arranged so that the centre of curvature lies outside the system

ray of light passing though the centre of curvature can be regarded as an optical axis of the system; in theory, therefore, the image quality is uniform and good throughout the large field of view because of the complete absence of coma, astigmatism and chromatic aberration. A Cassegrain combination is obtained by using a small convex mirror and making a central aperture in the large concave spherical mirror (→ 2). The light path is thus enclosed in the system; the focal plane lies outside the system and is therefore easy of access. The *M-m.s.* is employed by J. W. Fecker, Inc., in the 8-inch telescope supplied to the City College of New York. It is also used by the Russians in their very big telescopes at Abastumani.

Mensa (Table Mountain), an indistinct constellation in the southern hemisphere, situated between 3 h. 25 min. and 7 h. 40 min. R.A. and between —70° and —85° Dec. (→)

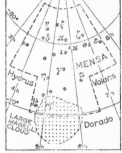

The constellation of Mensa

Merak, the star β Ursae Majoris, apparent magnitude 3·4, spectral class A 2.

Mercury (v. Pl. 16), the planet of the solar system closest to the Sun. The smallest after Pluto (→ 3, Solar system). *M.* is not remarkably striking in the sky since for us it is always close to the Sun. Indeed *M.* is only to be seen low down in a twilight sky, and then only around the time of the greatest elongations. Since the synodical rotation period is 116 days, 3 eastern and 3 western greatest elongations may occur in a year. Since, too, this planet is always in the region of the ecliptic the only greatest elongations that are favourable are those that occur when the ecliptic makes a large angle with the horizon. *M.* then stands at its highest point above the horizon. During a western elongation *M.* rises before the Sun and is then a 'morning star'. During an eastern elongation* *M.* sets after the Sun and becomes an 'evening star'. As a morning star it is most plainly visible during the autumn; as an evening star, in the spring. The greatest elongation depends on the point of the orbit which *M.* happens to have reached: if the elongation coincides with the aphelion* of the planet it is 28°, with the perihelion, 18°. In ancient Mesopotamia *M.* (as 'morning star') was called the 'messenger of the rising Sun'. Few details are visible through a telescope. A few indistinct patches have been charted (by Schiaparelli in 1889 and by Antoniadi in 1929) and have been used to determine the axial rotation. The time taken for one axial rotation is the same as for one orbital revolution round the Sun, so that *M.*, like the Moon with respect to the Earth, always has the same side turned towards the Sun. This means that the sunlit side will always have a very high temperature (up to 400°C., which is higher than the melting point of lead), whereas the side turned away from the Sun will not be much above absolute zero. Since the axial rotation is constant but the orbit eccentric, which means that the orbital speed is not constant (→ 1, Libration), it is not always exactly the same hemisphere which is turned towards the Sun. For a wide zone of the planet's surface the Sun rises and sets but remains close to the horizon.

The surface of *M.* bears some resemblance to that of the Moon. There will be hardly any atmosphere. Since *M.*'s orbit makes an acute angle with the plane of the ecliptic (→), for us it usually passes above or below the Sun. When the Earth is in the region of the nodes (v. Orbit) of *M*.'s orbit, we may see *M*. passing in front of the Sun (a transit of *M*.). These transits can occur about 13 times in one century. One of them,

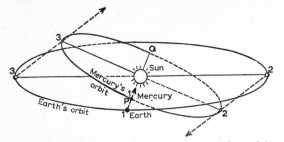

When Earth and Mercury are at 1, we see Mercury in front of the solar disk. As seen from Earth, Mercury is below the Sun at 2 and above it at 3. PQ is the line along which the orbital planes of Earth and Mercury intersect. At 1 the Earth is in line with the nodes (P and Q) of Mercury's orbit. The inclination of the orbit of Mercury to the Earth's is deliberately exaggerated

which occurred in November, 1953, is shown on Pl. 16. The transits for the next 40 years will fall on the 9th May, 1970, the 10th November, 1973, the 13th November, 1986, the 6th November, 1993, and the 15th November, 1999.

M. has no moons; its average distance from the Sun is 36 million miles, the eccentricity of its orbit is 0·206, the inclination of the orbit 7°, the period of axial rotation and orbital revolution 88 days, the diameter 3,200 miles, the greatest elongation 18° to 28°, the mass 0·05 that of the Earth, the albedo 0·06, the magnitude at the greatest elongation —0·2.

Meridian of the place of observation is the vertical circle (perpendicular to the plane of the horizon) passing through the northern celestial pole and the zenith (→ Celestial sphere).

Meridian circle, a telescope mounted so that it can rotate in the meridian. It is used to determine right ascensions and declinations of stars or, using stars of known co-ordinates, to determine time.

Messier, French astronomer. He compiled the first catalogue of 103 star clusters and nebulae, since named after him. It was intended as a list of nebulous objects which might confuse astronomers in the search for a new comet. Many nebulae and star clusters are still known by his catalogue number. M42, for example, is the great Orion nebula, and M31 the Great Nebula in Andromeda. His list was later superseded by the much more comprehensive *New General Catalogue (N.G.C.) (v.* Nebulae).

Metagalaxy is the name given to the whole complex system of extragalactic nebulae*. Within the area that can now be surveyed with the largest telescopes there are roughly one thousand million extragalactic systems. The name originated during the period when it was still thought that the whole complex of extragalactic nebulae was sharply circumscribed at a distance of about 100 million light-years. This idea later proved to be completely unfounded.

Meteors are stony or metallic particles revolving round the Sun. They become visible when they are rendered incandescent by the Earth's atmosphere (*v.* Pl. 34, right). *M.* are also called shooting stars, and the brightest, fireballs. They occur twice or three times as frequently in the morning sky as in the evening. Those in the morning sky are bluer. This is because the speed of the *M.* in relation to the Earth's atmosphere is greater in the morning sky than in the evening

sky (→). A good observer, under good conditions, can perceive an average of 6 *M.* an hour. Many others are not visible to the naked eye. The number of visible *M.* which penetrate the Earth's atmosphere in a day has been estimated at about 25 million. In general they are extremely small: a normal meteor is caused by a particle of 1 mm size, a bright meteor by one of about 1 cm, and fireballs by 1–10 cm and larger. They begin to glow at a height of about 65 miles, and the trail of light ends at a height of about 50 miles; the meteor is then completely burnt out.

From calculations of their orbits it follows that all, or

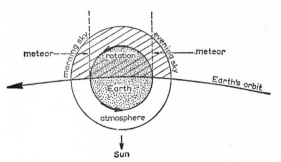

at least the greater part, belong to our solar system. When the Earth encounters a meteor stream* in its orbit, a meteor shower results.

Meteor streams are large numbers of meteors moving through the solar system in parallel orbits. If the Earth meets a stream of meteors in its orbit the effect of perspective makes us see a large number of shooting stars, or a meteor shower, diverging from the same point, the 'radiant' (→). Several of these meteor showers occur yearly at a fixed time and are given the name of the constellation in which lies the point from which they appear to come. We have thus the Perseids, which can be seen in the weeks around the 11th August, the Lyrids, the Geminids, the Draconids, etc. When the meteor particles form a condensed group we see them reappearing after a certain number of years, whenever the Earth and the meteors reach the intersection of their two orbits together. The Draconids, for example, return in great numbers every 13 years. When the meteors are spread out over almost the entire orbit we can expect them every year.

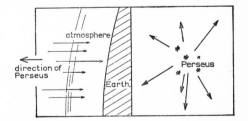

It is thought that various *M.s.* were produced by comets. The Draconids, for example, have the same orbit as one of the comets of the Jupiter family (*v.* Jupiter's family of comets). A case is known where a comet was seen to disappear and a meteor shower to appear: in 1846 Biela's comet (also a member of the Jupiter family) split in two at its approach. In 1852 the double comet returned (it had a period of 6½ years) and later, about the time when it was expected again, there appeared a magnificent shower of shooting stars, the Andromedids, which, after a few appearances, were not seen again.

Meteorites are meteors which reach the Earth before they are completely burnt out. Most have a thin, dark, vitreous molten crust. Some consist mainly of iron and nickel, others are stony and contain silicates.

About 30 *M.*, each weighing more than one ton are known. During this century two very large *M.* have fallen in Siberia, one on the 30th June, 1908, which destroyed an area of about 20 square miles, and one on the 12th February, 1947. The great crater in Arizona, 4,000 ft. across, 600 ft. deep, with sides rising 130 ft. above the surrounding countryside (*v.* Pl. 25, 26), was caused by a meteorite in prehistoric times. This giant meteorite displaced millions of tons of rock.

Microcosm, the 'little world'—the world of small dimensions, *v.* Pl. 91.

Micrometer, an instrument used in conjunction with a telescope to measure small angles such as the angular distance between the components of a double star or the diameter of a small planetary disk. The *M.* has two fine wires or spider webs, one of which is fixed. The other is moved by a screw with a graduated head on which the amount of turn can be read. The wires stand out dark against a background illuminated by, for instance, a small lamp, and are placed at the focus of the eyepiece so that they can be viewed simultaneously with the object under observation. To measure the distance between the components of a binary, the two wires are set at right angles to the line joining the components. The fixed wire is then aligned on one of the components and the screw is turned until the movable wire coincides with the second component. The amount of turn is then equivalent to the angular separation between the components in seconds of arc, which can be read directly from the graduated head. The entire instrument can also be rotated on the eyepiece, so that by causing the wires to coincide with the line joining the components it is possible to determine the position angle, i.e. the bearing of one component from the other.

Microscope, *v.* Miscroscopium.

Microscopium, (the Microscope), an insignificant constellation in the southern sky, lying between 20 h. 25 min. and 21 h. 25 min. R.A. and between —28° and —45° Dec. (→)

Milky Way or **Galaxy** (*v.* Pl. 45, 46, 60, 62), a system of stars, gas and dust, of which the Sun forms part. The *M.W.* consists of a spherical system, markedly concentrated towards its centre, and a flattish disk surrounding the central part. *a.* The spherical system is called the halo, its densely concentrated part the central region

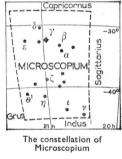

The constellation of Microscopium

(nucleus). The halo and central region consist of stars of Population type II, and the halo also includes the globular star clusters*. No dust is found there. Approximately 99% of all stars in the *M.W.* are in the halo and central region. Stars in the halo, like the globular clusters, probably describe very elongated orbits with one focus in the central region. The diameter of the halo is of the order of 100,000 light-years.

b. The flat round disk, the plane of which passes through the central region, consists of spiral arms (*v.*

Pl. 60, 62). As in other similar systems (*v.* Extragalactic nebulae), the arms probably emerge from the edge of the central region. They consist of Population type I stars, such as the Sun, and of open star clusters, gas and dust. The entire disk revolves around the centre but not as a solid body. The innermost part and the outer-

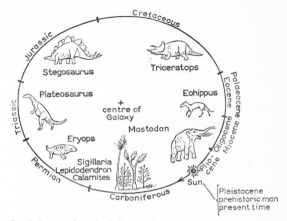

Fig. 1. Survey of the Sun's last revolution about the centre of the Galactic system (220 million years). The Earth's geological periods are shown alongside the solar orbit

most both rotate more slowly than the part between. The spiral arms are therefore not permanent features but will eventually be torn completely out of shape by the rotation of the *M.W.* unless the process is counteracted by a magnetic field.

In the vicinity of the Sun the period of revolution is 220 million years and the orbital velocity 135 m.p. sec. (216 km/sec.) (→ 1). While the halo and central region together contain more than 100 thousand million stars, the spiral arms are estimated to comprise a comparable number. The dimensions of the disk formed by the arms are: diameter 100,000 light-years, thickness in vicinity of Sun 2,500 light-years, Sun's distance from the Galactic centre 30,000 light-years. Various researches in the last few years have led to the identification of the spiral arms in the vicinity of the Sun; this result has been obtained by studying the distribution of ionized hydrogen, the location of O-type associations, B-class stars and galactic clusters (*v.* Pl. 61) and by using the radio-telescope to pick up the radiation from non-ionized hydrogen of wavelength 21 cm (*v.* Pl. 2, 62 and Radio astronomy). The Sun lies on the inside of a spiral arm. The various arms so far traced have been given names as follows (*v.* Pl. 61): Orion arm, in which the Sun is situated; Perseus arm, which contains the open star clusters χ and h Persei (*v.* Pl. 61) and is farther from the Galactic centre than the Orion arm; Outer arm, which lies beyond the Perseus arm; Sagitt-

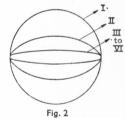

Fig. 2

Sub-systems:

I. RR Lyrae stars, globular star clusters (spherical)
II. Long-period variables (Mira Ceti type) (ellipsoidal)
III. Long-period Cepheids (much flattened ellipsoids)
IV. Novae (much flattened ellipsoids)
V. Open star cluster (much flattened ellipsoids)
VI. O-type stars (much flattened ellipsoids)

arius arm, which is next after the Orion arm in the direction of the Galactic centre. Because of the nature of the Galactic rotation, the distance of the spiral arms from the Galactic centre increases in the direction opposite to that of rotation, i.e. the arms trail. The *M.W.* is thought to be of a type intermediate between Sa and Sb (*v.* Extragalactic nebulae and Pl. 76).

The total mass of the *M.W.* is estimated to be 2×10^{11} solar masses. In the plane of the spiral arms 50% of the mass is accounted for by stars and the other 50% by gas and dust (*v.* Pl. 45). From the fact that the Population type found in the halo and central region is different from that predominant in the spiral arms, it can be concluded that the halo and nucleus consist of older stars and the spiral arms of younger stars. Only in the latter, where there is gas and dust, are new stars being formed.

The simple division of stars into two main Population types (with possibly some transitional types) was proposed by Baade. The diagram illustrates another possible and more complicated structure of the *M.W.* put forward by the Russian Parenago (→ 2).

Mimas, one of the moons of Saturn, the closest to the planet, discovered by Herschel in 1789. Mean distance from Saturn 115,000 miles, revolution 22 h. 37 min., diameter 300 miles (?), magnitude at opposition 12·1.

Minor planets, *v.* Asteroids.

Mira Ceti, the star *o* Ceti (→ Cetus), after which the *M.C.* class of long-period variables is named (*v.* Variable stars). Mira, 'the wonderful', was known to antiquity as a variable star and rediscovered as such by D. Fabricius in 1596. Apparent magnitude at maximum brightness 2–5, at minimum 8–10; period about 330 d.; spectrum at maximum M6, at minimum M9; temperature at maximum 2,600° K., at minimum 1,900° K. A simple calculation shows that the star radiates 3·5 times as much energy per unit of surface area at maximum brightness as it does at minimum. As the total amount of visible light is 100 times greater at maximum than at minimum (the difference is about 5 magnitudes), other factors must obviously be at work. In the first place the star pulsates, so that its surface area is greater at maximum brightness. Then there is considerable light absorption by molecules (particularly TiO). It is also thought that clouds consisting of solid and liquid particles (e.g. ice crystals and drops of water) form in the star's atmosphere at minimum and screen the light.

Moreover, it was discovered in 1923 that *M.C.* is a binary. The companion is a B-class star. Thus *M.C.* not only shows light variations due to the pulsation of the star and changes in its atmosphere, but its companion's apparent luminosity also varies over a 14-year cycle, being occulted in the vicinity of its periastron* by the extensive atmosphere of the primary.

Mirach, the star *β* Andromedae, apparent magnitude 2·4, spectral class Mo.

Miranda, one of the moons of Uranus, discovered by Kuiper in 1948. Mean distance from Uranus 81,000 miles, revolution 1 d. 10 h., magnitude at opposition 19 (*v.* Pl. 22, upper right).

Mizar, the star *ε* Ursae Majoris (this name is also sometimes used for the stars *β* Andromeda and *ε* Boötis). Apparent magnitude 2·4, spectral class A2. *M.* was the first visual double star and the first spectroscopic double star to be discovered. Discovered as a visual double star by Riccioli in 1650. The orbital movement is unknown; apparent magnitude of both components 2·4 and 4·0, distance between the two stars 300 A.U. The bright component *A* was spectroscopically divided into two almost equally bright stars by E. C. Pickering in 1889. The period of this system is 20·5 days. The weaker component *B* was discovered to be a spectroscopic double star by Frost in 1908.

Modulus of distance, *v.* Distance modulus.

Molecules. When two or more atoms of the same or different elements combine into a stable association, the complex is called a molecule.

On the Earth and other planets, most atoms exist in this form. The only elements which can exist as free and uncombined atoms are the rare gases, helium, neon, etc., whose atomic structure is so complete and stable that they cannot be induced to form *M.* with any other element.

M. predominate over free atoms on earth and the planets because these are both cold and dense. In this respect, they are unique in the universe as we know it. All other matter exists either in stars or in interstellar matter.

In stars, the temperature is usually so high that if two atoms do combine, they are knocked apart very quickly. On the surface of the Sun, a few of the simplest and most tenaciously bound *M.* can be observed. On stars cooler than the Sun the number and variety of *M.* is greater, and in some of the very coolest it is suspected that the atoms may be able to combine into particles similar to soot. But even here, this is a surface phenomenon; the great bulk of the coolest stars consists of free atoms.

In interstellar space, on the other hand, although matter is not hot, it is very rarefied. This means that the atoms seldom approach close enough to combine so that most of the matter is in the form of an atomic gas. In some of the denser clouds however, it does become possible for *M.* to form and possibly to build up into dust particles. Even here, 99% of the matter is atomic.

Monoceros (the Unicorn), a constellation situated on the celestial equator. It includes a part of the Milky Way; is rich in interesting objects. R.A. from 5 h. 55 min. to 8 h. 10 min., Dec. 11° S. to 12° N. (*v.* Pl. 57). (→)

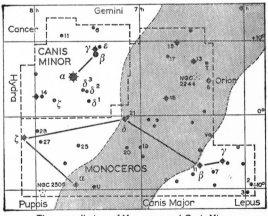

The constellations of Monoceros and Canis Minor

Monochromatic filter or **Lyot filter** is used to observe the outer layers of the Sun without being hindered by the blinding light of the deeper layers. It was perfected in 1938 by B. Lyot and admits only an extremely narrow band of the spectrum (up to 0·5 Å). The filter consists of a series of polaroid filters divided by quartz plates.

When this instrument is attached to a telescope between objective and eyepiece the Sun can be observed only in the filtered light obtained (v. Pl. 30). By suitably selecting the size and number of the quartz plates we can observe the Sun in, for example, the red Hα light which renders the chromosphere* with the prominences, dark filaments and solar flares plainly visible.

Month, a. the time taken by the Moon to return to the same point of its orbit (anomalistic month): 27 d. 13 h. 18 min. 37 sec.;

b. the draconic month is the time taken by the Moon to return to the same node; it is shorter than the anomalistic month since the nodes move to meet the Moon: 27 d. 5 h. 5 min. 36 sec.;

c. the sidereal month is the time taken by the Moon to return to the same place among the stars: 27 d. 7 h. 43 min. 11 sec.;

d. the tropical month is the time taken by the Moon to regain the same longitude; as a result of precession* the tropical month is 6·9 sec. shorter than the sidereal;

e. the synodic month is the period of time between two similar phases of the Moon (29 d. 12 h. 44 min. 3 sec.). This is so much longer because the Moon must always overtake the Sun, which is also moving eastwards, although more slowly;

f. the ordinary calendar month (28–31 days).

Moon (v. Pl. 13), the satellite of the Earth. Since it is much larger in relation to the Earth than the other moons of the solar system in relation to their main planets, the Earth—Moon system is nowadays often called a double planet (→ 1).

Origin of the Moon. It was formerly thought that the M. came into existence by fission from the Earth, leaving the Pacific Ocean as a 'scar'. While the Earth was still liquid and pulsating, the force of the Sun's attraction caused tidal mountains to develop. The resonance action between the two became so strong that the tidal mountains attained a height of some 600 miles. A quantity of matter then broke loose and became the ball that is now the M. (O. Fisher, 1882). This process, however, is physically impossible. Nowadays it is thought that, like the planets, the M. originated in a cold state at the time when the entire solar system was formed (v. Pl. 93).

Internal structure. According to B. G. Escher there is a core of nickel iron (radius 480 miles), around this a layer of basaltic magma (360 miles thick) with, as outer layer, a skin of granitic magma (240 miles thick).

This is merely a hypothesis based on the density, so as to explain various phenomena as the result of vulcanism. Nothing is known for certain about the internal structure of the M.

Movement of the Moon (→ 2). Every day the M. crosses the meridian later than the day before (about 51 minutes). This means that it does not take part in the apparent daily motion of the stars on the celestial

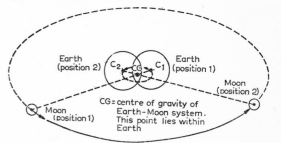

Fig. 1. The common centre of gravity of Earth and Moon lies within Earth

sphere (due to the rotation of the Earth), but has its own motion. It moves around the Earth in an elliptical orbit which makes an angle of 5° with the ecliptic. The angular distance between the Sun and the M. is called elongation. Thirteen times a year the M. overtakes the Sun, and this is called conjunction. If the M. as viewed from the Earth is opposite the Sun, it is said to be in opposition. The point of the M.'s orbit which is closest to the Earth is called the perigee, the point farthest away is the apogee. The M. always keeps the same side turned towards the Earth, i.e. a rotation lasts exactly as long as one revolution in its orbit. The time taken by the M., as viewed by an observer on the Earth, to accomplish one revolution on the celestial sphere (from one star back to the same star), is called the sidereal month (on the average it is 27 d., 7 h., 43 min., 11·47 sec.). Perturbations can make this month vary in length (up to 7 hours). The time which elapses between two equal phases of the M., from new M. to

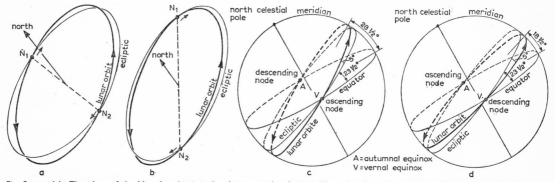

Fig. 2. a and b. The plane of the Moon's orbit is inclined at an angle of about 5° to the plane of the ecliptic. The points where the two planes intersect are called the nodes. The ascending node (N₂) is where the Moon crosses from the south to the north of the ecliptic. At N₁ (the descending node) the Moon passes from the north to the south of the ecliptic. The nodes move along the ecliptic (see arrow) and complete one revolution in about 19 years. c and d. The displacement of the nodes alters the position of the lunar orbit in relation to the celestial equator. c. The ascending node here coincides with the vernal equinox*. The lunar orbit is now at an angle of 28½° to the equator (23½° + 5°). d. When the nodes have completed half a revolution (i.e. in about 9¼ years), the descending node reaches the vernal equinox and the lunar orbit is inclined at 18½° (23½° — 5°) to the equator. At c the Moon is high on the meridian and hence high above the horizon; at d it is lower on the meridian and less high above the horizon

new *M*., for example, is the synodic month (29 d., 12 h., 44 min., 2·78 sec. on the average). The length of this month may vary up to 13 hours, mainly through the eccentricity of the *M*.'s orbit. (The synodic month is what we usually mean when we speak of 'a month'.) Since the nodes of the *M*.'s orbit (places where this orbit meets the ecliptic) move along the ecliptic (period of revolution about 19 years) the maximum height of the *M*. above the horizon at the meridian is not always the same from year to year. The two extreme cases are sketched in Fig. 2: *c*, the ascending node stands in the spring position (the *M*. stands higher in the sky) and *d*, the ascending node stands in the autumn position (the *M*. stands lower in the sky).

Libration (*v*. Libration). The *M*. makes a sort of nodding and shaking movement in the 'yes' and 'no' directions. From Earth we can therefore see more than half of the *M*.'s surface: 41 % of the globe is always visible, 18 % is visible now and then, and 41 % never visible.

Phases of the Moon (→ 3) are the changing shapes of that part of the Moon illuminated by the Sun, as seen from the Earth. These phases are caused by the ever-changing positions of Earth, *M*. and Sun relative to each other. If the *M*. is between the Earth and the Sun, we see the non-illuminated side: this is the new *M*. On the side of the *M*. turned towards us it is night. As the *M*. proceeds on its course about the Earth, the light, from the point of view of the observer on Earth, appears first in the west in the form of a crescent. After this the *M*.'s disk is half illuminated: first quarter. The terminator moves across the *M*. towards the east until the disk is seen as fully illuminated: full *M*. The *M*. now stands in a straight line with the Earth and the Sun.

The terminator which the observer perceives from the new to the full *M*. is the 'morning terminator', i.e. the Sun rises for those places on the *M*. touched by this shadow limit. After a full *M*. one can see shadow

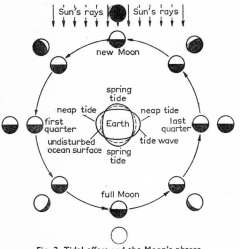

Fig. 3. Tidal effect and the Moon's phases

appearing again in the western part of the *M*.'s disk. This is the 'evening terminator', i.e. the Sun sets for these places. When the evening terminator has again travelled half way across the disk one speaks of the last quarter. The shadow continues to grow larger and the crescent becomes narrower until the light has

disappeared and it is once again new *M*. This progress from new *M*. to new *M*. lasts on an average 29 days; this is the synodic period.

Surface. (*v*. Pl. 10, 12, 14). With the naked eye we can see upon the *M*. dark patches, 'maria' or 'seas'. (Galileo gave them this name because he mistakenly thought they were oceans.) With the telescope we can detect, besides the flat seas, mountain ranges and an immense number of round formations, 'moon craters'. Since the shadows at the terminator are the most pronounced, the picture at full *M*. is less interesting than during the first or last quarter. Even with com-

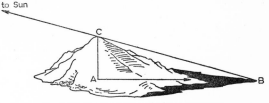

Fig. 4. Finding the height of a lunar mountain

paratively small telescopes we can see very many details since the lack of atmosphere renders the image extremely sharp.

Atmosphere. The *M*. has no atmosphere of any importance. This is deduced because, *a*. there is no twilight, and the terminator is a sharp line; *b*. an atmosphere above the surface would be illuminated longer at nightfall than the surface itself and the light cusps of the crescent *M*. would then have to be longer; *c*. when the *M*. by its own movement covers a star in the sky, this star suddenly disappears and does not slowly become weaker and redder as would happen if it were obscured by an atmosphere; *d*. the surface temperature in the middle of the *M*. at the vertical solstice (i.e. at full *M*.) is more than 100° C. At sunset the temperature has already sunk to — 50°, at night it is — 150° or colder. When, during a lunar eclipse, the *M*. comes within the shadow of the Earth the temperature drops quite rapidly to — 50°. If there were an atmosphere, it would prevent radiation and make such a difference in temperature impossible.

There can be no water on the *M*., for this would evaporate in the great heat of a lunar day. At the most there can be water only in the form of ice or snow in clefts or pits where the Sun never penetrates.

Maria (*v*. Pl. 10, 13). This name originated when the dark patches were taken to be seas (Lat. *mare*). They are plains with low hills, scattered craters and a few isolated rock formations. They may be composed of ash which covered the original formations. Roughly 50 % of the visible side of the *M*. consists of these ash plains which occur mainly in the northern hemisphere. Originally they may have been lava plains. The lava has penetrated some of the mountain circles which were already in existence at that time. They are still visible as partly buried rings (*v*. Pl. 10). One can also detect 'flow-lines' (*v*. Pl. 10) at the places where the flowing lava must have cooled off. They now extend over the 'seas' as visible crusts. A layer of ash and dust may have formed around them and remained intact owing to the absence of wind and water.

Mountain ranges (*v*. Pl. 10). These resemble terrestrial mountains but are higher in proportion to the diameter of the globe. This may be in some way connected with the much weaker pull of gravity on the *M*. and the absence of erosion (no atmosphere and no water). The summits are between 10,000 ft. and 30,000 ft. high. The shape is not that of the Earth's folded mountains but consists of separate summits without much connection between them. The height of a lunar mountain can easily be calculated from the length of its shadow and the height of the Sun with relation to the mountain.

In triangle ABC (→ 4), AB can be measured at the telescope or on photographs. Angle ABC is known at a given point of time (it may be calculated from the distance of the mountain from the terminator). CAB is a right angle. It is thus possible to calculate AC. On the Mare Imbrium there are still a few isolated summits like Pico (8,000 ft.) and Piton (7,000 ft.), v. Pl. 10.

Ring formations. These are divided according to shape into *walled plains*, diameter from 40 to 150 miles, e.g. Clavius (v. Pl. 14), and Grimaldi; *ring mountains*, diameter 15 to 50 miles; *craters*, diameter less than 12 miles; and *crater pits*, small recesses in the ground without ring rampart. The ring formations often have a central mountain (v. Pl. 12). The floor of the formation is lower than the surrounding *M.* surface.

Owing to the strong play of shadow the relief of these formations appears much higher than it really is (→ 5). If we were to stand in the centre of the Clavius, the strong curve of the *M.*'s surface and the comparative lowness of the ring walls would mean that they did not rise above the horizon!

Ray systems (v. Pl. 9, 12). In several ring formations one can see systems of bright rays issuing radially from the ring plain or from the surrounding wall. The centre sometimes lies outside the ring formation. These rays are especially clear by a full *M.*

The most striking system is that of the mountain circle Tycho in the southern hemisphere. One of these rays has a length of 1,100 miles. Rays are light in colour, cast no shadow and have thus no plastic form. It is not yet known what these systems really are. One suggestion is that they are a light powder distributed in various directions by an explosion and deposited rectilinearly owing to the absence of wind on the *M.*

Rills. These are splits in the ground or narrow valleys from 10 to 100 miles in length. Their depth is unknown. Some of these rills have crater-shaped widenings which appear to be connected with volcanic activity along a fault in the *M.*'s crust.

Thus one also finds countless rows of linked smaller craters which extend over a great length and in a fairly straight line. These are probably the result of volcanic activity. Such activity is also indicated by the

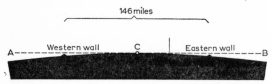

Fig. 5. Section through the lunar globe at Clavius. The observer is at C; his horizon is A–B. The walls of the walled plain (some peaks rise to 16,500 ft.), therefore, cannot be seen from C. Similarly, the eastern wall would be invisible to anyone standing on the western wall. Lunar relief is much lower than is generally supposed

very many craterlets or crater pits on the summits of the central mountains of the ring formations (v. Pl. 12).

Such a crater is also found on the top of Piton and on the top of an isolated mountain of 4,000 ft. a little south of Pico, both situated in the Mare Imbrium (v. Pl. 10). It would be too much of a coincidence if

all these craters were caused by falling meteorites! It is impossible to avoid a comparison with the Earth's volcanoes. Many people believe, nevertheless, that most crater structures are the result of falling meteorites which have a much greater effect due to the lack of atmosphere. Some of the *maria* too (the Mare Imbrium, for example, v. Pl. 10), according to the defenders of the meteorite theory, are the result of large lumps of stone or metal falling from space.

In November, 1958, a Russian astronomer, N. Kosirev, observed something that may have been volcanic activity near the central peak of the ring mountain Alphonsus. The occurrence lasted about 15 minutes. Dr. Kosirev obtained emission spectra of this possible eruption, which indicate the presence of carbon. An earlier observation of the same ring mountain had been made by D. Alter (Mount Wilson). After the explosion a grey-red spot remained which was studied by various observers. In January, 1957, the mean albedo of this area was 0·046, which is not far from that of basalt (0·044) or stony meteorites (0·045). Previous observations make no mention of this spot and it can therefore be assumed to have resulted from the explosion of November, 1958.

The first information ever obtained about the 'dark' side of the *M.* was provided by Lunik III (→ 6). Reports stressed that this side looks quite different from the side presented to the Earth, but it should be remembered that when the published photographs were taken by Lunik III the *M.* was full. This means that few shadows can be seen and makes the landscape seem much flatter than it possibly is. In any case, there is no immediate need to seek an explanation of the fact, if it is a fact, that the hemisphere facing the Earth has more craters than the 'dark' side. Even on the Earth, for instance, the oceans and land masses are not evenly distributed over the surface area.

Dust on the Moon. A large part of the surface is thought to be covered by a thick layer of dust. Some believe that this dust is quite loose and will prove a greater hindrance to future visitors than would drifting sand. This is not inconsistent with observations, for the smallest details visible with telescopes have a diameter of about half a mile. The dust is thought to have been formed by incident meteorites, ultra-violet rays and X-rays, and to have collected on the lowest lying parts of the surface, being transported there by the meteorites and also by electrical forces. Radar observations of the Moon have shown that not more than 5%, and probably less, of the visible surface is inclined at 15° or more to the horizontal.

Z. Kopal, who has compared the heights and bases of the lunar mountains, states that the slope is almost everywhere less than 10°. This appears to accord with the idea that outlines are rounded off by a layer of dust. Only where it was 100 yards deep would this layer be firm enough for a possible landing.

Others think that the dust changes into a porous but solid mass under the action of falling meteorites and particularly of atomic nuclei from the Sun, which have a velocity of 600 m.p. sec. Consequently, there would be practically no loose dust on the Moon and the surface would be firmer than desert sand.

Moreover, degassed material in a vacuum has been found to possess a property whereby its particles adhere firmly to each other.

It would be possible to explode a bomb on the Moon and observe the result, but there is general opposition to the idea of deliberate damage to the Moon.

Little is known with certainty about changes in the *M.*'s surface. Colour changes, however, are regularly observed. In some walled plains and smaller formations darker patches have been observed which change with a greater or lesser degree of regularity (e.g. in Schickard). When the Sun is high they do not grow

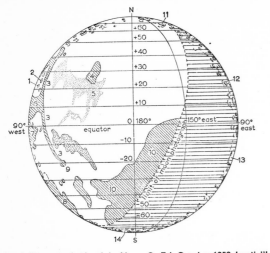

Fig. 6. The 'other' side of the Moon. On 7th October 1959, Lunik III photographed a part of the far side of the Moon. A portion of that side had already been mapped because librations in latitude and longitude – the shaking and nodding movements of the Moon (respectively) as much as 7° and 8° in both directions – occasionally offer glimpses of the border regions to the observer on Earth. The broken line approximately represents the limit of the photographs and shows that the Lunik was north of the lunar equator when they were taken. The shaded portion still remains unknown. 1. Juliot-Curie; 2. Lomonosov; 3. Sovietsky Mountains (length about 1250 miles); 4. Mare Moscovianum (diameter about 185 miles); 5. Astronauts' Bay; 6. Mare Marginis; 7. Mare Smythii; 8. Mare Australe; 9. Tziolkovsky (ring mountain with central peak); 10. Mare Somnii (Sea of Dreams); 11. Thornton; 12. Caramuel; 13. Mare Orientale; 14. Amundsen.

lighter as one might expect in the case of shadow; on the contrary, they grow darker. During the 'afternoon' of these parts of the *M.* they are usually darkest. The explanations which have been offered for this are: *a.* there exists some form of vegetation on the *M.* which during the lunar day of 14 terrestrial days blooms and then dies away; *b.* the lunar surface changes structure or colour under the influence of light and heat. Both explanations are still purely speculative.

Data: apparent (angular) diameter, 33′ 33″, minimum 29′ 24″; true diameter 2,160 miles (= 0·273 diameter of the Earth).

volume	0·02 that of the Earth
density	0·6 that of the Earth
mass	0·01227 that of the Earth
force of gravity on the *M.*'s surface	0·16 that on the Earth's surface
libration in longitude	± 7·9°
libration in latitude	± 6·9°
average speed in orbit	0·6 m. p. sec.
distance, average	238,860 miles (= about 60 times the Earth's equatorial radius)
maximum	252,700 miles
minimum	221,500 miles

Length of one degree measured along the *M.*'s equator = 18·8 miles.

The light of the full *M.* (reflected sunlight) is only 1/465,000 that of the Sun. Its magnitude then is — 12·55.

Albedo* (average)	0·07
Synodic period (from new *M.* to new *M.*)	29 d. 12 h. 44 min. 2·78 sec.
Sidereal period of rotation	27 d. 7 h. 43 min. 11·47 sec.

The centre of gravity of the mass of the Earth—Moon system lies inside the terrestrial globe, 2,975 miles from the centre of the Earth.

The *M.* is the favourite object for observers with small telescopes, through which the most important details can be seen. In 1609 Galileo was the first to view the *M.* with his home-made telescope and his works contain the first, still extremely primitive, sketches of the *M.* viewed in this way: *Siderius Nuncius* (1610) and *Opere del Galileo* (1655). The construction of his telescope was still rather simple (→ Telescope, *v.* Pl. 1), so that only a few details could be seen (*v.* Pl. 9).

The first map with names was drawn by Michael Floris van Langeren or Langrenus. The names were linked with the glorification of the European royal houses ruling at that time. The work was called *De lichten van Philips van Oostenrijk op de volle maan* (1645) In 1647 Hevelius published his *Selenographia: Sive, Lunae Descriptio,* a work containing 40 different phase maps and a detailed description. Of the 250 names he gave, 5 have been retained. In his work *Almagestum Novum* (1651), Riccioli gives a map of the *M.* with names which are still in use today. They are derived from geographical names and from the names of important scientists. In the eighteenth century astronomers began to draw their maps according to measurements made by telescope. A modern map of the *M.* is that of H. P. Wilkins: a 100-inch reproduction of a 300-inch map.

Morning star, *v.* Mercury and Venus.

Mount Palomar, a mountain 125 miles south-east of Los Angeles, on the west coast of North America. Because of its altitude (5,600 ft.), the absence of unwanted lights and the large proportion of cloudless days there, it was chosen as the site of the famous Hale telescope*, at present the largest in the world. The position is more suitable than Mount Wilson, where the lights from the town of Pasadena are beginning to prove troublesome. In addition to the 200-inch Hale, 18- and 48-inch Schmidt telescopes are also in use. The Mount Palomar Observatory shares a common work programme with the Mount Wilson Observatory (*v.* Pl. 81, 87).

Mount Wilson, a mountain north-east of Los Angeles and Pasadena on the west coast of North America. It was chosen by George Ellery Hale as the site of the great Hooker telescope*. In addition to this 100-inch telescope, the observatory also has a 60-inch telescope (installed in 1909) and tower telescopes for observation of the Sun. The Mount Wilson Observatory shares a common work programme with the Mount Palomar* Observatory (*v.* Pl. 81, 87).

Mounting of a telescope, *v.* Telescope.

Musca (the Fly), a con-

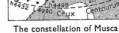

The constellation of Musca

stellation in the southern hemisphere, situated between 11 h. 20 min. and 13 h. 45 min. R.A. and — 64° and — 75° Dec. (→)

N

Nadir, the point where a vertical line through the observer's position intersects that part of the celestial sphere* which is below the horizon. It is diametrically opposite the zenith.

Nebulae, a former collective name for various kinds of objects (*v.* Interstellar matter, Planetary nebulae and Extragalactic nebulae). To the naked eye or a medium-sized telescope they all appear as hazy nebulous spots or clouds and are therefore distinguishable from stars. As was eventually recognized, the term embraced all external galaxies and even star clusters, because these could not be resolved into stars with the telescopes formerly available. At the beginning of this century astronomers still spoke of 'green' *N.* (line spectra, i.e. emission nebulae) and 'white' *N.* (continuous spectra, mainly external galaxies). External galaxies of spiral structure were also called 'spiral nebulae'. The *N.* were listed in special catalogues, e.g. Messier's and the *New General Catalogue of Nebulae and Clusters of Stars* by J. L. E. Dreyer (1888), usually abbreviated to *N.G.C.*

Only during the present century has it been possible, thanks to the development of the telescope*, spectrography (*v.* Spectrum) and photography (*v.* Astrophotography), to form a clear picture of these 'nebulae'.

TABLE OF NEBULOUS OBJECTS

nebulous objects	resolvable into stars	extragalactic nebulae (external galaxies)	
		galactic nebulae	globular star clusters
			open star clusters
	not resolvable into stars	continuous spectrum (reflection nebulae)	
		line spectrum	diffuse nebulae
			planetary nebulae

Neptune, the eighth planet in the solar system, counting outwards from the Sun. Of the planets beyond Saturn, Uranus* is seen as a weak star (magnitude at opposition 5·7) and *N.* and Pluto are invisible without a telescope (*N.*'s magnitude at opposition 7·65). These planets were therefore not discovered until after the advent of the telescope. After Uranus was discovered by W. Herschel (1781) its orbit was carefully calculated and observed. The calculations made allowance for perturbations due to other planets (particularly Saturn and Jupiter). These influences are anything but large, but orbital deviations due to them are perceptible. Nevertheless, the observed positions of Uranus did not accord with the predicted orbit, and astronomers tried to account for this discrepancy by assuming that the deviations observed were caused by another planet, as yet unknown. The difference between the actual and the predicted position of Uranus in 1845 was about 2 minutes of arc. Independently of each other, Leverrier (Paris) and Adams (Cambridge) endeavoured to work out where the unknown planet must be. They based their work on Bode's law*, which indicated what the unknown planet's distance from the Sun should be. This proved later to be incorrect, but it enabled the astronomers to calculate the direction in which the celestial body

would be found. In 1846 Leverrier wrote to Galle at the Berlin Observatory: 'Train your telescope on the point of the ecliptic in the constellation of Aquarius (longitude 326°) and within a degree of that point you will find a new planet, looking like a 9th-magnitude star and showing a small disk.' On the evening following receipt of the letter, i.e. on the 23rd September, 1846, Galle found the new planet 52′ from the place indicated by Leverrier. Adams had actually completed his calculations before Leverrier, but lack of a good map of that part of the sky meant that the accurate observations required could not be carried out quickly enough in England.

After a series of observations the orbit of the new planet, *N.*, was computed, and it was found that various astronomers had observed it in the past but had mistaken it for a star without suspecting its true nature. As the planet's disk has a diameter of only 2″, it can be seen only with a fairly large telescope (6-inch). It proved possible to calculate *N.*'s mass accurately (17·26 × the Earth's) from its disturbing effect on Uranus and from the orbital motion of *N.*'s satellite Triton, discovered shortly after *N.* Its spectrum* (i.e. of sunlight reflected by the planet) shows absorption bands which are attributed to methane. As practically no surface details are visible, our knowledge of *N.*'s rotation depends on spectroscopic observations, which show its period of rotation to be 15 h. 40 min. As in the case of other major planets, what we see is an atmosphere, consisting of hydrogen and methane. The temperature at the surface is estimated at 70°. With regard to the composition of the planet there are once more two main theories (*v.* Jupiter): either the atmosphere of methane and hydrogen is underlaid by a thick layer of ice round a solid core, or *N.* consists mainly of hydrogen with marked condensation towards the centre, and no solid core.

Satellites: a. Triton* (→ 3, Solar system), observable with a 6-inch telescope; *b.* Nereid*.

N.'s mean distance from the Sun is 2,793 million miles, period of revolution 164·78 years, mean orbital velocity 3·4 m. p. sec., (5·4 km/sec.) diameter approx. 28,000 miles, mass 17·26 × Earth's, period of rotation 15 h. 40 min., albedo 0·62, magnitude at mean opposition 7·65.

Nereid, the second moon of Neptune*, discovered photographically by Kuiper in 1949. *Details:* period of revolution 359 days, distance from Neptune about 3½ million miles, diameter about 200 miles, inclination of orbit to the ecliptic 5–6°, magnitude 17.

Net, *v.* Reticulum.

Neutron, *v.* Atom and Nuclear reaction.

New stars, *v.* Novae.

Newtonian telescope, a reflecting telescope in which the incident light is reflected by the main mirror to a prism or small flat mirror, set at an angle of 45°, which deflects it from the telescope tube into the eyepiece through which the image is viewed. Most telescopes built by amateurs are constructed on this principle (→ Hale telescope, *v.* Telescope).

NGC, *v.* Nebulae.

Node is one of the two points where the orbit* of a moon or planet intersects the plane of the ecliptic. In the case of a double star, the *N.s* are where the orbit intersects the plane of the sky (*v.* Orbit).

Norma (the Square), a constellation situated in the Milky Way between 15 h. 10 min. and 16 h. 30 min. R.A. and — 42° and — 60° Dec. (→)

North America nebula (NGC7000), a bright nebula about 3° east of Deneb (α Cygni). The name refers to the shape, which is due to the contours of dark clouds adjacent to the nebula. This nebula is perhaps made luminous by Deneb. It can be seen only in photographs.

Northern Crown, *v.* Corona Borealis.

North Star, *v.* Polaris.

The constellation of Norma

Novae or **New stars** (*v.* Pl. 38, 77, 78), stars which suddenly become much brighter and then gradually return to their previous magnitude. A special kind of *N.* is the supernova. The brightness of *N.* often increases by 10 magnitudes, i.e. their luminosity becomes 10,000 times greater. In the case of supernovae, the luminosity increases to about 100 million times its original intensity. If a supernova were to explode in the Sun's position, the earth would be vaporized; a supernova at the same distance as Sirius from us would give more light than the full Moon.

Before their discovery novae and supernovae are usually very faint stars; explosion makes them so bright within a matter of hours that they often become visible to the naked eye. Their spectra suggest very high temperatures and their absorption lines are considerably displaced to the violet, indicating that the luminous material is moving towards us at a high speed (*v.* Doppler effect) and that the star is expanding.

A few days later the brightness decreases rapidly and eventually, after some fluctuations, returns to normal

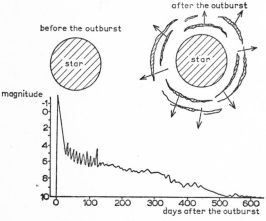

The light-curve of Nova Persei 1901

after a period of months or years. By that time a nebula moving at a high velocity outwards from the star (→) has sometimes formed. At first this nebula is only observable spectroscopically (it has a spectrum characteristic of a nebula) but later it may become visible on photographs (*v.* Pl. 38).

About 5 *N.* are observed each year, though 20 are thought to occur annually in our Galaxy. Supernovae are much rarer, appearing perhaps once in 300 years. Two well-known supernovae are: Tycho's star (1572), which was as bright as Venus, and Kepler's star (1604). The Crab nebula is the remains of a supernova which appeared in 1054 (*v.* Pl. 39). Novae and supernovae have also been discovered in extragalactic nebulae (*v.* Pl. 77, 78).

What exactly happens and what is the cause of the phenomenon are not yet fully understood. It is thought to be due to the sudden explosion of a star in which nuclear reactions have formed too much helium. The energy released is perceptible to us as light and the ejected shell of gas later as a nebula. The entire process seems to take place on or near the surface of the star. In the case of supernovae a larger part of the star is probably affected. Nova-like stars are also known in which a similar phenomenon takes place but on a much smaller scale. A relation has been found to exist between the explosive violence of these stars and the period between their outbursts, viz. the longer the period, the more violent the explosion. If this relation also applies to novae and supernovae, it would explain why we do not observe more outbursts than we do: their periods are too long.

Nuclear reaction, a reaction between atomic nuclei whereby nuclei of one element are transformed into those of another. Nuclear reactions are the source of the energy emitted by the Sun and the stars.

At the very high temperature prevalent in the interior of the stars (of the order of 15,000,000° for the Sun) the electrons with a negative electrical charge are stripped from the positive nuclei. The nuclei consist of positively charged protons and electrically neutral neutrons. The atomic nuclei of the various elements are formed by different combinations of protons and neutrons. Under certain circumstances the nucleus of one element can change into the nucleus of another element (*N.r.*). A nucleus is held together by attraction (binding force), which is effective only over a very short distance equal to a nuclear diameter. The high temperatures in stars produce the very great velocities of all the various particles, and thus cause them to collide violently so that, despite the presence of repellent forces (particles of like charge repel each other), the particles fuse together. A simple nucleus may become a more complicated one as a result of the penetration of a particle, e.g. a proton. This proton then distributes its energy over all the particles composing the nucleus. There is now an excess of energy and this the atomic nucleus may remove in various ways: *a.* the excess is returned to the intruding particle which is then ejected again; *b.* it may dislodge and eject a particle originally present in the nucleus; *c.* the extra energy disappears in the form of gamma rays, which are radiated; *d.* beta particles (electrons) may be emitted.

A proton and a neutron may be regarded as two different states of the same particle. A (neutral) neutron may change into a (positive) proton by releasing a (negative) electron. A (positive) proton can become a (neutral) neutron by releasing a (positive) electron (positron).

When simpler nuclei are converted into more complicated nuclei by the penetration of individual particles, energy is released (binding energy). Various *N.r.s* are possible inside stars. The reaction that occurs in a particular star will depend on the star's temperature.

Most stars consist of hydrogen, and the first $N.r.$ to occur in them is the transformation of hydrogen into helium. The process which effects this transformation in the Sun and in stars with a fairly low central temperature (about 15,000,000°) is the proton-proton chain (→ facing).

A hydrogen nucleus consists of one proton. A helium nucleus may consist of two protons and one neutron (He^3), or two protons and two neutrons (He^4). Two hydrogen atoms (protons) may together form a nucleus consisting of one proton and one neutron. This composite nucleus, which is not stable, is called a deuteron.

The reaction proceeds in a number of stages as follows:

a. proton + proton = deuteron + released energy. The energy liberated takes the form of a neutrino (a small neutral particle) and a positron (a positive electron).

The positron will combine with a free electron (negatively charged) and all the matter composing the two particles will be converted into energy (radiation).

b. deuteron + proton = helium³ + released energy. Thus a third proton combines with the deuteron, which, of course, is unstable. The liberated energy disappears as radiation.

c. helium³ + helium³ = helium⁴ + two protons + released energy. Two nuclei of He^3 thus together form one He^4 nucleus. He^4 is the end-product and two protons are again available.

The net result of this chain is, therefore, that four hydrogen nuclei (protons) yield one helium nucleus + released energy.

In stars with a higher central temperature (hotter than the Sun), the hydrogen is converted into helium by the carbon-nitrogen cycle as follows (carbon = C, nitrogen = N, oxygen = O; the number of particles in a nucleus is indicated by the figure to the right of the element symbol):

a. C^{12} + proton = N^{13} + radiation. C^{12}: 6 protons, 6 neutrons. N^{13}: 7 protons, 6 neutrons.

b. N^{13} = C^{13} + positron. C^{13}: 6 protons, 7 neutrons. The positron and a free electron disappear as radiation.

c. C^{13} + proton = N^{14} + radiation. N^{14}: 7 protons, 7 neutrons.

d. N^{14} + proton = O^{15} + radiation. O^{15}: 8 protons, 7 neutrons. O^{15} is unstable.

e. O^{15} = N^{15} + radiation. N^{15}: 7 protons, 8 neutrons.

f. N^{15} + proton = C^{12} + He^4.

The net result once more is that four hydrogen nuclei are converted into one He^4 nucleus. The carbon nucleus C^{12} which started the cycle is available again at the end.

When all the hydrogen in a star has been transformed into helium, the central temperature has been raised (to 100 million degrees) and the helium may in turn be transformed by $N.r.$ into carbon ($3 He^4 = C^{12}$), the carbon into neon ($C^{12} + He^4 = O^{16}$, $O^{16} + He^4 = Ne^{20}$), and thence, at much higher temperatures possibly into even heavier elements, up to iron (Fe^{56}), energy being released in these processes too. If the temperature in the interior of a star is not sustained, no further $N.r.s$ are possible and the star will gradually cool down.

Nutation, a small periodic term in the precession* of the Earth's axis.

Oberon, the outermost satellite of Uranus, discovered by Herschel in 1787. Observable with an 8-inch telescope. Average distance from planet 364,000 miles, period of revolution 13 d. 11 h. 7 min., diameter 500 miles (?), magnitude at opposition 14·2.

Objective, the image-forming lens or system of lenses in a refracting telescope, or the image-forming mirror in a reflecting telescope*. The greater its diameter, the greater the light-gathering and resolving power of the telescope. Theoretically, the light-gathering power increases in proportion to the square of the diameter of the O. Thus, an O. with a 3-inch aperture gathers over twice as much light as a 2-inch aperture. The resolving power determines: *a.* the size of the details that can still be seen on the surface of a planet; *b.* the shortest angular distance between the components of a binary that can just be separated.

The maximum magnification that can be used without causing the image to become blurred also depends on the diameter of the O.

Diameter of O. in inches	1	2	4	8	12
Limit of stellar mag.	9·0	10·5	12·0	13·5	14·4
Theoretical limit of ang. dist. between components of binary (components approximately equally bright)	4·56″	2·28″	1·14″	0·57″	0·38″

The diameter of the O. is thus also important when faint stars are photographed. For equal exposure times, a larger O. gives a fainter magnitude limit. The following rough table applies to slow plates or films:

| Diameter of O. | Exposure time in minutes | | | | | |
	1	3	9	27	81	
1 inch	9	10	11	12	13	average limit in magnitudes
2 inches	10·5	11·5	12·5	13·5	14·5	
3 inches	11·5	12·5	13·5	14·5	15·5	
4 inches	12	13	14	15	16	

Thus, a 2-inch O. and a 27-minute exposure will enable stars down to a magnitude of 13·5 to be photographed.

In practice, a refractor employs not a single lens but a combination of different lenses in order to correct lens defects (*v.* Optics). This arrangement is unnecessary in reflectors.

Objective prism, (*v.* Spectograph) a prism fitted in front of the objective in a photographic telescope so that on photographs of the sky, the stars appear as elongated spectra instead of as round images. These are not sufficiently refined for detailed study, but are useful for quick classification of stars. A crown-glass prism (angle 3–5°) is generally used for the stars, and a flint-glass prism (angle 25–30°) for comets.

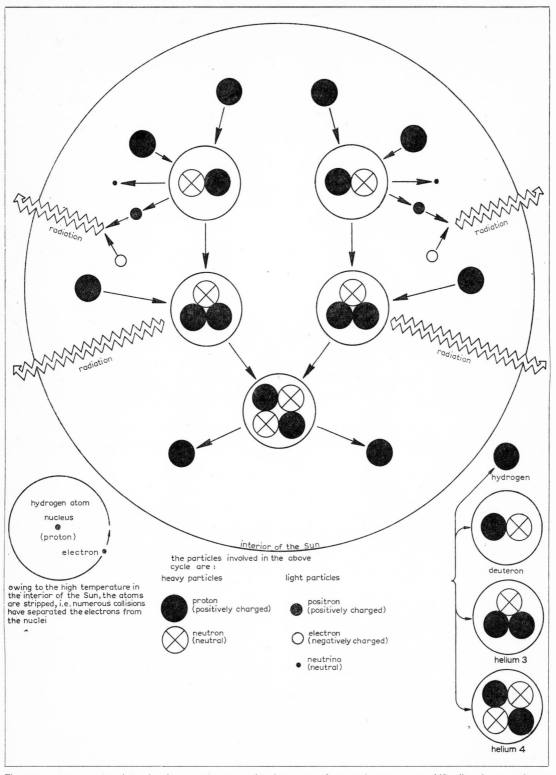

The proton-proton reaction chain whereby energy is generated in the interior of stars with temperatures of 15 million degrees or lower, such as the Sun

Oblateness of celestial bodies and systems of celestial bodies is usually a result of their rotation, which alters them from spheres to spheroids or ellipsoids*. The numerical value of the oblateness is found by dividing the difference between the largest and smallest diameters by the largest diameter. The *O.* of the Earth is $1/_{297}$; that of Saturn is much greater, viz. $1/_{9.5}$.

Observatory is an institute where astronomical phenomena are observed and studied (*v.* Pl. 20, 87, 88). The *Astronomical Ephemeris* publishes annually a list of 200 to 250 astronomical observatories (including private ones), distributed over the entire world. This list is not exhaustive but names only the observatories whose positions must be known accurately for the reduction of observations.

Occultation takes place when the Moon or a planet in its orbit passes between the observer and another celestial body, and hides the latter. The occulting body is usually the Moon because of its large apparent diameter. In this case, the disappearance of a star or planet occurs at the east side of the Moon, and the reappearance at the west. The *O.* of Jupiter's moons can be observed as they pass behind the planet (*v.* Jupiter's system of satellites, under Jupiter, and Pl. 19).

Observations of *O.s* are used to determine the motion of the Moon and the planets with ever-increasing accuracy. Moreover, the light variation of the star during the *O.* enables deductions to be made concerning the atmosphere of the occulting body.

Occulting variables, another name for eclipsing variables (*v.* Double stars).

Octans (the Octant), an indistinct constellation in the southern hemisphere, including the south celestial pole; situated between — 75° and — 90° Dec. (→)

Octant, *v.* Octans.

Open star cluster, *v.* Star cluster and Stellar association.

Ophiuchus (the Serpent-bearer), a constellation on the celestial equator, situated between 16 h. and 18 h. 45 min. R.A. and 14° N. and 30° S. Dec. (→)

Opposition, the position of one of the superior planets (Mars to Pluto) or asteroids* when it lies on the extension of the line joining the Sun to the Earth, and is therefore diametrically opposite the Sun (→). The longitude of the celestial body then differs from that

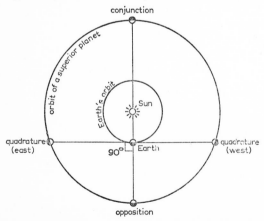

Positions of a superior planet in relation to the Earth and the Sun

of the Sun by 180°, the body is on the meridian* at midnight and a relatively short distance from the Earth. Owing to its nearness to the Earth at this moment a planet or asteroid is best observed during *O.* Mars and most asteroids come into *O.* annually. The Moon is also in *O.* at 'new Moon'.

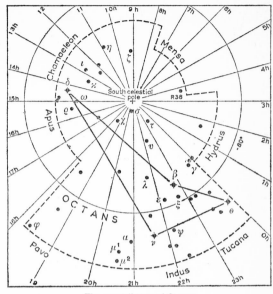

The constellation of Octans

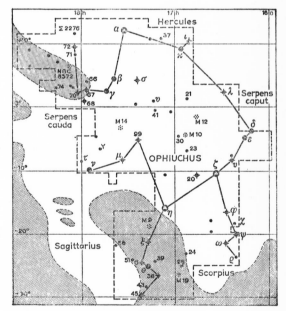

The constellation of Ophiuchus

Optics, originally the study of light but now restricted to the study of image formation in optical instruments. A convex lens changes a beam of parallel rays into an image at the focus. The distance from the lens to the focus is called the focal length. The lens gives an inverted image of an object, but that is not a drawback in viewing groups of stars, the planets or the Sun. The lens which forms this image is called the objective. The image formed by the objective is then viewed through a magnifying glass (eyepiece). This is the principle employed in the lens telescope or refractor.

The image formed by a lens is never perfect. It is impossible entirely to prevent a point from appearing as a very small circular disk. This is due to the diffraction of light. Other faults in image formation (aber-

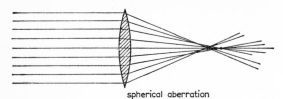

spherical aberration

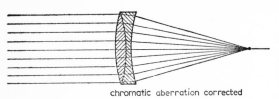

chromatic aberration corrected

Fig. 1

rations) may be divided into: monochromatic aberrations, which occur with light of a single colour, and chromatic aberrations, which only appear when white light is involved.

MONOCHROMATIC ABERRATIONS are:

Spherical aberration ($\rightarrow$1): The rays are not brought to a common focus. Can be avoided by combining lenses made of different types of glass, and by the use of aspherical surfaces.

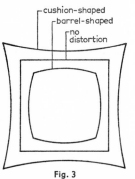

P

Fig. 2

Coma or sine aberration: Each point forms a small pearshaped image, point P (the actual image) being the brightest ($\rightarrow$2). This can also be avoided by using a suitable combination of lenses. A system of lenses from which both spherical aberration and coma have been removed is called 'aplanatic'.

Astigmatism: The image of a point consists of two small focal lines, a and b. This can also be rectified with a suitable combination of lenses, which is then called an 'anastigmatic' lens. The image obtained is sharp but does not lie in a flat plane. This fault is called:

Image curvature: This, too, can be almost entirely corrected. When all the above defects have been corrected in a lens system, there is always one defect left. It is:

Distortion ($\rightarrow$3), whereby a square appears barrel-shaped or cushion-shaped.

CHROMATIC ABERRATIONS comprise:

cushion-shaped
barrel-shaped
no distortion

Fig. 3

Chromatic axial aberrations: The red, yellow, green, etc. rays of white light are refracted to different degrees and therefore focus on different planes situated close to each other ($\rightarrow$4). Can be corrected by a combination of two or more lenses of different types of glass.

Chromatic magnification defect: The red image and

blue image, for example, are not equally large. These defects can be largely obviated by using a combination of at least 4 lenses.

Spherical mirrors can be used in place of lenses to form images ($\rightarrow$5). They have the great advantage that, since all colours are reflected in an identical

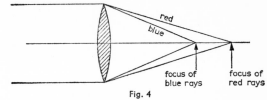

focus of   focus of
blue rays   red rays

Fig. 4

manner, no chromatic aberrations can occur, although most of the other aberrations do remain. If a paraboloidal mirror is used instead of a spherical mirror, then on the axis there is also no spherical aberration. A reflecting telescope usually consists of a paraboloidal objective mirror to form the primary image which is then viewed with a lens eyepiece (*v.* Telescope).

Orbit, the path followed by a celestial body. Most orbits are elliptical, although some deviate only slightly from a circular shape. An orbit is defined by its elements ($\rightarrow$):

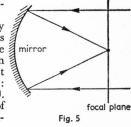

mirror

focal plane

Fig. 5

a. The semi-major axis *(a).* This determines the size of the orbit, e.g. in astronomical units* ($a = AM$).

b. The eccentricity *(e),* which determines the shape of the *O.* and is MS/a.

c. The angle between the orbital plane and the plane of the ecliptic (in the case of planets), the plane of the equator (satellites), or the plane of the sky (double stars). This is called the inclination (i).

d. The longitude of the ascending node (Ω). N^1N^2 is the line of nodes, or the line of intersection of the orbital plane and the plane of the ecliptic.

A planet is moving from south to north of the ecliptic when it passes through point P^1, so that N^1 is called the ascending node. At point P^2 the planet, as seen from the north, drops below the plane of the ecliptic, so N^2 is the descending node. The longitude of the ascending node is the angular distance between the vernal equinox and the ascending node as seen from the Sun, and is measured in the direction of the planet's motion. This angle, therefore, lies in the plane of the ecliptic and is the angle VSN^1.

e. The angular distance, as seen from the Sun in the case of a planet, between the ascending node and the perihelion (ω) indicates the direction of the major axis and is measured in the direction of the planet's motion.

These five elements determine the shape of the elliptical *O.* (in planetary orbits the Sun is at one of the foci) and the position of the *O.* in space.

The period P, or time required for one revolution by the celestial body, is known if the semi-major axis is known. A sixth element must also be known in order to determine the position of a body on its *O.*; it is:

f. The time T of perihelion transit or periastron transit. In the case of a satellite with retrograde motion (i.e. opposed to the general direction of motion in the solar system—e.g. Phoebe*) the inclination i of the O. is regarded as being greater than 90°. For example, if the angle formed by the orbital plane of a retrograde

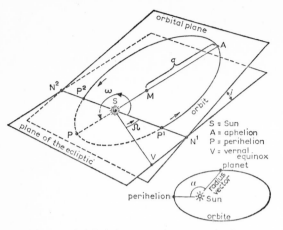

α = the anomaly (which determines the position of a planet on its orbit at a particular moment)

satellite and the plane of the ecliptic is 30°, then $i = 180° - 30° = 150°$.

Orbiting astronomical observatory. Most of the ultra-violet and X-radiation from outer space is absorbed in the upper atmosphere of the Earth, *never* reaching the surface of the Earth. The only way to observe such regions of the spectra of the Sun or stars is to mount telescopes and spectographs in rockets and satellites which can travel above the absorbing layers. During recent years, the U.S.A. have been using rockets to collect data on the Sun's ultra-violet spectrum and this is now known in some detail down to 80 Å. Solar radiation and also certain regions of the solar ultra-violet spectrum are also being monitored from satellites. There are now plans in the U.S.A. and Britain for astronomical telescopes which, with their spectrographs and other equipment, are destined to be put into orbit. The telescopes proposed for them are large (up to 50 inches in diameter) and will be controlled from the ground. The difficulties (particularly of pointing control) are obviously considerable, but it seems likely that astronomers will soon be able to examine the universe in a new range of wavelengths that may produce data as important as that given by the radio range of wavelengths.

Orion, a constellation on the celestial equator, between 4 h. 40 min. and 6 h. 20 min. R.A. and 11° S. and 23° N. Dec. (*v.* Pl. 3, 4, 52–6). Orion was a hunter who pursued the Pleiades*. He was slain by Diana and placed in the sky as a constellation.

Orion's belt, formed by stars δ, ε and ζ (sometimes also called the 'three kings'), is very striking. This constellation contains a bright nebula visible with the naked eye (*v.* Orion nebula).

Orion nebula, (M42 and M43), example of a bright nebula comparatively near the Earth. It is visible with the naked eye as a hazy spot under Orion's belt. Photographs of the area taken with long exposures show

M42 and M43 to be concentrations of a much more extensive nebula covering a large part of the constellation of Orion. The *O.n.* is best viewed with a telescope of small magnification. The 'star' at its centre is seen, even with a small telescope, to consist of four stars, the 'trapezium'. The nebula is approximately 1,000 light-years away. Its density is strikingly low—only one millionth of that of the best vacuum obtainable in a laboratory—viz. 10^{-17} gm/cc. At the centre of the nebula there are approximately 4,000 free electrons per cc. The nebula is composed mostly of hydrogen, but oxygen, nitrogen, sulphur, argon and chlorine are also present. The age of the trapezium is 300,000 years.

A large number of red stars has been found in the vicinity of the trapezium (41 within a radius of 1 minute of arc). These are thought to constitute an association (*v.* Star cluster and stellar association). The group is regarded as a young group of stars still in the process of formation (*v.* Evolution of the stars). The movements of various parts of the *O.n.* have been studied and found to be chaotic. The nebula as a whole is receding from us with a velocity of 11 m. p. sec. (17·5 km/sec.) but the velocity varies from one part to the other. Recent and more accurate research shows that the velocities of some parts differ from the average by as much as 19 to 25 m. p. sec. (30 to 40 km/sec.) (*v.* also Interstellar matter and Pl. 53, 54).

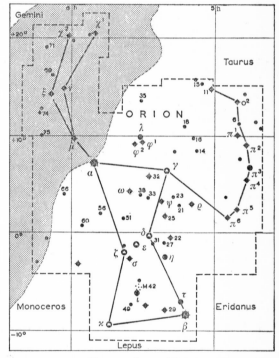

The constellation of Orion

Ozone, a molecular form of oxygen. It occurs in the high Earth's atmosphere and absorbs much ultra-violet radiation (*v.* Pl. 5).

Painter, *v.* Pictor.

Pallas, one of the largest asteroids*, diameter 280 miles. Discovered by Olbers in 1802. Inclination of orbit to the plane of the ecliptic 34·8°.

Parallax (heliocentric or annual) of a star is the angle subtended at the star by the radius of the Earth's orbit (→ 4 Distance finding). The geocentric (or diurnal) horizontal parallax of the Sun, Moon or a planet is the angle subtended at it by the radius of the Earth itself.

Parsec is the unit used for distances outside the solar system. If the parallax* of a star is 1 sec. of arc, its distance is said to be 1 parsec.

1 parsec = 206,265 astronomical units = 3·26 light-years (*v.* Distance finding).

Pavo (the Peacock), a constellation in the southern hemisphere lying between 17 h. 35 min. and 21 h. 25 min. R.A. and —57° and —75° Dec. (→)

Peacock, *v.* Pavo.

Pegasus, a constellation in the northern hemisphere, situated between 21 h. 5 min. and 0 h. 15 min. R.A. and 2° and 36° N.Dec. (→)

Pelican nebula, a bright nebula west of the North America nebula* (NGC7000) and east of the star

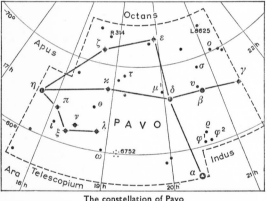

The constellation of Pavo

Deneb (α Cygni). The name refers to the shape of the nebula's outline, which is due to dark clouds surrounding it (*v.* Interstellar matter and Pl. 49,50).

Penumbra, *v.* Umbra.

Periastron, the point on the orbit of the smaller component of a binary star at which this component is nearest to the primary.

Perigee, the point on the Moon's orbit round the Earth where the distance from the Earth to the Moon is smallest.

Perihelion, the point on the orbit of a planet or a comet where it is nearest the Sun.

Period, (*a*) the time taken by one celestial body to complete a revolution round another.

1. The sidereal *P.* is the time necessary to complete one revolution of the celestial sphere in relation to the stars, as seen from the centre of the motion. 2. The synodic *P.* is the time necessary for a single revolution as seen from the centre of the Earth, counting from, for example, one opposition to the next. 3. The ano-

malistic *P.* is the time necessary for a single revolution starting and finishing at the same point of the orbit (e.g. the perihelion). The anomalistic is practically the same as the sidereal *P.*

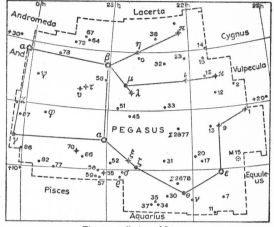

The constellation of Pegasus

(*b*) The period of rotation or the time taken by a celestial body to rotate once on its axis. 1. The sidereal period of rotation is the actual time necessary for one rotation, i.e. the interval between two successive appearances of a particular star on a particular meridian of the celestial body. 2. The synodic period of rotation is the interval between successive transits of a certain meridian of the body through the centre of the visible disk, as seen from the Earth.

Period–luminosity law defines the relationship between the period and absolute magnitude of a particu-

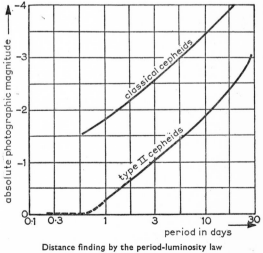

Distance finding by the period-luminosity law

lar class of variable stars, the cepheids*. The figure (→) gives a graphical illustration of the law. The period is plotted along the horizontal axis and the absolute magnitude along the vertical.

Perseids, a meteor shower* whose radiant lies in the constellation of Perseus. Observable about 11th

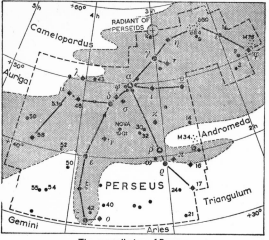

The constellation of Perseus

August, associated with the comet 1862 III (v. Meteor) (→ Meteor streams).

Perseus, a constellation in the northern hemisphere, situated between 1 h. 25 min. and 4 h. 45 min. R.A. and between 31° and 59° N. Dec. This constellation contains the double star cluster NGC 869 and 884, also known as χ and h Persei, visible with the unaided eye (v. Pl. 41). (→)

Phase, the appearance or form of that part of the disk of the Moon, or of an inferior planet, which is

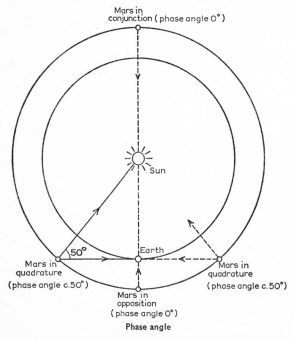

Phase angle

illuminated by the Sun, as seen from the Earth (v. Moon, Venus, and Pl. 16).

Phase angle is the angular distance between the Sun and the Earth as seen by an observer on the Moon or a planet. At full Moon the phase angle of the Moon is 0°, as it is for an inferior planet at superior conjunction, or for a superior planet at opposition or conjunction. In the case of Mars, for example, the phase angle may vary from 0° to about 50°. The greater the *P.a.*, the greater the part of the planet's disk that is dark as seen from the Earth. *P.a.* is greatest during quadrature (→).

Phecda, the star γ Ursae Majoris, apparent magnitude 2·5, spectral class Ao.

Phobos, the inner satellite of Mars, discovered by Hall in 1877. Mean distance from Mars 5,810 miles, period of revolution 7 h. 39 min., diameter 10 miles (?) magnitude at opposition 11·5. It revolves in the same direction in which Mars rotates. As Mars completes one rotation in about 24 hours and *P.* one revolution in only 7·5 hours, *P.* moves faster than a point on Mars' surface; as seen from Mars, it therefore rises in the west and sets in the east.

Phoebe, the outermost of Saturn's satellites, discovered by Pickering in 1898. Mean distance from Saturn 8,050,000 miles, period about 550 days, retrograde motion (opposite to that of the other satellites in the system), diameter 190 miles (?), magnitude at opposition 14·5.

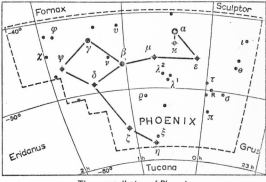

The constellation of Phoenix

Phoenix, a constellation in the southern hemisphere, situated between 23 h. 25 min. and 2 h. 25 min. R.A. and —40° and —58° Dec. (→)

Photographic magnitude is the magnitude of a star as measured with a blue-sensitive photographic plate. As these photographic plates are more sensitive to blue and violet than the human eye, the *P.m.* will usually differ from the visual magnitude (v. Colour index and Star).

Photography, v. Astrophotography.

Photometry is the measurement of the intensity of light. In astronomy, it particularly refers to the measurement of the brightness of stars.

Photon, a 'particle' of light. According to the quantum theory, light consists of small quantities of energy possessing the character of matter. The amount of energy in each particle depends on the wavelength.

Photosphere, the apparent surface of the Sun, which radiates light and below which no observation can be made. The *P.* merges on the outside with the chromosphere, the next layer in the Sun's atmosphere (v. Sun).

Pic du Midi, observatory in the Pyrenees (v. Pl. 20).

Pictor, (the Painter), a constellation in the southern hemisphere, situated between 4 h. 30 min. and 6 h. 50 min. R.A. and —43° and —64° Dec. (→ Dorado).

Pioneer, the name for a series of American moon rockets (*v.* Space travel and Artificial satellite).

Pisces (the Fishes), a zodiacal constellation in the northern hemisphere situated between 22 h. 50 min. and 2 h. 5 min. R.A. and between 7° S. and 33° N. Dec. (→)

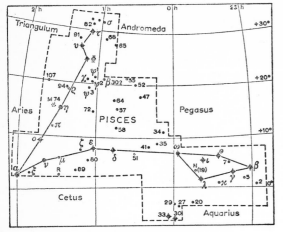

The constellation of Pisces

Piscis Austrinus (the Southern Fish), a constellation in the southern hemisphere, lying between 21 h. 25 min. and 23 h. 5 min. R.A. and between — 25° and —37° Dec. (→)

Planetary nebulae (*v.* Pl. 44) are gaseous spheres or shells formed round the central stars. *P.n.* are so named because, when seen through a small telescope, they mostly appear as faint, luminous disks somewhat reminiscent of planets, with which, however, they have nothing else in common. Most *P.n.* have a single central star of very high temperature (40,000–170,000°K), which is physically related to the nebula. In spectral type and absolute magnitude, the central stars are very similar to ex-novae. The *P.n.* are expanding at a speed of 5–30 m. p. sec. (10–50 km/sec.). A familiar example is the Ring nebula in Lyra. About 370 *P.n.* are known in the Milky Way. They are all telescopic objects, their great distance rendering them too faint to be visible to the naked eye. They belong to stellar Population type II and are strongly concentrated towards the centre of the Galaxy. In 1927 Prof. Oort (Leiden) used the *P.n.,* *inter alia,* to show that our Galaxy is rotating and that the centre of the rotation (i.e. the centre of the Galaxy) lies in the direction of the constellation Sagittarius. A typical *P.n.* has a diameter of over 50,000 astronomical units and a mass which is only a fraction of that of the Sun (the mass of NGC7293, for example, is thought to be about 1/10 of the Sun's mass). They are therefore very tenuous and consist mainly of ionized hydrogen. They are believed to be formed when the central star, at a certain stage in its development, sheds layers of material by explosion. This matter is then made incandescent by very hot ultra-violet radiation from the star (*v.* Emission nebulae under Interstellar matter). Shklovsky estimates the number of *P.n.* in our Galaxy at 60,000,

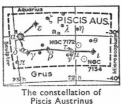

The constellation of
Piscis Austrinus

and Gurzadian considers the life of *P.n.* to be 20,000 years, so that 3 new *P.n.* must appear in the Galaxy every year to keep their numbers up to strength. While the nebulae are developing, the central stars are also thought to be undergoing a change, viz. to white dwarfs. It may possibly be that all white dwarfs have originated from central stars of *P.n.* It is not certain which kind of stars produce *P.n.* but supergiants are one possibility. Shklovsky thinks that RV Tauri variables may be the original source.

Planetarium, originally a device used to illustrate the motion of the planets round the Sun. A sixteenth-century *P.* is still preserved in Strasbourg Cathedral. One type encountered frequently nowadays is the Zeiss *P.* A very complicated projector simulates on a dome the apparent movements of the Sun, Moon and planets against a background of the constellations, also projected on the inside of the dome. The diurnal motion is illustrated at an accelerated tempo. The Sun rises and sets. We see the Moon crossing the sky in her various phases. The planets follow their elliptical orbits. The accelerated speed at which projection takes place gives an excellent general idea of the celestial phenomena illustrated. The Zeiss *P.* is an invention of Dr. Bauersfeld (about 1924). Planetaria are to be found in many of the cities of Europe and America. The London Planetarium was opened in March, 1958.

Planetoids, *v.* Asteroids.

Planets, *v.* Solar system, and under individual names.

Pleiades (the Seven Sisters) (*v.* Pl. 3, 4, 40), an open star cluster in the constellation of Taurus; R.A. 3 h. 45 min., Dec. 24° N. Six stars are visible with the naked eye, several hundred with a telescope. That these stars are also physically associated was proved when they were found to have the same direction and speed of motion in space. The brightest stars are giants of spectral class B. Photographs show that some of these stars lie in a nebula which is illuminated in the neighbourhood of the stars and is an example of a reflection nebula. (*v.* Interstellar matter, also Star cluster and stellar association).

Pleione, the star 28 Tauri, apparent magnitude 5·0, spectral type B. One of the stars of the Pleiades* (*v.* Pl 40), near the star Atlas (27 Tauri). Spectroscopic research revealed that *P.* has a fast axial rotation*, viz. 125 m. p. sec. (200 km/sec.) for a point on the equator (cf. Sun: 1¼ m. p. sec. or 2 km/sec.). It is thought that this high-speed rotation makes the star unstable at the equator. It is probably much flattened and is losing mass at the equator. In fact, a gaseous ring was detected, with the aid of the spectroscope, in 1938. By 1952, this ring had disappeared, presumably under the influence of the star's radiation pressure. Repetition of the process, which may be a stage in the evolution of B-type stars, causes the star to lose part of its mass.

Pluto, the outermost known planet of the solar system, discovered in 1930 (*v.* Pl. 22). Following the discovery of Neptune, and after due allowance had been made for its effect on the orbital motion of Uranus, the latter still deviated slightly from its computed path. Lowell worked on the basis of these slight differences between observed and calculated positions, and assumed that they were due to the presence of an unknown planet. In 1915 he computed the orbit of this planet. The actual orbit proved to be in reasonable agreement with that computed by him. *P.* was found, after Lowell's death, by Tombaugh who compared two photographs of the same part of the heavens taken at different times. In the interval the planet had moved in relation to the stars. The name *P*. begins with the initials of Percival Lowell.

Nevertheless, *P*.'s mass is too small to account for the perturbations observed in the orbit of Uranus. Consequently, the discovery of the planet did *not* depend on the calculations, as in the case of Neptune. Not until 1950 did Kuiper succeed in measuring *P*.'s diameter with the Hale telescope*; it is about 3,700 miles. According to its dimensions and mass, *P*. should be classified with the terrestrial planets and asteroids, rather than with the major planets. Its orbit is very eccentric and steeply inclined to the ecliptic (*v*. Pl. 15). Although *P*., by its mean distance from the Sun, is the outermost planet of the solar system, its perihelion actually lies within the orbit of Neptune. It will be there in 1989. *P*. is so faint that it can be seen only with large telescopes. It moves across the celestial sphere at an average rate of $1 \cdot 5°$ per year. *P*.'s mean distance from the Sun is 3,666 million miles, perihelion distance 2,760 million miles, aphelion distance 4,570 million miles, period of revolution 248 years, diameter $0 \cdot 46 \times$ Earth's, mass $0 \cdot 9 \times$ Earth's.

Polaris, Pole star or North star, α Ursae Minoris, apparent magnitude $2 \cdot 08$–$2 \cdot 17$, spectral class F7. It is a cepheid variable star with a period of 4 d. and nowadays approximately marks the position of the north celestial pole, from which it is at present 1°, or twice the apparent diameter of the Moon, away. All stars describe their apparently circular orbits around the pole. α Ursae Minoris is also a double star, its components (one blue and the other white) having apparent magnitudes of $2 \cdot 0$ and $9 \cdot 0$, and being $18 \cdot 3''$ apart (1924).

P. will reach its shortest distance from the north celestial pole ($0° \ 27' \ 31 \cdot 50''$) in 2102. The next pole star will be γ Cephei (ca. 4145), then α Cepheid (ca. 7530).

Polarization is a condition of light in which the vibrations all take place in a single plane. Light reflected by a material may be partly polarized by that material. The degree of *P*. depends on the reflecting surface and on the angle of incidence of the light. Natural (unpolarized) light vibrates in all possible planes perpendicular to the direction of propagation. By testing the degree of *P*. in light reflected by the surfaces of planets, it is possible to learn more about the state and structure of their solid surfaces.

Pollux, the star β Geminorum, apparent magnitude $1 \cdot 2$, spectral class K0.

Poop, *v*. Puppis.

Population types are groups into which stars are divided according to their situation and age. The stars in galaxies are frequently classified into two population types (*v*. Pl. 60). Population I is associated with regions containing interstellar dust and gas, and is found in the arms of spirals and in irregular galaxies. Population II is found in the central regions of spirals and in the spheroidal halo surrounding these galaxies. This population type is also found in globular star clusters* and in elliptical galaxies*. Both populations are now believed to co-exist in the central regions, as well as in the arms, of spirals, but with type I predominating in the latter and type II in the former.

The flat disk formed by the spiral arms and consisting of Population I rotates round the centre of the galaxy. The stars forming the halo* do not share in the rotation. In our Galaxy, the Sun belongs to Population I and shares in the galactic rotation. The few stars forming part of the halo and which happen to be near the Sun thus appear to have high velocities because they do not share in the motion of the Sun, and other stars, around the centre of the Milky Way. Such stars are called high-velocity stars*.

The fact that the two populations differ from each other physically is shown by the difference between the Hertzsprung-Russell diagrams* for the two types. Stars of Population II are probably, in the main, old stars, whereas young stars occur in Population I. Our Galaxy—Population I: perhaps some 500,000 million stars. All stars forming the spiral arms, including O and B giants, supergiants, cepheid variables, members of the galactic star clusters, probably some of the stars in the central portion. Population II: perhaps 100,000–200,000 million stars. All stars in the halo, including sub-dwarfs, RR Lyrae stars, long-period variables, planetary nebulae, novae and a large proportion of the stars in the central region.

In the case of the Great Nebula in Andromeda (M31), it is estimated that, although the spiral arms come out clearly in photographs, at least 80% of the total light is derived from the central region and the halo (*v*. Extragalactic nebulae).

Many observers now believe that the division into two populations is an over-simplification. The Galaxy is suspected by some (Parenago, Zwicky) to be more complicated in structure (*v*. Galaxy).

Positional astronomy, another name for Spherical astronomy*.

Positron, *v*. Atom and Nuclear reaction.

Praesepe (the Beehive) (M44), an open star cluster in the constellation of Cancer. It appears as a hazy spot to the naked eye but can be resolved into stars with even a small telescope.

Precession, the movement of the points where the equator and the ecliptic intersect. The Earth is not a true sphere, the equatorial diameter being greater than the polar diameter. It can be regarded, however, as a sphere with a superimposed shell which is thickest at the equator and extremely thin at the poles. The gravitational attraction of the Sun is thus made up of a force on the sphere, which acts through the Earth's centre, and another one on the shell, which does not. Since the Earth's axis is not perpendicular to the direction of the Sun's attraction, the latter portion is equivalent to a mechanical couple tending to tip the axis of rotation. Since, however, the Earth is spinning, it acts as a gyroscope and instead of tipping, it precesses, describing a cone about the pole of the ecliptic. This is seen as a change in the north celestial pole, which describes a circle of $23\frac{1}{2}°$ round the pole of the ecliptic. At present the north celestial pole is $1° \ 2'$ from the star α Ursae Minoris, which we therefore call the (north) pole star. In 2,800 B.C. α Draconis was the pole star and in 26,000 years from now the north celestial pole will again approximately coincide with the present star. The attraction of the Moon and the planets also produces precession.

This change in the position of the north celestial pole is also accompanied by a shift of the vernal and autumnal equinoxes; the vernal equinox moves $50''$ annually along the ecliptic in a direction opposite to that of the Sun's motion. The declination and right ascension of the stars consequently also change. To find the correct position of a star, it is necessary to correct the listed declination and right ascension by consulting *P.* tables.

Procyon, the star α Canis Minoris, one of the stars in the vicinity of the Sun (*v.* Pl. 35). It is situated at a distance of 11·3 light-years and is a double star. Details of main component: apparent magnitude 0·5, absolute magnitude 2·8, spectral class F3, luminosity 5·8 × Sun's. Details of component B: apparent magnitude 10·8, luminosity 0·00044 × Sun's.

Prominence, a cloud of incandescent gas issuing from the Sun's surface and sometimes extending to very great distances from it (*v.* Sun and Pl. 28, 31).

Proper motion of a star is its displacement on the celestial sphere as a result of its movement in relation to the Sun. The average annual *P.m.* of stars is very small, the largest known being 10·2″. Stars which move with exceptional velocity are called 'high-velocity' stars (*v.* also Star).

Proton, a positively charged elementary particle, *v.* Atom.

Proton chain, a series of nuclear reactions which generate the Sun's energy. This source of energy is active in stars with a central temperature not greatly exceeding that of the Sun (*v.* Nuclear reaction).

Proxima Centauri, the star believed to be closest to the Sun. Distance 4·3 light-years, apparent magnitude 11, absolute magnitude 15·4, spectral class M5, luminosity 0·000052 × Sun's. It forms a binary with the brighter star α Centauri, which itself consists of two components. α Centauri is roughly the same distance from the Sun as Proxima is. The distance from Proxima to α Centauri (*v.* Pl. 35) is of the order of 0·15 light-year. *P.'s* period of revolution, if any, must be very long (e.g. 1 million years).

Ptolemaic system, a former theory of the structure of the solar system, according to which the apparent daily motions of the Sun, Moon and planets about the Earth were real. The problem of how to account for the circular orbits of the (apparent) motions of the celestial bodies had already been raised by Plato (ca. 428– ca.

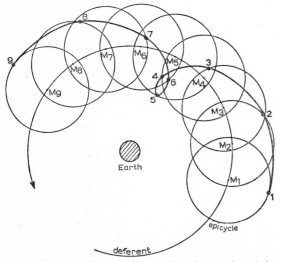

Fig. 1. The orbit of a celestial body along the epicycle and the deferent according to the Ptolemaic system

348 B.C.) and occupied a prominent place in astronomy until the Renaissance. Claudius Ptolemaeus (Alexandria, ca. 150 A.D.) further elaborated the system of his various predecessors (Eudoxus, Apollonius and Hipparchus) in his work, *Syntaxis*, better known by its

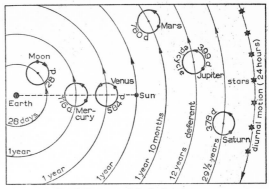

Fig. 2. Diagram of the Ptolem·c system

later Arabic title, *Almagest*. He asserted that all observable movements of the Sun, Moon and planets could be accounted for by an involved system of orbits, with the Earth as the immovable centre. Each of the then known celestial bodies (Moon, Mercury, Venus, Sun, Mars, Jupiter and Saturn, in order of distance from the Earth as it was thought at that time) revolved on a small circle, called an epicycle (→ 1), the Moon from east to west and the planets from west to east (→ 2).

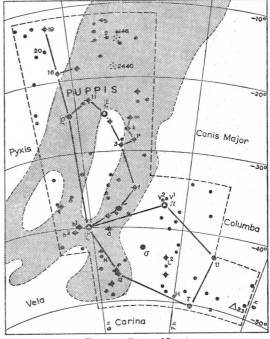

The constellation of Puppis

The centre of each epicycle revolved from west to east on a larger circle (the deferent) with the Earth at its centre. The period of this circular orbit was one sidereal year for Mercury, Venus and the Sun, 1 y. 10 m. for Mars, 12 y. for Jupiter, 29·5 y. for Saturn and about 27 d. for the Moon. The centres of the Mercury and Venus epicycles always remained on the line joining the Earth and the Sun, so that the motion of these planets on their epicycles caused the various

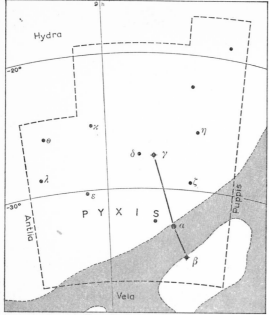

The constellation of Pyxis

elongations relative to the Sun (→ 2). Beyond the deferent of Saturn lay the celestial sphere containing the stars, which revolved once every 24 hours. This was the cause of the diurnal rotation in which the planets, Sun and Moon also shared. To explain irregularities in the movements of the planets, the epicycles and the deferents, although circular, had to be eccentric, the

epicycles in relation to the corresponding deferent and the deferents in relation to the Earth. The system was made more and more involved to explain every slight deviation of the apparent motions, and small new epicycles had to be added time after time. Copernicus (1473–1543) drastically modified the picture of the solar system by assuming axial rotation of the Earth and placing the Sun at the centre of the system; Kepler abolished the epicycles.

Pulsating stars, stars in which variation of brightness is believed to be caused by expansion and subsequent contraction of the stellar body. Examples: cepheids and β Canis Majoris stars (v. Variable stars and Cepheids).

Puppis (the Poop), a constellation in the southern hemisphere which was formerly part of the Ptolemaic constellation Argo Navis (the Ship Argo). It lies between 6 h. and 8 h. 25 min. R.A. and 11° and 51° S. Dec. This constellation is largely situated in the Milky Way and is rich in stars. (→ p. 187)

Pyxis (the Compass), an inconspicuous constellation in the southern hemisphere, situated between 8 h. 25 min. and 9 h. 25 min. R.A. and between —17° and —37° Dec. (→)

Quadrant, an instrument formerly used in astronomy to measure the elevation of stars. It consisted of a graduated arc of 90°. It was used, for instance, by Tycho Brahe in measuring the positions of planets.

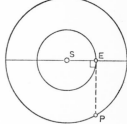

Planet (P) in quadrature. Sun is at S, Earth at E

Quadrature is the position in which the Moon or a planet is said to be when the angular distance between the Sun and the Moon or planet, as seen from the Earth, is 90°. The inferior planets can never be in Q (→ and → Opposition)

R

Radar in astronomy is limited to objects within the solar system. The principle is as for aircraft detection– a pulse of radio radiation is transmitted and the small amount of it that is reflected back from an object is received on radio antennae. The direction from which the echo returns can be measured and also the time delay between emitting the pulse and receiving the reflected signal. Assuming the velocity of light, the latter gives the distance of the object. Radio contact was made with the Moon in 1946; with Venus in 1958.

Radial velocity is the line-of-sight component of the velocity vector. The velocity of a star can be resolved into proper motion, which is perpendicular to the line of sight and can be calculated from the star's displacement on the celestial sphere, and the *R.v.*, which we can calculate from the shift of the spectral lines as a result of the Doppler effect* (v. also Hubble's constant).

Radiant is the point on the celestial sphere from which the members of a meteor shower appear to diverge (v. Meteor streams).

Radiation laws, the laws of Stefan-Boltzmann, Wien and Planck concerning the energy emitted by a perfect radiator. The formulae in which these laws are expressed all include the temperature of the radiator, and enable the surface temperature of the Sun and stars to be determined approximately. In particular, Wien's law states that the higher the temperature of the radiator, the more the wavelength of maximum intensity of the radiation is shifted towards the shorter wavelengths. Expressed as a formula, the law says: $T = 0.290/\lambda$ max. The maximum intensity in the solar spectrum is situated at a wavelength (λ) of 4,800 Å or 0.000048 cm, which gives a solar surface temperature of: $T = 0.290/0.000048 =$ approx. 6,000° K. K (= Kelvin) is the absolute temperature and equals the Centigrade temperature plus 273°.

Radiation pressure, the force exerted by radiation on the objects which it strikes. Lebedew showed by a laboratory experiment in 1900 that radiation can exert pressure. Once we recognize the material character of

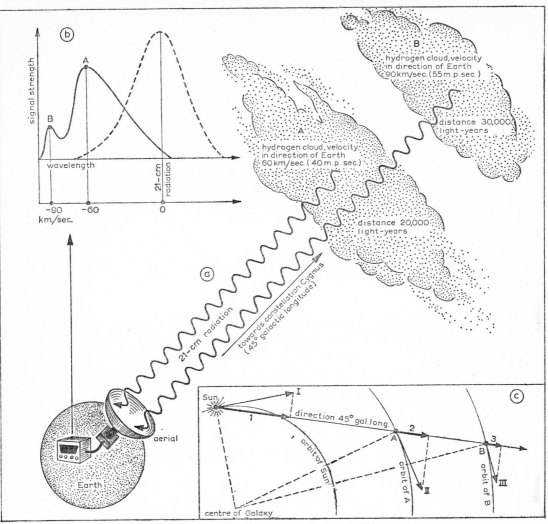

Fig. 2. Interception of radiation on a wavelength of 21 cm

radiation (light rays consist of photons; v. Light), it is not surprising to find that rapidly moving photons are able to exert pressure (v. Space travel). The generation of a comet's tail as the comet approaches the Sun was formerly attributed to R.p., but it has been suggested that the tail may be caused by ions being stripped from the comet by electrically charged particles emitted by the Sun (v. Pl. 31).

An important factor in theoretical studies of the interior of stars is the enormous R.p. which prevails there.
Radio astronomy, a new branch of astronomy which obtains information about celestial objects by using radio waves instead of light-waves.

In 1932 Jansky (in the United States of America) discovered that the Galaxy emitted radio waves on a wavelength of a few metres. At first this fact was regarded as a curiosity of little value to science. The systematic study of R.a. began after the Second World War and owed its rapid development primarily to the experience of radar acquired during the war. Radio telescopes came into use in many countries: Great Britain, the United States of America, Canada, France,

India, Holland, Japan and the Soviet Union, each with its own research programme. In 1951 the 'World-wide Survey of the Sun' was initiated, in which radio observatories in Australia, Japan, France, the Netherlands, Britain and Canada collaborated to keep the Sun under continuous observation.

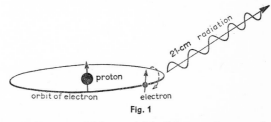

Fig. 1

Telescopes which use visible light can observe only processes which emit electromagnetic waves of lengths between 3,000 and 8,000 Å. With radio telescopes we can intercept waves over a much wider range of lengths (from 1 cm to 10 metres) and thus observe 'invisible' processes. The work of conventional telescopes is restricted to clear and preferably moonless nights, while radio telescopes are equally effective in cloudy conditions and by day.

The radio waves are reflected on to an aerial by a large 'mirror' of metal mesh. Special amplifiers raise this radiation to a measurable level. The chief discoveries so far have been:

a. point sources: small clearly defined areas in the sky which emit powerful radiation in the radio wavelength. By 1955 over 2,000 had been found. Some, such as Cassiopeia A and Cygnus A, with wavelengths of several metres are almost as powerful as the quiet Sun. Baade and Minkowski have photographed with the 200-inch telescope areas containing point sources and occasionally found faintly visible objects, including the remains of supernovae (Crab nebula* in Taurus), nebular wreaths, colliding spiral nebulae (*v.* Pl. 84) and other external galaxies.

b. the *Sun* emits powerful radio radiation—'solar noise'—which furnishes new information concerning its structure (*v.* Sun).

c. the detailed *structure of the Galaxy* has come within the scope of observation only as a result of research with the radio telescope. Optical observation is practically ruled out by large, dark nebulae which obscure much of our view of the Milky Way. A maximum intensity of radio radiation occurs in that position in the sky which visual observations suggest to be that of the centre of our Galaxy, and a weaker maximum from the direction of Cygnus. The most spectacular results came from studying radiation at a wavelength of 21 cm (*v.* Pl. 61, 62).

THE BEST KNOWN DISCRETE RADIO SOURCES

Name	*Right ascension*	*Declination*	*Known objects with which identified*
Andromeda	0 h. 40 min.	41° 00′ N.	Andromeda nebula, M31
Perseus	3 h. 16 min.	41° 19′ N.	NGC 1275 – two colliding galaxies
Taurus A	5 h. 31 min.	21° 59′ N.	Crab nebula, M1
Puppis A	8 h. 20 min.	42°48′ S.	galactic nebulosity
Virgo A	12 h. 28 min.	12° 40′ N.	peculiar galaxy M87
Centaurus A	13 h. 22 min.	42° 46′ S.	NGC5128, probably two colliding galaxies
Cygnus A	19 h. 58 min.	40° 36′ N.	two colliding spiral galaxies
Cassiopeia A	23 h. 21 min.	58° 32′ N.	galactic nebulosity

In 1944, van de Hulst, then a student, now a professor at Leiden, predicted that the hydrogen clouds in our Galaxy emit radiation of wavelength of 21·1 cm which should be powerful enough to be observed on Earth. This radiation is produced when the single electron orbiting round the nucleus changes its spin. Both nucleus and electron rotate round their own axes. If the electron spin changes (→ 1, broken line) radiation of wavelength 21·1 cm is transmitted which is comparable to an emission line in the spectrum of visible light. This happens in each hydrogen atom on an average of once in 11 million years. Radio engineers have worked out ingenious methods for observing this slight irregularity of intensity against the great intensity of the surrounding wavelengths and the inherent noise of the receiver. The profile of this signal varies considerably with the direction along which we examine the Milky Way. In the direction of the central region (→ 2b, broken line), and also in the opposite direction, we find a peak exactly where we should expect to observe the 21 cm line. In other directions we find several peaks displaced in relation to the position

where the 21 cm should occur. This is due to the Doppler effect*; as a result of galactic rotation the clouds are moving relatively to us, and from this information it is possible to deduce the distances of the clouds, provided we know how fast the various parts of the Milky Way are rotating. This is explained in Fig. 2c. The neutral hydrogen clouds A and B in the spiral arms of our Galaxy emit radiation with a wavelength of 21 cm. Owing to galactic rotation (→ 2c) the Sun is approaching clouds A and B. Arrows I, II, and III respectively represent the orbital velocity of the Sun, A and B. We are only concerned with the components in the line of sight, viz. 1, 2, and 3. It will be obvious from these arrows that clouds A and B must appear to be moving towards us, cloud B more rapidly than cloud A. Owing to the Doppler effect, the wavelength observed is shorter if the source is approaching us, so that the radiation at 21 cm is slightly shifted towards shorter wavelengths (→ 2a, 2b). The radio telescope receiver records these shifts. From them it is possible to calculate the velocities of the clouds and consequently their distances from the Sun. These distances are 20,000 and 30,000 light-years for A and B respectively. It has thus been possible to plot these hydrogen clouds and the 'map' obtained has given us our first idea of how the spiral arms of the Milky Way are arranged (*v.* also Galaxy) (→ 2a).

Optical methods could never have led to this result, for the rays of visible and infra-red light are absorbed by intervening clouds of dust and do not reach Earth. Only radiation on much greater wavelengths can penetrate these clouds. Radiation at 21 cm has also been picked up from the Large and Small Magellanic Clouds.

d. improvements in radio telescopes have enabled astronomers to pick up radio waves from the Andromeda nebula. The strength of these waves is roughly the same as the radiation from our Galaxy would be if it were situated as far from us as the Andromeda nebula is.

e. the radiation on radio wavelengths observed from Jupiter and Venus is probably associated with atmospheric disturbances on these planets.

f. the principles of radar can also be applied to radio telescopes. The radio telescope emits a directional signal, which is reflected by a celestial object and then received again by the radio telescope. Echoes reflected from the Moon were detected in this way in 1946, and recently have been obtained from Venus. (This technique will enable us to check previous determinations of the distance-scale of the solar system). The method has also been applied very profitably to the study of the orbits and velocities of meteor showers: on the 10th October, 1946, a meteor shower was observed when the sky was clouded and optical observation was impossible. Since 1946 meteor showers have been regularly observed in the daytime.

R.a. is also applied in planetary research, the wavelengths used ranging from 1 cm to 15 metres. The temperatures of the Moon, Venus, Mars, Jupiter and Saturn have been determined in this way. The polarization of radiation of radio wavelengths from Jupiter has led to the belief that this planet possesses an ionosphere and a magnetic field.

Radio noise, radiation picked up from distant celestial bodies by radio receivers (*v.* Radio astronomy).

Radio sources, *v.* Radio astronomy.

Radio telescope is an instrument for collecting radio waves from celestial bodies and making them perceptible. The radiation is reflected from a parabolic 'mirror' of metal to an aerial (dipole), situated at the focus, from which the signals are led to a radio receiver.

The resolving power of a telescope (i.e. the angular distance between two sources which the telescope can just distinguish as individual points) is directly proportional to its aperture and inversely proportional to the wavelength of the radiation.

Because the wavelength of radio waves is very large in comparison with that of light, a *R.t.* capable of showing details as clearly as they could be seen by the unaided eye would have to have an aperture of more than 6 miles for a wavelength of 1 metre. *R.t.s* therefore always have a lower resolving power than optical telescopes. On the other hand the design of the reflector is simpler than for an optical telescope. It must not contain any unevenness exceeding one-tenth of the wavelength received, but this means that an imperfection of as much as 10 cm in the parabolic shape is permissible for reception on a wavelength of 1 metre.

A considerable increase in resolution can be obtained by using an interferometer—an array of identical antennae spaced at regular intervals. Such an instrument, however, has other complications which limit its usefulness.

The largest *R.t.* in the world (*v.* Pl. 2), which has a reflector 250 feet in diameter, is at Jodrell Bank, near Manchester.

Ram, *v.* Aries.

Ras Algheti, the variable star α Herculis, apparent magnitude 3·1–3·9 spectral class M3. It also has a G-type companion of magnitude 5·4.

Ray systems, systems of bright streaks on the surface of the Moon, which appear to radiate from various craters. Nothing is known with certainty about their origin. The best known are those radiating from Tycho and Copernicus (*v.* Moon and Pl. 12).

Re-appearance, *v.* Emergence.

Red giant, *v.* Giant.

Red shift, displacement of spectral lines towards the red, observed in the spectra of extragalactic nebulae* (*v.* Doppler effect). Hubble and Humason photographed and studied the spectra of many external galaxies. In 1929 Hubble discovered that the *R.s.* is directly proportional to the distance of these galaxies (*v.* Extragalactic nebulae and Hubble's constant).

External galaxies in	Right ascension	Declina-tion	Distance in light-years	Velocity in m.p. sec	Velocity in km/sec.
Virgo	12 h. 25 min.	+ 12°	33	750	1,200
Pegasus	23 h. 17 min.	+ 8°	100	2,400	3,800
Perseus	3 h. 15 min.	+ 41°	150	3,250	5,200
Coma Berenices	12 h. 56 min.	+ 28°	240	4,750	7,500
Ursa Major I	11 h. 43 min.	+ 57°	500	9,500	15,000
Leo	10 h. 24 min.	+ 11°	650	12,000	20,000
Gemini I	7 h. 4 min.	+ 35°	750	14,000	23,000
Boötes	14 h. 30 min.	+ 32°	1,300	25,000	39,000
Ursa Major II	10 h. 55 min.	+ 58°	1,400	27,000	42,000

There are some galaxies for which a velocity of 75,000 m. p. sec. (120,000 km/sec.) has been found. The theory of the expanding universe* regards the *R.s.* as an actual effect of velocity (*v.* Extragalactic nebulae and Pl. 83). Objections have, nevertheless, been raised to these enormous velocities of recession, but, if upheld, they would necessitate a new explanation of *R.s.* such as: *a.* that the photons lose energy on their long journey, causing us to observe longer wavelengths; *b.* that the atoms at the time of departure

were larger and produced light of a longer wavelength; or *c.* that the constants in atomic physics are in fact not constant over long periods of time.

None of these explanations is generally regarded as satisfactory. Moreover, the relativity theory can cope with the concept of an expanding universe, and if we calculate when all matter must have been collected in a single small volume we arrive at an age which accords reasonably well with estimates arrived at by other means (*v.* Universe).

Red spot, *v.* Jupiter.

Red sunset results, as does the blue sky* from the fact that the Earth's atmosphere scatters blue light more than red light. Near sunset or sunrise, the Sun's rays, slanting through a long atmospheric path, have nearly all the blue light scattered out of them. Consequently, there is only red and yellow light left in the direct beams, hence the red colour of the Sun's disk. Further, such light as illuminates the clouds is also mainly of this colour.

Reflecting telescope or **reflector,** a telescope in which mirrors are used to collect the rays of light (*v.* Hale telescope). The advantage of a mirror is that it has no chromatic aberration. Moreover, mirrors can be manufactured to much larger dimensions than lenses. This is because light does not penetrate them but is only reflected from the surface, and they can be supported underneath. Lenses have to transmit light and can therefore only be supported round their edges. Large lenses sag in the middle and distort the received image. Reflectors can also be made from a great variety of materials, because all that matters is the reflecting surface, whereas lenses have to be made from special types of glass (*v.* Telescope).

Refracting telescope or **refractor,** *v.* Reflecting telescope and Telescope.

Refraction is the change in direction of a ray of light when it passes from a medium of one refractive index to another with a different index. This is particularly noticeable when light passes between air and water or air and glass.

Regulus, the star α Leonis, apparent magnitude 1·3, spectral class B8.

Relativity Theory, a theory developed by Einstein on the subject of space and time. The Special Theory (1905) teaches that measurements of time and length are not absolute quantities but are dependent on the condition of motion of the observer and the object observed. In 1916 Einstein expanded his theory into the General Theory. This theory, with its remarkable con-

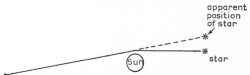

sequences in the domain of physics, does not lend itself readily to an elementary explanation. Only its astronomical consequences need be mentioned here:

a. Einstein was able to explain a previously inexplicable but very small deviation in Mercury's orbit. The amount of deviation calculated by Einstein corresponds very closely to the deviation actually observed (43 seconds of arc per century).

b. Einstein forecast that rays of light which pass close to the Sun would be bent by its gravitational field. The predicted effect was very small, a displacement of at most $1\cdot7''$ ($\rightarrow$). It can be observed only during a solar eclipse and then only if conditions are favourable. A photograph of the stars in the immediate vicinity of the Sun is taken during a total eclipse. It is then compared with photographs of the same stars in the night sky.

This apparent displacement of the stars seen near the Sun was first observed on the 29th May, 1919, by a British expedition in Brazil.

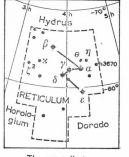

The constellation of Reticulum

c. In stars of very great density (*v.* Dwarf stars), and particularly the dark companion of Sirius, a displacement of the spectral lines towards the red was observed which could not be entirely accounted for by the Doppler effect*. Einstein's theory predicted a red shift of this kind in the case of such dense stars.

Resolving power of a telescope determines the size of details which are only just visible as separate objects. The greater the diameter of the objective*, the greater the *R.p.* (*v.* Telescope).

Reticulum (the Net), a small constellation in the southern sky, situated between 3 h. 15 min. and 4 h. 35 min. R.A. and between $-53°$ and $-67°$ Dec. ($\rightarrow$)

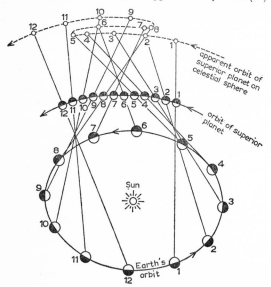

The actual orbit of a superior planet (e.g. Mars) round the Sun, and its apparent orbit in the sky. The positions of the Earth and the outer planet, and the latter's apparent positions in the sky as seen from Earth are shown at intervals of a month and numbered correspondingly. From 1 to 5 the planet's apparent orbital motion is 'direct', becoming stationary about 5; it is 'retrograde' from 5 to 8, where it again becomes stationary; then it is once more direct. Retrograde motion is always observed a short time before and after opposition (planet, Earth and Sun in line, in this case between 6 and 7)

Retrograde motion, *a.* the east to west motion of a satellite round a planet; *b.* the apparent east to west motion of a planet among the stars as seen from the Earth ($\rightarrow$).

Reversing layer is that part of the Sun's atmosphere where Fraunhofer lines are produced. It lies above the photosphere but is not readily distinguished from the chromosphere.

Revolution is the motion of a celestial body in an orbit (*v.* Rotation).

Rhea, one of Saturn's satellites, discovered by Cassini in 1672. Distance from Saturn 330,000 miles, period of revolution 4 d. 12 h. 25 min., diameter 1,000 miles (?), magnitude at opposition $10\cdot0$ ($\rightarrow$ 3 Solar system).

Rigel, the star β Orionis, apparent magnitude $0\cdot3$, spectral class B8.

Right ascension of a star is the angular distance, measured in the direction opposite to diurnal rotation, from the vernal equinox to the intersection of the declination circle of the star and the celestial equator (*v.* Celestial sphere). The celestial equator is usually divided into 24 'hours'. *R.A.* is therefore normally expressed in hours, minutes and seconds, and it is independent of the daily rotation of the celestial sphere. It is one of the two co-ordinates (the other is declination) used in star atlases and star catalogues.

Rills, cracks in the Moon's surface, up to several hundred miles in length. Their depth is unknown (*v.* Moon).

Ring mountain, a ring-like formation on the Moon's surface, a more or less circular wall enclosing an area which is generally lower than the surrounding surface of the Moon. Some ring mountains possess a central peak (*v.* Moon and Pl. 8, 10, 12).

Ring nebula in Lyra, a planetary nebula*, oval in shape, in the constellation of Lyra (NGC6720 or M57). Its position on the celestial sphere is 18 h. 52 min. R.A. and 33° N.Dec. It lies one third of the way along a line joining β Lyrae and γ Lyrae. Its distance from the Sun is estimated at 2,000 light-years. Its diameters are $0\cdot6$ and $0\cdot9$ light-year. The nebula contains a central star visible only through a large telescope (apparent magnitude 15).

Rocket astronomy, *v.* Orbiting astronomical observatory.

Rotation is the motion of a celestial body as it turns about a diameter called the axis of rotation (*v.* Revolution). The points where this axis cuts the surface of the body are called the poles. All celestial bodies and systems appear to rotate. The Earth's rotation causes the stars to appear to move in circular orbits round a point near the Pole star, i.e. the point where the

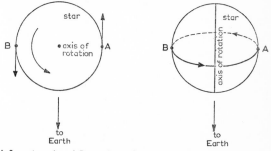

Left: points A and B on the surface of a star respectively move towards and away from Earth (motion perceptible owing to Doppler effect). *Right:* the axis of rotation of the star lies in the direction of Earth, and A and B move in a plane perpendicular to the line of sight (motion not perceptible)

Earth's axis, produced, cuts the celestial sphere. This *R.* causes the division of each period of 24 hours into day and night (*v.* Celestial sphere). That the Sun rotates is clear from the movement of sunspots across the solar disk (*v.* Sun). The *R.* of many stars can be deduced from their spectra as *R.* makes one side of the star recede from us while the other approaches. Doppler effect* displaces the spectral lines corresponding to the approaching parts of the star, slightly towards the violet, and those of the receding parts towards the red, a fact which is seen in the widening of these lines (*v.* Spectrum). The speed of rotation can be calculated from the amount of widening. Absence of widening does not necessarily mean an absence of *R.*: it is possible that the star's axis of rotation is in line with the Earth, so that no part of the star's surface is in radial motion relative to the Earth (→). In general, the stars with the fastest rotation are the B-type (*v.* Spectral type) stars with rotational velocities of up to 300 m. p. sec. (500 km/sec.) at the equator.

A large proportion of O-, B- and A-class stars have equatorial rotational velocities of the order of 60 m. p. sec. (100 km/sec.) (*v.* Pleione). Other stars rotate much more slowly, e.g. the Sun, 1·25 m. p. sec. (2 km/sec.). If it is assumed that the stars were formed by vortices in a primeval nebular mass (*v.* Evolution of the stars), the rotation was imparted to them then. The original total rotation of the nebular mass was divided among the stars formed from it.

The entire Galaxy * (*v.* Pl. 60) has also been found to rotate. A stellar system of this kind, however, does not rotate as a solid body. Instead, stars close to the centre have a small angular velocity, and those somewhat farther from the centre a larger angular velocity, while the outermost stars again have a smaller angular velocity.

Runaway stars, *v.* High-velocity stars.

Russell diagram, *v.* Hertzsprung-Russell diagram.

Sagitta (the Arrow), a small constellation in the northern hemisphere, situated between 18 h. 55 min. and 20 h. 20 min. R.A. and between 16°N. and 21° N. Dec. (→)

Sagittarius (the Archer), one of the zodiacal constellations and therefore astride the ecliptic. It is in the southern hemisphere and in the Milky Way between 17 h. 40 min. and 20 h. 25 min. R.A. and between —12° and —45° Dec. The centre of the Galaxy lies in the direction of this constellation. It is rich in bright stars and in bright and dark nebulae. (→)

Sails, *v.* Vela.

Saros is the period of 18 years 11 days in which eclipses of the Sun and Moon occur in the same sequence and at the same intervals as in the previous similar period. The *S.* was known to the Babylonians, who were thus able to predict solar and lunar eclipses. Eclipses can occur only if the Sun and Moon are together near a node* of the Moon's orbit. The nodes of the Moon's orbit move towards the Sun, so that the latter needs only 346·6 days to pass the same node on two successive occasions. The Moon returns to the same node every 29·53 days. After a multiple (19) of 346·6 days which is also a multiple (223) of 29·53

Satellite or moon, a heavenly body which revolves about a planet (→ 3 Solar system) (*v.* also under names of planets).

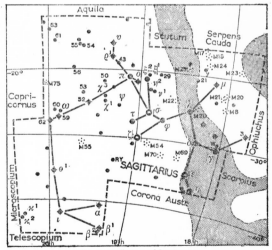

The constellation of Sagittarius

Satellite astronomy, *v.* Orbiting astronomical observatory.

Saturn (*v.* Pl. 21), the most distant of those planets of the solar system that were known before the eighteenth century. *S.* is one of the major planets and with its satellite system and rings forms a unique feature in the heavens. The planet's distance from the Earth is greatest at a conjunction*, when it is 1,025 million miles, and smallest at an opposition*, when it is 742 million miles. Its sidereal period* is 29·5 years, its synodic period* 378 days (*v.* Period). Oppositions thus take place two weeks later every year. Observing *S.* through a telescope, we see, as in the case of Jupiter, only the outer layers of its atmosphere. Although not so clear as those on Jupiter, there are several belts visible which run

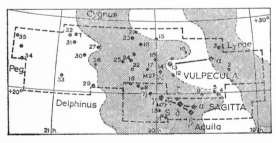

The constellations of Sagitta and Vulpecula

days (the *S.* satisfies this condition), the Sun and Moon will again be together at the same node, so an eclipse can occur.

parallel to the equator. These bands are cloud formations in the atmosphere which have assumed this shape as a result of the planet's rapid rotation. The planet is yellowish in the neighbourhood of the equator and greenish at the poles. That *S*. revolves rapidly round its axis can be seen from its pronounced oblateness: the equatorial diameter is 75,000 miles, the polar diameter 68,000. Since the belts of *S*., unlike those of Jupiter, reveal no clear features which are more or less permanent, it is difficult to determine the period of axial revolution. Spectroscopic investigations have shown that rotation is faster at the equator than at higher latitudes. The period of revolution at the equator is 10 h. 14 min.

The spectrum* of the solar light reflected by *S*. includes absorption lines of methane and ammonia. Compared with Jupiter, there is less ammonia and more methane. The low temperature (120°K at the surface of the atmosphere) causes the ammonia to crystallize and form clouds in the gaseous methane. There are two main hypotheses concerning the constitution of *S*. (→ 1): *a*. the planet possesses a deep atmosphere consisting of hydrogen and methane with clouds of ammonia floating in it (with the ammonia in crystal form), and beneath this lies a very thick layer of ice, inside which the rocky nucleus is enclosed; *b*. the entire planet, except the methane and the ammonia at the surface of the atmosphere, consists mainly of hydrogen and helium thickly concentrated towards the centre.

The density of *S*. is so small that the planet would float in water.

THE RING SYSTEM (→ 2) was unknown before the discovery of the telescope. With his telescopes (*v*. Pl. 1), Galileo* was unable to distinguish enough detail to perceive it. In 1610 he saw the planet as three parts: the disk of *S*., and the ring projecting on either side of it. Other observers thought that the planet had projections attached to it—the ansae or handles. It was not until 1655 that Huygens first saw the actual shape, a discovery which he announced with the words: 'Annulo cingitur, tenuis, plano, nusquam cohaerente, ad eclipticam inclinato'—'It is surrounded by a thin flat ring, which nowhere touches it, at an angle to the ecliptic.' In 1675 Cassini discovered that a dark band

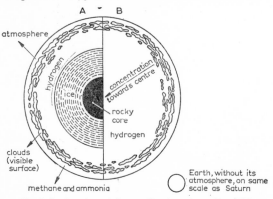

Fig. 1. Section through Saturn. Two hypotheses (A and B)

divided the ring into two—Cassini's division (*v*. Pl. 21). The 'crape ring' was first observed in 1850 by G.P. Bond. The system of concentric rings lies in the planet's equatorial plane and consists, from outside to inside, of: the outer ring (ring A), the main ring (ring B), and the crape ring (ring C). The existence of a very

faint ring round the outer ring is sometimes suspected. The outer and main rings are separated from each other by Cassini's division. As seen through a telescope, this is a dark gap through which a star can be clearly seen during an occultation. This band therefore consists not of dark matter but of empty space. The main

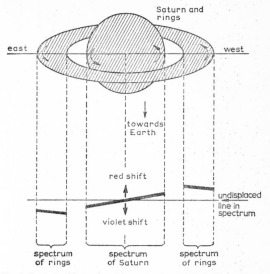

Fig. 2. Because of Saturn's axial rotation its eastern half is moving in the direction of the Earth; Doppler effect displaces the spectrum to the violet. The western half is receding from us: its spectrum is displaced towards the red. The centre of the visible disk is moving from east to west but has no motion towards or away from Earth; its spectrum is therefore not shifted. Similarly, the whole eastern half of the ring moves in the direction of the Earth, with a resultant shift to violet. Its western half recedes from Earth, resulting in a red shift. It can be seen that the inner part of the ring has a greater velocity than the outer, for the spectrum shift of the inner part is greater. From this it may be deduced that the ring is not solid but consists of individual particles having various velocities of revolution

ring is the brightest, and the crape ring is much fainter than the other two. Other concentric dark bands have been seen; these probably are not empty space, but are merely less bright than their surroundings.

The ring system is very thin in relation to its diameter. Outer ring: outer diameter 171,000 miles, inner diameter 149,000 miles; main ring: outer diameter 144,500 miles, inner diameter 118,000 miles; crape ring: inner diameter 91,500 miles; equatorial diameter of *S*. 75,000 miles; estimated thickness of ring system 10 miles (0·002″).

With the equatorial plane of the planet it is inclined at an angle of 27° to the plane of *S*.'s orbit round the Sun. In the course of the sidereal period of 29·5 years, therefore, the Sun and the Earth will be once 27° above and once 27° below the plane of the ring. When the Sun passes through the plane of the ring, the annular system is a nearly invisible line or entirely invisible. This was the case in 1891, 1907, 1921, 1937 and 1951. For the next few years the ring will be wide open and occupy a good position for observations (*v*. Pl. 21).

In 1895 spectroscopic observations revealed that the inner parts of the system are rotating faster than the outer parts (→ 2). The ring therefore does not rotate as a solid body, a result which was previously advanced on theoretical grounds by Clerk Maxwell in 1858. It is believed nowadays to consist of fragments of ice, or at least of particles coated with hoar frost. A small part of the ring system is usually invisible in the shadow

	Average distance from Saturn in miles	Period	Diameter in miles	Magnitude in opposition	Remarks
Mimas	115,400	22 h. 37 min.	300 (?)	12·1	
Enceladus	148,000	1 d. 8 h. 53 min.	300 (?)	11·6	
Tethys	183 200	1 d. 21 h. 18 min.	700 (?)	10·5	visible with 4-inch telescope
Dione	234,700	2 d. 17 h. 41 min.	700 (?)	10·7	visible with 4-inch telescope
Rhea	327,800	4 d. 12 h. 25 min.	1,000 (?)	10·0	visible with 3-inch telescope
Titan	760,000	15 d. 22 h. 41 min.	2,600	8·3	visible with 2-inch telescope
Hyperion	922,200	21 d. 6 h. 38 min.	250 (?)	13·0	
Iapetus	2,215,000	79 d. 7 h. 56 min.	800 (?)	10·1–11·9	visible with 3-inch telescope
Phoebe	8,050,000	550·5 d.	400 (?)	14·5	retrograde motion*

of the planet. At opposition this shadow is hidden behind the planet itself. Similarly the ring system casts a shadow on *S.* This is visible as a dark belt on *S.*'s surface adjacent to that part of the ring which is in front of the planet as seen from the Earth. The ring system is believed to be a permanent feature. Concerning its origin, Roche showed in 1850 that the existence of a satellite within a certain distance of the planet (Roche's limit) is impossible owing to the disruptive effect of the planet's power of attraction. The external diameter of the ring system lies within this limit (2·5 radii of the planet). It is thought that matter originally in the vicinity of *S.* conglomerated to form the satellites. It was not possible for matter within Roche's limit to do so, and if a satellite approached *S.* to the distance of the ring it would have been disrupted into small fragments. Since the distance of Cassini's division from the centre of *S.* is known, the period of a particle, if it were placed in this division, can be calculated by appeal to Kepler's third law*. It is found to be precisely one-half of that of *S.*'s nearest satellite, Mimas. Because of this commensurability of the two periods, the perturbations exerted by Mimas on the particle would be cumulative and it would soon be removed from Cassini's division. Other less conspicuous divisions in *S.*'s ring-system can be explained in a similar way.

THE SATELLITE SYSTEM. Several satellites are visible with even a small telescope. Titan, the largest of them, has a diameter greater than that of our Moon (→ 3 Solar system), possesses an atmosphere and is visible with a 2-inch telescope. Only Phoebe has retrograde motion. The orbital planes of moons I–VII do not deviate much from the plane of the ring system.

Scales, *v.* Libra.

Schmidt telescope, a very important optical system with excellent definition and a large field. It is a combination of a refractor* and a reflector*. The system was invented in 1930 by B. Schmidt of Bergedorf. Many *S.t.* are in use, e.g. the large (48-inch) telescope at Mount Palomar, used to take the photographs for the National Geographic Society-Palomar Observatory Sky Atlas (*v.* Star atlas, and Pl. 81).

The *S.t.* is employed only as a camera. Its optical system consists of a concave spherical main mirror with a glass plate in front of it. As the mirror is made with a large aperture ratio (i.e. mirror diameter: focal length) of 1:1 or 1:2, its aberration would be very great. This aberration (spherical, *v.* Optics)

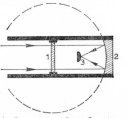

1. Correcting plate; 2. mirror; 3. position of film

is neutralized by the correcting lens, a specially designed glass plate (→ 1). This plate is nearly flat and so thin that it introduces practically no chromatic aber-

ration. The centre of the corrector plate is placed at the centre of the imaginary sphere of which the mirror's surface forms part. The photographic plate or film is placed between the lens and the mirror (→, 2), at the focus of the system. As the focal plane facing the mirror is convex, the plate is constrained to a convex shape (→, 3). Because of its large aperture ratio, the system has great light-gathering power, enabling faint stars and nebulae to be photographed with relatively short exposures. Its large field, which makes it possible to photograph a considerable part of the sky (5° × 5°) at a single exposure, is another advantage of the *S.t.* over the ordinary reflecting telescope.

Scintillation, *v.* Twinkling.

Scorpion, *v.* Scorpius.

Scorpius (the Scorpion), a zodiacal constellation in the southern hemisphere, situated in the Milky Way between 15 h. 45 min. and 17 h. 55 min. R.A. and

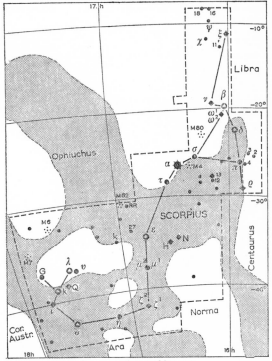

The constellation of Scorpius

between —8° and —45° Dec. It contains very many bright stars and bright and dark nebulae. (→)

Sculptor is a constellation in the southern hemisphere, between 23 h. 5 min. and 1 h. 45 min. R.A. and between —25° and —40° Dec., occupying an inconspicuous part of the sky where few bright stars are to be seen. This is not surprising since the south galactic pole lies in this constellation; in other words we are looking in a direction perpendicular to the galactic

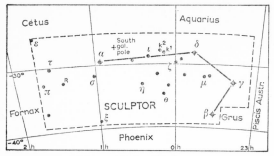

The constellation of Sculptor

plane and therefore through a relatively thin disk of stars. (→)

Scutum or **Scutum Sobieskii,** (Sobieski's Shield), a small constellation in the Milky Way, situated in the vicinity of the celestial equator between 18 h. 20 min. and 18 h. 55 min. R.A. and between —4° and —16° Dec.

Sea-goat, v. Capricornus.

Seeing, v. Twinkling.

Selected areas, small areas distributed evenly over the entire celestial sphere, in which stars down to a certain magnitude* are closely studied. This scheme was worked out by the Dutch astronomer Kapteyn for the purpose of obtaining statistics on the part of the universe surrounding us. To study the entire sky would have taken too long and been nearly impossible. He therefore suggested that as many observatories as possible should collate the following details of 206 small areas evenly distributed over the entire sky: stellar positions, visual and photographic magnitudes, proper

motions (v. Pl. 35), parallaxes, spectral classes and radial velocities.

Much of the work is now completed: the Mount Wilson Catalogue and the Bergedorfer Spectral-Durchmusterung are two of the most important contributions. From the information obtained, Seares (Mount Wilson) and Van Rhijn (Groningen) concluded that the Galaxy* is flattened and that the Sun occupies a position removed from the centre.

Selenography is the study of the surface of the Moon. Hevelius (1611–87) called his lunar atlas (one of the first) *Selenographia* (v. Moon).

Serpens (the Serpent), a constellation consisting of two parts, Serpens Caput (head) and Serpens Cauda (tail). Serpens Caput is situated between 15 h. 10 min. and 16 h. 20 min. R.A. and between 25° N. and 3° S. Dec. Serpens Cauda extends from 17 h. 15 min. to 18 h. 55 min. R.A. and from 6° N. to 16° S. Dec. (→).

Serpent, v. Serpens.

Serpent-bearer, v. Ophiuchus.

Seven Sisters, v. Pleiades.

Sextans (the Sextant), an inconspicuous constellation on the celestial equator, stretching from 9 h. 40 min. to 10 h. 50 min. R.A. and from 7° N. to 11° S. Dec. (→)

Sextant, v. Sextans.

Shadow transit, transit of the visible disk of a planet by the shadow of one of its satellites (v. Jupiter and Pl. 19).

Shield, v. Scutum.

Shooting star is another name for a meteor*.

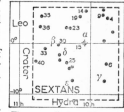

The constellation of Sextans

Sidereal period, the time taken by a planet to complete one revolution around the Sun in relation to the stars, as seen from the Sun (v. Period). The sidereal period of a satellite round a planet is similarly defined.

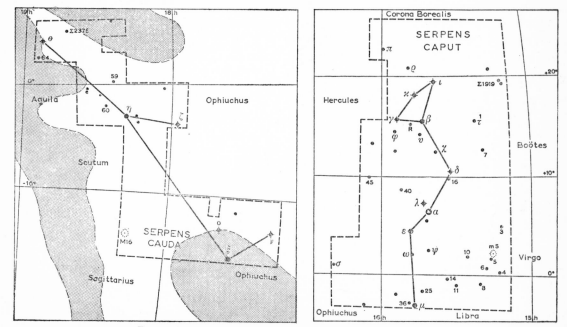

The constellation of Serpens; *left:* Serpens Cauda, *right:* Serpens Caput

Sidereal time, a local time based on the rotation of the celestial sphere*. The sidereal day of 24 sidereal hours begins when the vernal equinox* crosses the observer's meridian* (upper transit). The local *S.t.* is therefore obtained from the hour angle* of the vernal equinox and is o h. when the vernal equinox transits the meridian.

Local *S.t.* (in hours) = $\frac{1}{15}$ of the hour angle of the vernal equinox (in degrees of arc).

The *S.t.* can also be calculated from the right ascension of any star. At the moment of the star's meridian passage, the *S.t.* is equal to the star's right ascension. In other words, the hour angle of a star plus its right ascension equals local *S.t.* The *S.t.* is therefore not a universal but a local time, depending on the place of observation (→ Celestial sphere).

Siderostat is a single mirror moved continually about two axes to reflect light from a star or, more particularly, the Sun, along a fixed direction into observing equipment. The coelostat* is more frequently used nowadays.

Sirius, (the Dog Star) α Canis Majoris, the brightest star in the sky and very close to the Sun. Distance 8·7 light-years, apparent magnitude —1·6, absolute magnitude 1·3, spectral class Ao, visual luminosity 23 × Sun's. In 1834 Bessel noticed that *S.'s* orbit in the sky was not straight but undulating, from which he deduced that *S.* had an invisible companion and that the motion of the two stars caused the undulation. Later the orbits were computed but the second star had not yet been seen. This companion was first observed by Clark in 1862. It proved, in fact, to be an 8th magnitude star and should theoretically have been easy to perceive with a small telescope. That it was not so easily seen was due to its being outshone by the bright light of *S.*

Sirius B was the first white dwarf ever found. Its diameter is only 0·034 × the Sun's, but its mass is 0·96 × the Sun's. The mean distance from A to B is 20 A.U. and the period 49·9 years.

Details of Sirius B: apparent magnitude 8·5, absolute magnitude 11·4, visual luminosity 0·002 × the Sun's (*v.* Pl. 35).

Sirona, a small asteroid with a periodic variation of magnitude, period 9 h. 40 min. (*v.* Eros).

Sobieski's Shield, *v.* Scutum or Scutum Sobieskii.

Solar constant, *v.* Solar energy.

Solar eclipse takes place when the Earth enters the shadow cone of the Moon. This is possible only when the Moon is new. As the Moon's orbit is inclined at 5° 9·0′ to the ecliptic, a *S.e.* cannot occur unless the Sun is at or near a node (*v.* Pl. 27, 28). Solar (and lunar) eclipses recur in succeeding cycles of 18 years and 11 days (*v.* Saros). On the average there are 2 or 3 *S.e.s* per year (maximum 5).

As the Moon has no atmosphere, its shadow cone is sharply defined. The length of the cone (→) is such that it sometimes extends beyond the Earth and sometimes falls just short of it, depending on the slightly varying distances between the Sun, Moon and Earth. In the former case we see the Moon's disk larger than the Sun's, in the latter case we see it smaller. That is why we are able to distinguish between three types of solar eclipse: *a.* total, when the lunar disk obscures the entire solar disk; *b.* annular, when the Moon leaves the rim of the Sun uncovered; *c.* partial, when the Moon does not pass through the centre of the solar disk. A total *S.e.* lasts not more than 7½ min. and is visible only in the limited area swept by the Moon's shadow. Observers outside this path see a partial *S.e.* The ob-

servation of eclipses is a matter of extreme importance to modern astronomy, for the outer layers of the Sun, such as the faint corona, can best be studied then.

Plate 19 shows a *S.e.* visible on a small area of Jupiter's surface (inside the black spot at the top, just left of centre), and caused by the Moon at the right.

Solar energy is energy emitted by the Sun in the form of radiation. The intensity of the radiation is normally expressed in terms of the 'solar constant'. The solar constant is the total radiation received in 1 minute on a surface of 1 sq. cm placed at right angles to the Sun's rays just outside the Earth's atmosphere, the Earth being at its mean distance from the Sun. Its value is approximately two calories per sq. cm per minute.

Only a very small percentage of *S.e.* is intercepted by the planets, including the Earth. By far the greatest part of it disappears into interstellar space. The total quantity of energy emitted annually is 3 × 10^{33} calories. We believe that this output of energy has been going on for thousands of millions of years and there is not the slightest indication that it is decreasing even slowly. Calculations show that this output is much greater than could be accounted for by the cooling of originally hot matter, by combustion or by bombardment by meteorites. It was formerly believed that the release of *S.e.* was the result of slow contraction, but this source too is realized to be quite inadequate.

This energy is now thought to be due to nuclear processes in the interior of the Sun, hydrogen being converted into helium (*v.* Nuclear reaction). The energy thereby released, e.g. in the form of gamma rays of very short wavelength, is changed on its journey to the Sun's surface by alternate absorption and emission by matter, into radiation of longer wavelengths, part of which reaches us as visible light (*v.* Pl. 32).

Solar flare, *v.* Flare.

Solar noise, *v.* Radio astronomy and Sun.

Solar system, (*v.* Pl. 15), system comprising the Sun, planets and their satellites, asteroids, comets, meteorites and dust. The Sun is at the centre and the outer limit is probably a cloud consisting of clouds of matter which occasionally become visible to us when, as a result of disturbance by neighbouring stars, they fall towards the Sun and, as comets, start following very elongated elliptical orbits (*v.* Comet and Pl. 23, 24). The diameter of this (hypothetical) cloud may be about 4 light-years.

Whereas it was formerly thought that the system was centred on the Earth (*v.* Ptolemaic system), it is now known that the Earth, like the other planets, follows an elliptical orbit round the Sun. In antiquity the then known planets were associated with deities. Together with 'Sun' and 'Moon' their names were used for the days of the week. This can still be clearly seen in some languages.

Sunday	Sun	(Du.: zondag, Ger.: Sonntag)
Monday	Moon	(Fr.: lundi, It.: lunedì, Du.: maandag, Ger.: Montag)
Tuesday	Mars	(Fr.: mardi, It.: martedì)

Wednesday	Mercury	(Fr.: mercredi, It.: mercoledì)
Thursday	Jupiter	(Fr.: jeudi, It.: giovedì)
Friday	Venus	(Fr.: vendredi, It.: venerdì)
Saturday	Saturn	(Du.: zaterdag)

Because of their striking appearance Mercury, Venus, Mars, Jupiter and Saturn have been known since antiquity. They were called 'planets' (i.e. wanderers) because they appeared to move quite freely among the other 'fixed' stars. They were important features of ancient astrology*. The other planets were discovered telescopically or photographically at a much later period: Uranus in 1781 by Herschel, Neptune in 1846 by Leverrier and Pluto photographically in 1930 by Tombaugh.

The Earth's orbit (→ 2) on the celestial sphere is visible to us in the apparent path of the Sun over a period of a year (v. Ecliptic). Almost all the orbits of the planets round the Sun lie in approximately the same plane. Only those of Mercury and Pluto are clearly inclined to this plane (Mercury 7°, Pluto 17° 9′). The inclination to the ecliptic is even greater in the case of many of the asteroids. The planets all orbit in the direction of the Sun's rotation, i.e. from west to east. The greater a planet's distance from the Sun, the longer its period of revolution and the smaller its orbital speed, as the table below shows (v. also Pl. 15).

Planet	Eccentricity of orbit	Inclination of orbital plane to ecliptic	Equatorial diameter in miles	Diameter Earth = 1	Gravitation at surface Earth = 1
Mercury	0·2056	7°00′	3,008	0·38	0·36
Venus	0·0068	3°24′	7,720	0·97	0·87
Earth	0·0167	——	7,926	1·00	1·00
Mars	0·0933	1°51′	4,226	0·53	0·38
Jupiter	0·0483	1°18′	88,740	11·2	2·6
Saturn	0·0559	2°29′	75,060	9·5	1·1
Uranus	0·0470	0°46′	29,600	3·7	0·9
Neptune	0·0087	1°46′	27,800	3·5	1·5
Pluto	0·247	17°10′	8,950	1·1	0·8

The smaller or terrestrial planets are: Mercury, Venus, Earth, Mars and possibly Pluto; the major planets are Jupiter, Saturn, Uranus and Neptune (→ 3). The densities suggest that the main difference between the terrestrial and the major planets is one of composition. The former, like the Earth, all have a solid core and in some cases, at least, an atmosphere. The major planets all have a very deep atmosphere, consisting of hydrogen, methane and sometimes ammonia. It is doubtful whether they have a solid core. Their cores are thought to consist of hydrogen, very condensed towards the centre (e.g. Jupiter*).

The fact that the smaller planets are nearer the Sun and all the major planets farther away must be due to the way in which the solar system originated.

The origin of the *S.s.* has long been one of the greatest unsolved problems of astronomy. An important aspect of the question is whether the *S.s.* is an unusual or a comparatively normal feature in the development of a star. If the former, then we must assume that life in the form it has assumed on Earth is a very rare development in the universe. If the latter, then we can probably expect to find rational beings throughout space. The various theories put forward in the last few centuries to account for the planetary system may be classified as follows:

a. Open systems, i.e. the origin of the planets is due to influence beyond the *S.s:*

1. Buffon, 1749. A collision of a comet with the Sun

caused matter to pour from the Sun; this matter then condensed to form the planets.

2. Chamberlin-Moulton, 1900. A star passed close to the Sun causing high tidal waves to form on both bodies. These flood waves were pulled out to form clouds, in which local condensations gave rise to planets. Thus a planetary system was created simultaneously around each star.

3. Jeans-Jeffreys, 1917. A star with a much larger

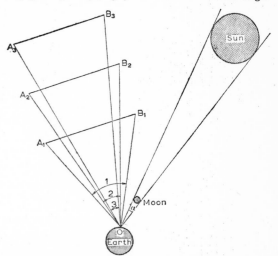

Fig. 1. The farther a celestial object is from Earth, the smaller its angular diameter will appear to an observer O; angles 1, 2 and 3 correspond to distances A_1B_1, A_2B_2 and A_3B_3. Although the Sun is many times larger than the Moon, it is also so much farther away that they both have approximately the same apparent diameter, viz. angle α (= 0·5°)

mass than the Sun passed very close to the Sun. Tides directed towards the star were raised on the Sun. These became so high that matter broke loose from the Sun forming a cigar-shaped cloud directed towards the other star and starting to revolve about the Sun. Some of it solidified to form the planets.

4. Lyttleton, 1936. The Sun was originally a double star. A passing third star removed the companion star and attracted a cloud of gas from the Sun; this cloud condensed to form the planets.

5. Alfvén, 1942. The Sun moved through a gaseous nebula situated in space. The gas particles of the nebula were electrically charged by the Sun. These gravitated towards the star and, depending on their mass and chemical composition, formed various concentric rings which condensed into the planets.

6. Hoyle, 1946. The Sun was originally a double star. Its companion exploded like a nova. As this explosion was directed towards the Sun, the distance between the two stars was increased and the nova disappeared into space. The gaseous material ejected from the nova was captured by the Sun and gave rise to the planets.

7. Hoyle, 1954. The Sun originated as one of the members of a star cluster. One of the stars in the vicinity of the Sun exploded like a supernova. The matter ejected mingled with the interstellar hydrogen. The Sun contracted and rotated at great speed, and from its equator lost material which collected in the form of a disk round the Sun. A magnetic field around the Sun slowed down the Sun's rotation and drove the disk farther from the Sun. Silicates and metals which

originated from the supernova explosion liquefied or solidified in the neighbourhood of the Sun. The lighter gases, including the original hydrogen, were still gaseous there. The solid or liquid particles remained behind when the gas disk was repelled by the magnetic field, and formed the nuclei of the smaller terrestrial planets. The lighter gases condensed farther from the Sun and formed the major planets. Under the influence of a very hot star in the neighbourhood of the Sun, the bulk of the hydrogen originally present in the nebula disappeared into space. If the magnetic field had not existed, the gaseous disk would have grown outwards from the Sun, giving rise not to a planetary system but to a small companion of the Sun. In other words, the Sun would have become a binary.

b. Closed systems, i.e. the *S.s.* was formed from matter already present in the space now occupied by the system, unaffected by outside influences.

1. Kant, 1755. A rotating cloud of gas and dust contracted. Local concentrations gave rise to the planets, while the central condensation created the Sun.

2. Laplace, 1796. Extended Kant's suggestion in greater detail. The greater part of the original Sun's rotation was imparted to the particles of this nebula and, as a result of cooling and contraction, the rotation became faster. Rings of matter were formed which condensed to form planets (the nebular hypothesis).

3. Berlage, 1929. Particles of a nebula originally present were driven outwards through the nebula by the Sun's radiation pressure, accumulating other particles in the process. Under the force of the Sun's electrostatic field they formed various concentric rings (round the Sun), the distances of which from the Sun depended on the atomic weights of the ions forming the nuclei of the planets-to-be: the smaller the atomic weight, the greater the distance from the Sun. These rings condensed into planets.

4. Von Weizsäcker, 1943. Eddies were formed in a gaseous nebula rotating around the Sun. These eddies lay in concentric rings and matter accumulated between them. The largest conglomerations captured the smaller fragments and formed the nuclei of the future planets.

5. O.J. Schmidt, 1944. The Sun was surrounded by a rotating cloud of gas and dust. Particles with the same moment of momentum combined and further accumulation took place round them as nuclei. From these the planets were formed.

6. G. Kuiper, 1954 (and later). The Sun originated from the contraction of a gaseous nebula, a part of the original material being left behind in the form of a flat disk, the solar nebula. The Sun was still cold. The rotating solar nebula contained streams of gas, which varied in force and were unstable and kept disappearing and reforming. The nebula broke up into large clouds of gas, the proto-planets. whose masses, dimensions and positions relative to the Sun depended on the local density of the nebular mass (*v.* Pl. 93).

There were two unstable regions, in which the four inner and the four outer proto-planets respectively were formed, and these were separated by a stable region in which the asteroids were formed by the accumulation of particles. In the outermost region of the solar nebula, which was also stable, the comets originated, likewise by accumulation. The body of each planet was formed by condensation towards the core of the proto-planet, and the proto-satellites by a similar process towards the outside of the proto-planet.

It was because of the tidal friction of the newly formed planet on the proto-satellites that the latter's axial rotation was not fast. The proto-satellites were thus unable to repeat the process of forming an unstable gas ring round themselves, and thus giving rise to a third generation of still smaller bodies (satellites of satellites). In the same way the tidal friction of the Sun prevented the formation of satellites round proto-Venus and proto-Mercury. The proto-Earth probably split into two, thus forming a double planet.

Some of the satellites may have escaped into space and have been recaptured again by the planets (hence the retrograde satellites) or have finally occupied a fixed position in the *S.s.* like the Trojan asteroids (*v.* Trojans).

When the Sun started to radiate, its heat destroyed a great proportion of the mass of the proto-planets, largely by evaporating it into interplanetary space,

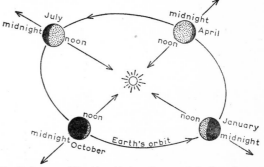

Fig. 2. Because of Earth's orbital motion round the Sun, the part of the sky seen at a particular hour of the night throughout the year varies continuously

for the outer atmosphere attained a high temperature (cf. even today: Earth's surface $250°$ K, exosphere probably $1,500–2,000°$ K). The proto-planets must therefore have been formed before the Sun started to radiate, i.e. while it was still in the state of a contracting gaseous nebula.

The interplanetary material derived from the proto-planets has now disappeared. Kuiper thinks that when the sun began to radiate, this material was ionized by the rays which then drove the ions into interstellar space. By far the greater part of the material thus evenly disappeared into interstellar space. Then part of the material forming the outermost layers of the proto-planets was also driven beyond the *S.s.* by evaporation. This entire process probably took about 10^8 or 10^9 years to complete. The planets nowadays have on the average less than 1 % of the masses of the proto-planets. The fact that the planetary orbits all lie in approximately the same plane is explained by assuming that the original gas nebula was very tenuous, so that it could contract to a very flat disk before reaching the critical density at which (according to Roche's limit) it would be torn to pieces. Kuiper believes that 1–10 % of main-sequence stars (*v.* Hertzsprung-Russell diagram) have formed planetary systems. If this is so, the total number of such systems in the Galaxy is of order 10^9 or 10^{10}.

Nowadays, at any rate, it is generally agreed that the planets were formed cold by the agglomeration of particles of material from an original cloud of gas and dust. Currents set up in this nebular mass may have given rise to turbulence and hence to local condensation of the material. If by chance such a condensation was large, it was also stable and attracted all individual particles of matter and smaller condensations in its neighbourhood.

To be acceptable, a theory must explain the peculiar distribution of angular momentum in the *S.s.* (98% in the orbital motion of the planets and only 2% in the rotating Sun, although the latter contains more than 99% of the mass) and also why the composition of the inner planets is different from that of the outer major planets. This separation of heavier from lighter material can be accounted for by the influence of a magnetic field, as in Hoyle's hypothesis, or by intense radiation which ionized the hydrogen in the vicinity of the Sun, the remaining nuclei and electrons being then removed by the Sun's intense emission of charged particles (*v.* above under 3. Berlage). The material left in the vicinity of the Sun was insufficient to form a major planet, so that the smaller terrestrial planets were formed there.

According to Kuiper, the initial solar nebula from which the planets were formed had a mass $\frac{1}{10}$ that of the Sun. Had this mass been smaller, e.g. $\frac{1}{100}$ of a solar mass, formation of the planets would have been impossible. At best, a swarm of small fragments, such as the meteor showers on the fringe of the *S.s.*, would have resulted. Had the mass of the initial nebula been much greater, e.g. comparable with the Sun's, no planets would have originated but the cloud would have condensed to form a second star, and the Sun would have become a binary.

Attempts are also being made nowadays to predict how the *S.s.*, and particularly the Earth, will fare in the remote future. The American astronomer M. Schwarzschild thinks that the Sun is slowly becoming hotter as its hydrogen stocks are used up (*v.* Nuclear reaction). In 5 or 6 thousand million years the Sun will have become an M-class giant (*v.* Giant). Mercury's orbit will then lie within the Sun's disk and the Earth's surface temperature will be well beyond the boiling point of water. Needless to say, all life will long since have been extinct. Then the Sun will cool rapidly and become a white dwarf, and the temperature at the Earth's surface will drop far below freezing point. Water vapour from the atmosphere, if there is any left, will cover all land with snow and the polar caps will extend to the equator. The Earth will then end its existence as a desert waste, dimly lit by a dying Sun.

LIFE IN THE SOLAR SYSTEM. It is quite certain that life as it has developed on Earth is possible only within very narrow limits of temperature. The upper limit is about 100–400° C., at which certain micro-organisms can still sustain life. The lower limit is remarkably low, for various bacteria and spores of algae, mosses and ferns remain alive if placed in liquid helium (−271°C.). Mosses, algae and lichens can survive for several weeks in liquid air (−109°C.) although there is no question of biological activity at these temperatures.

Some bacteria and fungi can live without oxygen. Certain plants, when placed in a vacuum, create their own atmosphere. Other bacteria can live in a 10% solution of sulphuric acid and in saturated solutions of boric acid, vitriol and nitric acid. There are bacteria which do not depend for their food supply on other organisms or on solar radiations, but live on minerals. Bacteria can withstand a pressure of 3,000–8,000 atmospheres. Micro-organisms thus appear to adjust themselves readily to all sorts of conditions.

Nevertheless, compared with the temperatures which occur in the universe as a whole, the temperature range for life is very limited. The normal temperature for a large proportion of the matter in the universe is between several thousand and several million degrees. Such material is confined to stars. The remaining material is in the form of clouds of gas and dust. Only in the neighbourhood of hot stars will these clouds have high temperatures (up to 10,000° K); elsewhere in space their temperature will be just a few degrees above absolute zero (−273°C.).

Only a small proportion of the matter in the universe is found between the temperature limits within which life is possible. Energy, at any rate, is necessary to sustain life. Plants on Earth absorb the Sun's rays and the animal kingdom lives on the energy stored by the plants. The quantity of energy available depends on the amount of sunshine absorbed. Thus, if the temperature on a planet is too low, either because the temperature of its sun is too low or because the planet is too far from its sun, insufficient energy is available to support life. If the energy needed for vital processes is absent, then life is impossible. The organic matter stored by plants and animals consists mainly of very complex compounds of carbon. The original energy of the Sun is stored in the human body, for instance, in the form of fats. The complicated molecules of these various compounds cannot, of course, occur above 100° C.

Possibility of life on other planets. Mercury: the side always presented to the Sun is too hot (400° C.), the side away from the Sun too cold. Moreover, *M.* has either no atmosphere or a very tenuous one.

Venus: the outer layers of its atmosphere are all we see of this heavily clouded planet. Recent radio observations indicate that the surface temperature is between 200° C. and 300° C., presumably due to a very intense greenhouse effect. The amount of carbon dioxide in the atmosphere is about 500 times that in the Earth's and is comparable with the amount which might have been expected in the latter if there had never been any terrestrial life and hence no carbon sediments had been biologically generated.

Moon: too hot in the daytime (over 100° C.), too cold at night (about absolute zero). Yet some observers try to attribute the colour changes observable on the surface of some walled plains to a sort of vegetation (lichens?). This appears most improbable.

Mars: in the last few years Russian biologists have carried out experiments in Pamir, where the climate corresponds to that of middle latitudes on Mars. The annual ground temperature range there is about 102° C., the daily range as much as 60° C. The mean annual temperature in the valleys of Pamir is below freezing point. Yet over 200 species of plants are found there.

The air in the valleys of Pamir is very dry, the relative humidity dropping in the afternoon to almost zero. The conditions prevailing there change plants which normally have considerable transpiration into forms with hardly any transpiration. The dry and cold climate of Mars therefore does not exclude the possibility of vegetation.

Plants use nitrogen which is plentiful on Mars. They give off oxygen, which they also need to breathe in. No oxygen has been revealed in the atmosphere of Mars, but it is possible that the Martian flora, like certain terrestrial aquatic plants, store a supply of oxygen in their cells.

No chlorophyll absorption band can be found in the spectrum of sunlight reflected by Mars. Chlorophyll is

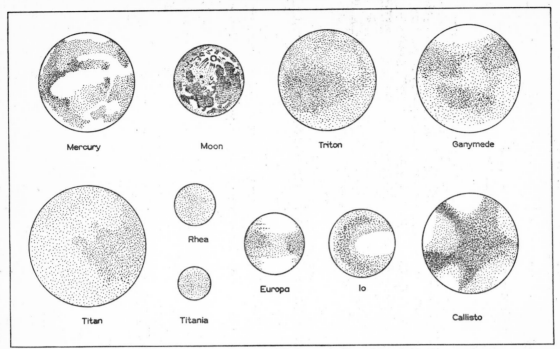

Fig. 3. Comparative sizes of Mercury and the largest satellites of the solar system

what gives terrestrial vegetation its green colour. It has, however, been discovered in Siberia that one variety of pine and other species of tree absorb chlorophyll only above 0° C. When the temperature drops below zero, the chlorophyll absorption disappears.

Moreover, the Russian Tikhov reaches the conclusion that plants absorb only that part of solar radiation which they can use. In higher temperatures, they can reflect almost all heat radiation, the part of it that is visible to the human eye being yellow in colour. In Pamir, in fact, bright orange-coloured algae are found living in hot springs where the temperature reaches 70° C. Some plants which are blue-green under normal conditions are yellow in the vicinity of these hot springs (e.g. *Verbascum thapsus*). Vegetation on a hot planet (e.g. Venus) would therefore be orange. In a cold climate, such as that of Mars, the plant will absorb all the heat available in order to take in as much energy as possible: it will then turn blue or violet. In an average climate, like that of the Earth, vegetation is green.

In a general way, ultra-violet radiation is probably destructive of living organisms, and therefore of vegetation, if any, on Mars. On Earth most of this radiation is kept out by the atmosphere. It is thought that the 'violet' layer which extends from $6\frac{1}{2}$ to $12\frac{1}{2}$ miles above Mars and consists of fine dust, can scatter and absorb radiation of short wavelengths (blue, violet and ultra-violet). Some sort of vegetation may therefore be expected on Mars, and this conclusion has recently been strengthened by some remarkable spectroscopic evidence obtained by Sinton, while using the 200-inch Hale reflector on Mount Palomar. Sinton discovered that infra-red radiation of certain wavelengths from the Sun is absorbed in the dark areas of the surface of Mars but not in the bright ones: two of the three absorption bands found were known to be shown by molecules in which carbon and hydrogen

atoms are linked. The third has since been found to be shown by cellulose, which is present in plants. Although not conclusive, Sinton's discovery must be regarded as the most important evidence so far as for the existence of plant life on Mars. The absence of oxygen, however, makes animal life, as we know it on Earth, impossible (*v.* also Mars). Micro-organisms certainly could live on Mars.

Jupiter, Saturn, Uranus and Neptune: the ammonia and methane in their atmosphere might indicate the presence of bacteria. Russian research convincingly shows that organic and inorganic methane and ammonia may contain different isotopes and therefore have different spectra. The spectrum of the methane (organic) used in household gas has been found to agree with that of the methane on these planets. The spectrum of inorganic ammonia (prepared in a laboratory) does not coincide with that of ammonia in Jupiter's atmosphere. It may therefore be that the methane in the atmospheres of the major planets is the product of bacterial activity in the deeper layers and that the ammonia is due to the decomposition of dead micro-organisms.

If other stars have planets, we cannot see them because they reflect far too little light. The question of the existence of other planets is linked with the problem of explaining how they originate. Planetary systems are thought by many astronomers to be a normal development of stars, the number of such systems in our Galaxy may thus be estimated at 1–100 thousand million. If the average system consists of 10 members and if 1 planet in 100 is suited to the development of higher forms of life, we should expect life to have developed in 100 million to 10 thousand million planets in the Galaxy.

Solar-terrestrial relationships cover phenomena in the Earth's atmosphere which can be correlated with observed occurrences on the Sun. The most common is the observation of a flare* on the Sun and subsequent terrestrial radio fade-outs and auroral displays (*v.* Aurora).

Solar tower is a tower with a coelostat mounted at the top to direct sunlight vertically downwards into a fixed telescope. In this way, the troublesome effects of shimmer, due to hot air near the ground, are minimized.

Southern Cross, *v.* Crux.

Southern Crown, *v.* Corona Australis.

Southern Fish, *v.* Piscis Austrinus.

Southern Triangle, *v.* Triangulum Australe.

Space station, *v.* Space travel.

Space travel, the propulsion of space ships beyond the Earth's atmosphere (*v.* also Artificial satellite), a futuristic idea which may be realized at a not-too-distant date. Both the Soviet Union and the United States of America hope to launch a manned rocket to the Moon within the next few years. *S.t.* is a logical stage in technical development, and also the outcome of a need for adventure. Just as the countries of the Earth were discovered in times gone by, the worlds of outer space now await discovery. The first artificial satellites put into outer space as part of the programme for the International Geophysical Year (1957–8) were the first step towards space travel to the Moon and the other worlds of the solar system. Various items of information needed for space travel, such as the effect of cosmic rays* on man, and the number and size of meteorites* in space, have been collected by the artificial satellites and radioed to Earth. In addition satellites enable rockets and their motors and fuels to be tested (*v.* Pl. 6).

The reactor produces the only propulsive power that is independent of the atmosphere and can therefore be used in empty space. Its basic principle is that every action in one direction causes a reaction in the

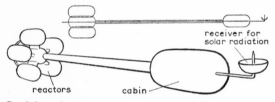

Fig. 1. Interplanetary space ship as designed by Krafft Ehricke of Convair (1957)

opposite direction; for example, when a gun fires a projectile, reaction causes the gun to recoil. In the reactor, gases, ions or photons expelled at great velocity from the rear cause the reactor motor itself to move forward. This does not mean that the ejected gases or other particles propel the motor by pushing against the air particles outside; in fact, the reaction principle works better in a vacuum. Various types of propellent are used to obtain the forward thrust. The power of that thrust depends, among other things, on the velocity of the jet of particles.

Some of the propellents in use or to be used in the future are: liquid fuels (e.g. acid) and solid fuels (e.g. rubber or asphalt), metal fuels (metal particles in a fluid), 'exotic' fuels (i.e. numerous combinations of various chemicals), ion propulsion and, finally, photon propulsion, in which light from the Sun is gathered and then ejected. Photon propulsion, because of the inexhaustible supply, may be able to produce velocities approximating that of light. The Russians and Americans appear to be experimenting with it already.

In outer space man will be exposed to many dangers, not all of which can be assessed as yet, such as the unknown effect of cosmic rays, or the effect the astronaut's weightless condition will have on his blood circulation. Already a special branch of medicine is studying the possibility of life under these conditions.

The navigation of a space ship poses many problems. It will be impossible to navigate in outer space without complicated instruments, and therefore little navigational responsibility will be given to the astronaut. A monitoring device consisting of freely suspended gyroscopes and accelerometers will be connected to the instruments aboard the rocket to correct every unwanted deviation from course.

Artificial Planets and Lunar Projectiles. On the 2nd January, 1959, the Russians launched Lunik 1 (Mechta) by means of a three-stage rocket. On the 4th January it passed within 3,750 miles of the Moon and then went into orbit around the Sun. The mean orbital velocity of this tiny planet around the Sun is 20 m. p. sec. (32 km/sec.), i.e. slightly greater than the Earth's. The greater part of the orbit lies in the space between the orbit of the Earth and that of Mars. As the period of its orbit around the Sun is about 1·2 years, Lunik 1 is expected to pass close to the Earth 5 years after launching. By emitting a cloud of luminous sodium gas, Lunik 1 revealed its position for a short time when 70,000 miles from the Earth.

The American Pioneer 4 was launched on the 4th March, 1959. It passed within 37,500 miles of the Moon, and, like Lunik 1, became a satellite of the Sun. Its period of revolution is 392 days (perihelion distance 93 million miles, aphelion distance 106·4 million miles).

The first material contact with the Moon was made on the evening of 13th September, 1959, when Lunik 2 landed a Russian flag and emblem on the Moon's surface. The speed of Lunik 2 was then 7,500 m. p. h. (12,070 km/h.). Precautions were taken to ensure that no micro-organisms were carried to the Moon. This Lunik, too, released a sodium flare.

Lunik 3 was launched on the 4th October, 1959. This projectile described an orbit around the Moon and then returned towards the Earth. It took photographs of the far side of the Moon, which had never before been seen, and radioed them back to Earth (*v.* Moon). On 12th Feb. 1961 the Russians launched a rocket designed to reach the area of Venus.

Both the Soviet Union and the United States of America have announced their intention of sending a manned rocket to the Moon in the near future. In preparation for that event the X-15 experimental rocket has been developed in America; this is a small 'space ship' which can attain a speed of about 4,400 m. p. h. (7,000 km/h.) and a height of about 175 miles. It is intended to carry out test flights of about 1 hour with this aircraft, during which the pilot will be weightless for 6 min. Then attempts will be made to place manned satellites and a permanent space station in orbit round the Earth. To make a space ship leave the Earth, so that it will not fall back but attain free flight, it must be launched with a velocity of 7 m. p. sec. (11.3 km/sec.).

One possible approach to the next stage of the problem is: *a.* to place material in an orbit round the Earth; *b.* to build a permanent space station in the same orbit beyond the Earth's atmosphere; *c.* to build space ships at the space station (these would not be suitable for travelling through an atmosphere); *d.*

to use the space station as a base for interplanetary journeys.

a. THE MATERIAL. This will be placed in the orbit of the projected space station with multi-stage rockets. The most suitable point of departure will be on the equator, with the rocket aimed in an easterly direction, because the Earth's rotation alone will give it an initial velocity of 1,000 m. p. h. (1,600 km/h.). Once its motors are shut off, the rocket will move on a trajectory farther and farther from the Earth, while the Earth's gravitational pull gradually slows it down. By the time it has reached say, 1,000 miles above the Earth's surface, where the space station is to be built, its velocity must be increased to about 16,000 m. p. h. This is just enough to keep the ship permanently in orbit at a height of 1,000 miles. The material for the space station will now be discharged and, owing to its velocity, will continue travelling in the same orbit. The return of the space ship with its crew is an extremely difficult undertaking which is by no means solved.

b. BUILDING THE SPACE STATION. It is thought that each rocket will be able to take 2 lb. of payload per ton of initial weight. Fifty trips will be necessary to transport all the material needed for the projected space station. The latter will be built *in situ* on the orbit round the Earth. It may be wheel-shaped, for instance, with a diametrical cross-piece, and an entrance at its centre. If the station were made to spin about its own axis in space, the resultant centrifugal force would set up an artificial gravity on the outer wall of the ring and make life on board more pleasant. The power required can be obtained from the Sun: a concave mirror would concentrate the solar rays (not attenuated here by an atmosphere) on a liquid, the hot gases from which could be used to drive turbines, etc. The gases would be cooled at the dark side of the station, where low temperatures prevail, and the fuel would be led back to the sunlit side.

c. CONSTRUCTION OF THE SPACE SHIPS. The space ships will be built at the space station. As they are not intended for use in an atmosphere, they can be made of very light material, and need not be streamlined. Krafft Ehricke of Convair (→ 1) has designed interplanetary ships to be built from the cylindrical parts of rockets sent aloft from the Earth. The cylindrical cockpit is built well away from the motors to protect the crew from harmful radiation.

d. INTERPLANETARY JOURNEYS. The first destination will be the Moon (→ 2). Just as advantage was taken of the Earth's rotational velocity at the equator upon departure from the Earth, the space station's orbital velocity of 16,000 m. p. h. will now be used as the initial velocity. If the ship's speed is now increased to about 22,000 m. p. h., the journey to the Moon will take only 5 days. On the fall back to Earth the velocity will increase. To brake, the space ship must turn through 180° and use its motors in the direction opposed to movement.

A journey to Mars or Venus would not require much more power than one to the Moon. For a trip to Mars (→ 3) advantage would be taken of the space station's velocity of revolution around the Earth and of the Earth's velocity of revolution around the Sun. The orbital velocity of the space station is 16,000 m. p. h. The Earth revolves around the Sun at a velocity of over 67,000 m. p. h. The departure has to be arranged to coincide with a moment when the motion of the space station and that of the Earth are in the same direction. The initial velocity of the space ship is then over 80,000 m. p. h. already, without further effort! A thrust slightly greater than that needed for a journey to the Moon then frees the ship from the gravitation of the Earth-Moon system and allows it to follow the path which will intersect the orbit of Mars. A round trip to Mars will necessitate far-reaching

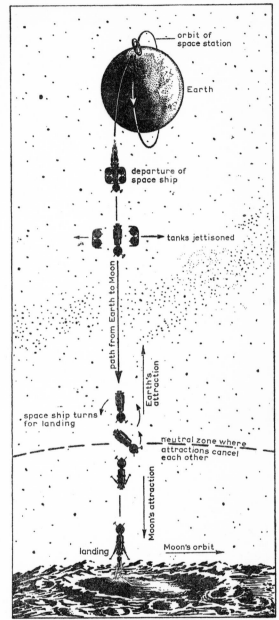

Fig. 2. Diagram of a journey by space ship to the Moon

preparations: (i) several space ships will leave the space station for Mars; (ii) a second space station will be built in an orbit round Mars; (iii) a rocket for use in the atmosphere will be built in this space station; (iv) this rocket can then land on the planet. The journey to Mars and back will take over three years.

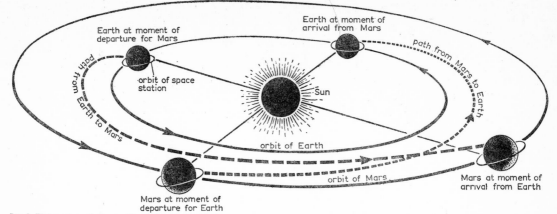

Fig. 3. The motion of a space ship orbiting with the Earth round the Sun has to be accelerated slightly in order to reach the orbit of Mars, which is farther from the Sun than the Earth's orbit

For the trip to Venus, the departure will coincide with the moment when the motion of the space station round the Earth is opposite to that of the Earth around the Sun. This will give the space ship an initial velocity of about 50,000 m. p. h. The space ship in its orbit round the Sun will now have a lower velocity than the Earth and will therefore move towards the Sun, so that the orbit of Venus can be reached. The dense atmosphere of Venus will render a landing on that planet very difficult.

The possibilities of journeys to the stars are, as yet, more doubtful. The vast interstellar distances can only be traversed by using extremely high velocities. Theoretically, it is possible for matter to travel at velocities up to nearly that of light (186,300 m. p. sec. or 300,000 km/sec.), and it is thought that these velocities can be obtained with photon propulsion. But the difficulty is that the light used for this purpose has first to be gathered from the Sun with parabolic reflectors, and that beyond the solar system the source of light is too remote. Photon propulsion can therefore be used only in the vicinity of the Sun or other stars but not for travelling in empty outer space. Nevertheless, a suitable source of power may perhaps be found some time in the future. Another problem is the immensity of the distances to be covered. The nearest star, α Centauri, is 4·3 light-years distant from the Sun (v. Pl. 45). The really interesting objects in our Galaxy are on the average at least 500 or 1,000 light-years away. Even at a velocity comparable to that of light, a journey of this kind would take about 1,000 years, and the round trip as many as 2,000 years! Life would therefore be too short to undertake such trips. Yet this objection is perhaps only apparent. According to Einstein, the speed at which time passes on a particle of material depends on the velocity at which the particle is travelling in space. The crew aboard a fast-moving space ship, might, for instance, become only a few weeks older on a journey of thousands of light-years, and timepieces on board might show only a few weeks' interval between start and end of the trip.

Spectral lines, bright or dark lines in the spectrum*. The bright lines are emission lines*, and the dark lines are absorption lines*. Each line corresponds to radiation on a particular wavelength* (v. Pl. 16, 32).

Spectral types are the various groups into which stars are divided according to their spectra (v. Spec-

trum). Secchi first classified stars by their colour, dividing them into white stars (such as Sirius, Vega and Rigel), yellow stars (Capella, Arcturus and the Sun), orange stars (Antares and Betelgeuse) and red stars. In 1885 Pickering studied a large number of stellar spectra and divided them into 16 classes named A to Q. Miss Cannon's final classification was based on Pickering's. The principal classes are: O, B, A, F, G, K and M, which, in that order, form a sequence in which the properties of the star vary gradually. This sequence is the one used in the Draper Classification*. The complete classification includes four more classes (W, O, B, A, F, G, K, M, R, N and S), while each class is subdivided into 10 groups. B5 thus refers to a spectrum which is halfway between Bo and Ao. A small c, g or d prefixed to the spectral class indicates respectively that the star is a supergiant, a giant or a dwarf. The suffix e refers to the presence of emission in the case of types where this is not a normal feature. Some examples: Rigel cB8, Arcturus gKo, Procyon dF5, Mira Ceti M9e, Sun dG2.

DESCRIPTION OF SPECTRAL TYPES

Type	Temp. in deg. K.	Colour	Spectral lines	Stars
W			continuous spectra with bright, broad emission lines of ionized helium, oxygen and nitrogen	rare, v. Wolf-Rayet stars
O	about 50,000		absorption lines of ionized helium, oxygen and nitrogen	
B	about 20,000	bluish	absorption lines of neutral helium; hydrogen lines more pronounced	Rigel, Spica
A	about 10,000	white	hydrogen lines attain maximum intensity	Sirius, Vega
F	about 7,000	white	hydrogen lines decrease, lines of metals (notably calcium) appear	Canopus, Procyon
G	about 6,000	yellow	lines of metals very pronounced	Sun, Capella
K	about 5,000	orange	lines of metals exceed hydrogen lines in intensity; bands of molecules appear	Arcturus, Aldebaran
M	about 3,000	red	prominent bands of titanium oxide	Betelgeuse, Antares

Between class O and class M, stars change in colour from white through yellow and orange to red, which immediately demonstrates the important fact that the sequence is also one of diminishing temperature. This is confirmed by the nature of the spectral lines. The O spectra contain the lines of ionized helium which can only occur at very high temperatures. The occurrence of molecules (which produce bands in spectra and are observed in type M) is a sign of relatively low temperature.

The study of *S.t.* in connection with the absolute magnitude of stars led to the Hertzsprung-Russell diagram, which has proved extraordinarily important in the development of astronomy.

Spectrograph or **Spectroscope,** an instrument for studying the spectrum* of a luminous source such as a flame or electric arc in a laboratory, or a star or a nebula in astronomy. The main types are the prism *S.*, the grating *S.* and the objective prism *S.*

In the first type, light from the source is concentrated by a lens L_1 ($\rightarrow$) on to a slit *S.* A collimating lens L_2 makes parallel the rays that have passed through the slit and this parallel beam falls on to a transparent prism P. In the prism, the light of shorter wavelength (say, blue light) is bent through a greater angle than that of longer wavelength (red). The transmitted rays are concentrated by a camera lens L_3 and form a band of coloured light in the focal plane F. The complete spectrum will consist of ultra-violet and infra-red in addition to the visible colours. It can either be photographed by putting a plate or film at F or the visible part of the spectrum can be viewed with a magnifying eyepiece. The physical length of the spectrum can be increased at will by making lens L_3 of longer focal length, but in order to increase the resolution of the spectrograph (i.e. the amount of detail actually in

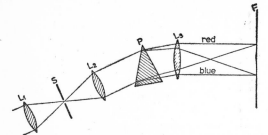

the spectrum), it is necessary to use a narrow slit and to increase the apex angle of the prism, or to use a series of prisms.

If the instrument is to be used on stars or nebulae, the lens L_1 is replaced by the actual telescope, the slit of the spectrograph then being at the focus of the telescope. The telescope may of course be a refractor or a reflector. The spectrograph itself may also be designed to use mirrors instead of lenses.

In the grating spectrograph, the prism is replaced by a reflecting plate with 10 or 20 thousand parallel scratches *per inch* ruled on its surface. The spectrum is now formed by diffraction at these rulings rather than refraction within the prism. The more the lines in the grating, the higher is the resolution. Most modern astronomical spectrographs employ gratings.

These types of spectrograph only allow the spectrum of one star to be obtained at a time. It is sometimes possible to employ another method— to place a large prism of small angle in front of the objective (lens or mirror) of the telescope. Such an *objective prism* draws out each star image into a short spectrum and many such spectra can be photographed at once.

Spectroheliogram, a photograph of the Sun, taken in light of one particular wavelength (e.g. in the light of a line of calcium or hydrogen). These photographs

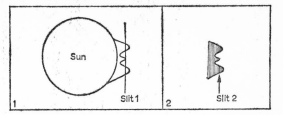

reveal details which are of great importance in the study of the Sun. A *S.* is taken with a ($\rightarrow$) spectroheliograph (*v.* Pl. 30).

Spectroheliograph, an instrument for photographing the Sun in monochromatic light (i.e. light of one particular wavelength). The objective of the telescope T ($\rightarrow$ 1, 2) forms an image of the Sun. Only a narrow strip of the image is admitted by slit 1. From this narrow strip prism P forms a spectrum that is projected via mirror 2 to slit 2. Only a particular colour (i.e. wavelength) is admitted by slit 2 and recorded on the photographic plate. By displacing the instrument I, it is possible to photograph the entire Sun strip by strip in the particular colour chosen (the photographic plate remains stationary). The solar image thus obtained is called a spectroheliogram*. A special modification makes the *S.* suitable for visual observations; it is then called a spectrohelioscope.

A *S.* can actually be used to photograph parts of the Sun, such as the chromosphere* and prominences* which are otherwise only visible during a total eclipse. If the limb of the Sun is scanned with the *S.* using the wavelengths of the monochromatic light which is being emitted by the prominences, we obtain slit image photographs which show the shape of the prominences in all details ($\rightarrow$ Spectroheliogram).

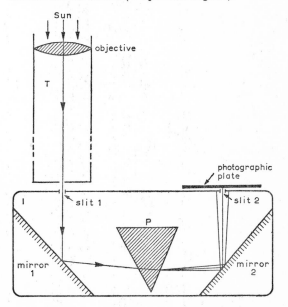

Spectrohelioscope, *v.* Spectroheliograph.
Spectroscope, *v.* Spectrograph.

Spectroscopic binaries are double stars whose components are so close together that they cannot be seen as individual stars with a telescope. As a result of the Doppler effect* the lines in the spectra of these double stars show periodic shifts which indicate that the components are alternately moving away from us and towards us (→ Double stars). If a spectroscopic binary is also an eclipsing variable (v. Double stars), it is possible, by studying the light-curve* as well as the

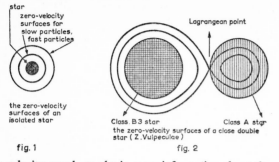

fig. 1   fig. 2

velocity graph, to obtain more information about the system. Close *S.b.* are particularly interesting. The tide-raising effect of the two components on each other is very powerful. Examination of their spectra reveals emission and absorption lines which cannot be

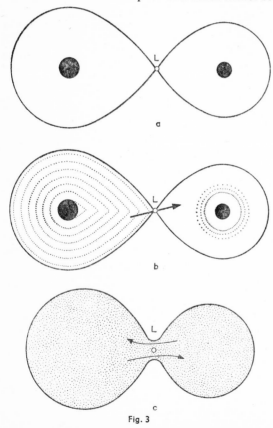

Fig. 3

accounted for as originating in any normal way in either of the stars. It is assumed in such cases that one or both of the stars are enclosed in an envelope of gas

and that excitation of this gas causes the peculiar spectrum lines. Theoretical considerations also lead to the same conclusion. When particles leave the surface of an isolated star at a certain velocity, they will be progressively slowed down by the gravitational attraction until their velocity is zero and they fall back to the surface. For particles with a particular velocity it is possible to imagine a sphere whose surface defines the positions in space where the velocity will be zero (zero-velocity surface, Fig. 1). For particles with higher initial velocities, the radius of this imaginary sphere will be greater. The two components of a close spectroscopic binary, however, deform each other's zero-velocity surfaces, with the result that the latter are elongated in the direction of the other component (Fig. 2). When the ejected particles have a certain velocity, the two zero-velocity surfaces touch at a point called the Lagrangean point (L). For a particle of material situated at this point, the gravitational attraction of the two stars cancel each other out. Point L will obviously be nearer the star with the smaller mass. The eclipsing variable Z Vulpeculae, for instance, consists of a B3 star (mass = 5 × Sun's) and an A-type star (mass = 2 × Sun's), both with a diameter of 3 million miles.

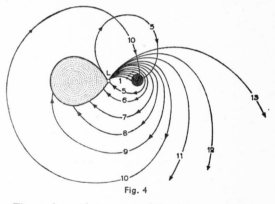

Fig. 4

Fig. 2 shows that a part of the A-type component (the one with less mass) of Z Vulpeculae is outside the critical zero-velocity surface. A slight disturbance may cause particles there to move freely into the space round the stars or to fall on to the other star.

A component of a spectroscopic binary which is greater than the critical zero-velocity surface cannot have originally been formed in that way, for there is no reason why material outside its sphere of influence should be attracted to it during its formation. Since stars change into giants at one stage of their development, it can be assumed that the unstable component was originally smaller and stable. In the course of the evolution which both stars have undergone at different rates, one component grew greater than the critical zero-velocity surface, then became unstable. The stars in Fig. 3a are stable. Those in Fig. 3b are also stable but one of them is surrounded by an envelope of gas, from which particles are able to pass freely through the Lagrangean point to the space round the other star, and land on its surface or form a ring of gas round it. In the case of double stars which are in contact with each other (Fig. 3c), material in the region of point L can flow freely from one component to the other. Computers have been used to check the various possible motions of particles ejected by one of the stars (*v.* Three-body problem). Fig. 4 shows the paths calculated for particles with 13 different velocities (after Z. Kopal). The two stars were assumed to be of equal mass, with the left-hand star rotating at a faster rate than that at which it revolves, counter-clockwise in the figure. Particles 1–4 (with the lowest velocities) fall on to the primary, particle 5 first orbits round the primary and again passes through the Lagrangean point, finally falling on the primary. Particles 6–9 return to the companion star. Particle 10 circles round both stars, then falls on the primary. The particles with the highest velocities (11–13) move away from the double star, eventually return by a spiral orbit and fall on one of the stars. The orbits described also depend on the masses of, and the distance separating, the two stars, and on the speed and direction of rotation of the companion.

Spectroscopic parallax, a way of finding the parallax* and hence the distance of a star, by comparing the strengths of certain spectral lines. Within a particular spectral class the strengths of some lines in the spectrum alter in proportion to the luminosity of the star. Once this relationship has been exactly established, it is possible to deduce a particular absolute magnitude from a particular strength ratio. The distance of the star can then be calculated from the absolute and apparent magnitude. This method has been applied to several thousands of stars. It is particularly useful for stellar distances exceeding 20 parsecs*.

Spectrum, the band of colour produced when white light is refracted by a prism (or diffracted by a grating) (→). White light is composed of light of various wavelengths*. Rays with a short wavelength (e.g. violet, about 4,000 Å) are refracted most, and those with a greater wavelength (e.g. red, about 7,000 Å) are refracted less, so that white light produces a band of colour: red, orange, yellow, green, blue, and violet. To form a *S.*, the instrument generally used is not a simple prism or grating, but a spectroscope*. Every source of light forms a *S.* Incandescent solids and incandescent gases under high pressure (e.g. the interior of a star) produce a continuous *S.*

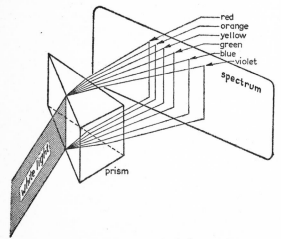

White light is resolved into a band of many colours

The *S.* of a luminous gas under low pressure is discontinuous. Monatomic gases (e.g. hydrogen and helium) give a line *S.* The spectral lines occur at definite wavelengths, so that the substance producing the light can be identified from its *S.* Polyatomic gases (e.g. nitrogen, titanium oxide) give a band *S.* If the light from a source which yields a continuous *S.* passes through a colder layer of gas, this gas absorbs from it those lines which it itself produces on being heated. The result is an 'absorption' *S.*, in which dark lines occur, that are characteristic of the absorbing gas. Like emission spectra, absorption spectra are subdivided into line and band spectra. The absorption lines in the solar spectrum are called Fraunhofer lines* (*v.* Pl. 32).

Spherical astronomy is a branch of astronomy concerned with the mathematical study of the positions and movements of celestial bodies as projected on the imaginary celestial sphere*, with the observer at the centre. *S.a.* is therefore not concerned with the distances of celestial bodies in space. Only measurements on the celestial sphere come within the scope of *S.a.* Also called positional astronomy.

Spheroid is the solid figure obtained when an ellipse is rotated about one of its axes. Most celestial bodies are spheroidal in shape because of their rotation.

Spica, the star α Virginis, apparent magnitude 1·2, spectral class B2.

Spicules, tiny spur-like mobile projections in the Sun's chromosphere, which can be observed on the limb of the Sun with a Lyot filter. Average duration 5 min., upward velocity 12–20 m. p. sec. (20–30 km/sec.), diameter about 700 miles (*v.* Pl. 29, 31). A theory of *S.* is that turbulent movements originating in the granules* attain the equivalent of the local velocity of sound at about 1,000 miles above the Sun's surface, and shock waves are set up. These heat up the chromosphere and give rise to *S.* more than 3,000 miles above the Sun's surface.

Spiral arms of a galaxy, *v.* Milky Way and Pl. 61, 66, 70, 74, 76, 77, 86.

Spiral nebula, a galaxy with a spiral structure. Two or more spiral arms consisting of stars and bright and dark nebulae emerge from the edge of the bright centre region. Examples are: our Galaxy, M31 and M33. According to the shape of the spiral arms, spiral nebulae are divided into normal and barred spirals, of which the former are the more common (*v.* Extragalactic nebulae and Pl. 66).

Sputnik, *v.* Artificial satellite and Space travel.

Square, *v.* Norma.

Star, an incandescent, gaseous celestial body such as the Sun. For most stars the only details directly accessible by observation are: apparent magnitude and spectral class. The absolute magnitude can be calculated once the distance is known. The temperature can be calculated from the spectrum. Knowing the temperature and the absolute magnitude of a star, we can calculate its radius. The radii of some stars (large and not too distant) can be directly measured with the interferometer*. A few other facts can usually be found about double stars*. There is one *S.* about which we can obtain more detailed information, viz. the Sun. Knowledge of the interior of a *S.* can only be deduced theoretically (*v.* Nuclear reaction and Sun).

Even in ancient times the stars were classified according to magnitude. Ptolemy called the brightest stars 1st magnitude stars and the faintest 6th magnitude stars. It was later found that the intensity of the radiation we receive from a 1st magnitude *S.* was about 100 times that received from a 6th magnitude *S.* The ratio between the two was fixed at exactly 100 : 1, so that a 5th magnitude *S*., for example, is by definition 2·512 times brighter than a 6th magnitude *S*. (2·512 is approximately the fifth root of 100).

Several stars proved to have a magnitude brighter than 1. Capella, for instance, is of magnitude 0·2 and Sirius — 1·6. When Venus is at its brightest, we must accord it a magnitude of —4·4. The full Moon has a magnitude of —12·6 and the Sun —26·8. With the largest telescopes we can see stars of the 19th magnitude, while those of the 22nd can be photographed with the 200-inch telescope at Mount Palomar Observatory. The magnitude of a *S*. depends not only on its luminosity but also on its distance from us. To eliminate this distance effect we consider all stars as they would appear at a distance of 10 parsecs*. The brightness of a star as we should then see it is called its *absolute* magnitude, as opposed to its *apparent* magnitude. If the apparent magnitude and distance of a *S*. are known, the absolute magnitude can be found from a simple formula. The Sun has an absolute magnitude of 4·9. The brightest stars have an absolute magnitude of —9 and the faintest, 18. The intensity of the brightest stars is therefore some 500,000 times that of the Sun, while the faintest have only 0·0005 of the luminosity of the Sun. The distances of the stars can be determined in various ways (*v.* Distance finding).

Table II gives various details about the stars nearest to us. Comparison of this with Table I shows that only a few near stars are of great apparent magnitude.

It was formerly thought that stars were motionless in the sky (whence the name 'fixed stars' as opposed to planets or 'wandering stars'), but Halley discovered in 1718 (on comparing the positions given by Ptolemy) that some bright stars had shifted nearly a degree. Later observations confirmed that most stars do move slightly.

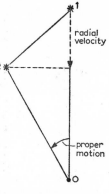

If a star moves from 1 to 2 (→), we perceive the movement only as it is projected on the celestial sphere. This we call the proper motion, once we have extracted the effect of the Earth's motion around the Sun. The proper motion is therefore relative to the Sun. The star's velocity towards or away from us, i.e. its radial velocity, is observable with the spectroscope as a Doppler effect*. The radial velocity (again with a correction applied to make it relative to the Sun) can be calculated from the displacement of the spectral lines. Barnard's Star (called after the discoverer), a weak star with a magnitude of 9·6, has the exceptionally large proper motion of over 10″ per year. In 180 years, therefore, it moves a distance in the sky equivalent to the diameter of the Moon. Several hundred stars have a proper motion of over 0·1″ per year.

The Sun, too, moves in relation to the stars surrounding it, with a velocity of 12½ m. p. sec. (20 km/sec.) towards a point in the sky called the 'apex', (R.A. 18 h., Dec. + 30°), about 10° from the bright star Vega. It is receding from the antapex (south of the constellation of Orion, not far from Sirius). This motion of the Sun was discovered by William Herschel in 1783. At that time the proper motions of no more than 13 stars were known, so that he could only calculate the positions of the apex and antapex approximately. By eliminating the effect of solar motion, Professor Kapteyn (Groningen, 1904) discovered that stars in the vicinity of the Sun move in two main directions (*v.* Star streaming).

The rotation of a *S*. can be demonstrated by means of the Doppler effect* if the axis of rotation is not in the line of sight.

The visual binaries have furnished us with valuable information about stellar masses. Once the orbit of a binary has been computed, the masses of the two components are very easily calculated from Kepler's third law (or, rather, the third law as extended by Newton). In 1924 Eddington found that in visual binaries there is almost always a definite relationship between the masses of the stars and their absolute magnitudes. The greater the mass, the brighter the *S*. We can therefore find the mass of any main sequence *S*. once we know its absolute magnitude.

It appears that the masses of the stars do not cover a very large range: they vary from 50 to 0·05 times the Sun's mass (which is 2,000 million million million million tons).

The diameters of stars can be found in various ways. Those of eclipsing binaries* can in fact be found without the distance of the stars being known, for we can work out from the light-curve how long one star takes to transit the other; the velocity of the occulting star can also be found from the shift of the spectral lines (*v.* Doppler effect). From these two data it is possible to calculate the radius.

A second method depends on the fact that the magnitude of a *S*. is determined by the size of the radiant surface and its temperature. Thus, if the absolute magnitude and temperature of a *S*. are known, the radiant surface and the diameter can be computed.

The diameters of very large, nearby stars can also be found directly with the aid of the interferometer.

These diameters may be compared with those found by the second method:

	Calculated	With interferometer
	(Sun = 1)	
Antares	300	290
Aldebaran	43	39
Arcturus	24	24

In general the intrinsically brightest stars are the largest. The diameters of stars vary between that of the Earth and the size of the orbit of Mars around the Sun.

The density (specific gravity) of a *S*. can be calculated if the diameter and the mass are known. A large variety of densities is found to exist, ranging from 1/2000 of the density of air to more than 1,000 times that of water (*v.* Dwarf stars). The stellar spectra provide us with much information about the atmospheres of stars, e.g. the elements that occur in them and their degree of ionization (*v.* Spectrum). The temperature of the stellar surface can also be computed from the spectrum (*v.* Radiation laws).

There are stars with such extensive atmospheres that we can talk of gas round the stars. These are Wolf-Rayet stars, P Cygni stars and class B emission stars.

The interiors of stars are not accessible to observation. Here we are compelled to fall back on theoretical considerations. We must assume that the interior of a star is in equilibrium. At a certain point *P*, the enormous pressure *A* of the gas layer whose weight rests on *P* is compensated for by a pressure *B*, consisting of the pressure of the gas and radiation pressure. At higher temperatures the radiation pressure predominates because it increases as the fourth power of the temperature, whereas the gas pressure increases in direct proportion to the temperature. The temperature of the centre of the Sun is estimated to be about 15 million degrees, and the pressure is so great that matter there is compressed to a density 100 times that of water. The greater part of the stars consists of hydrogen.

For the source of the energy produced by the stars v. Nuclear reaction.

TABLE I. THE BRIGHTEST STARS

Name		Apparent magnitude	Spectral type	Parallax	Distance in light-years	Absolute magnitude
α Canis Majoris	Sirius	—1·58 D	Ao	0·378″	8·7	+1·3
α Carinae	Canopus	—0·86	Fo	0·033″	650?	—7·4?
α Centauri	—	+0·06 D	Go	0·760″	4·4	+4·4
α Lyrae	Vega	+0·14	Ao	0·123″	26	+0·5
α Aurigae	Capella	+0·21	Go	0·077″	52	—0·6
α Boötis	Arcturus	+0·24	Ko	0·098″	41	—0·1
β Orionis	Rigel	+0·34 D	B8	0·006″	540	—5·8
α Canis Minoris	Procyon	+0·48 D	F3	0·288″	11·3	+2·8
α Eridani	Achernar	+0·60	B5	0·045″	66	—1·1
β Centauri	—	+0·86	B1	0·011″	300	—3·9
α Aquilae	Altair	+0·89	A5	0·204″	15·7	+2·4
α Orionis	Betelgeuse	+0·92 V	M2	0·011″	200	—3·4
α Crucis	—	+1·05 D	B1	0·014″	230	—2·7
α Tauri	Aldebaran	+1·06 D	K5	0·057″	57	—0·1
β Geminorum	Pollux	+1·21	Ko	0·101″	32	+1·2
α Virginis	Spica	+1·21	B2	0·027″	120	—1·6
α Scorpii	Antares	+1·22 D	M1	0·009″	360	—3·2
α Piscis Austrini	Fomalhaut	+1·29	A3	0·139″	24	+2·0
α Cygni	Deneb	+1·33	A2	0·008″	650	—5·2
α Leonis	Regulus	+1·34	B8	0·049″	67	—0·3

D = Double star. The combined magnitude is given.
V = Variable star.

TABLE III. DIMENSIONS OF BRIGHTER COMPONENTS OF SOME ECLIPSING BINARIES

Name	Spectral type	Period in days	Radius (Sun = 1)	Mass (Sun = 1)	Density (Sun = 1)
H.D. 1337	O8	3·52	23·8	36·3	0·003
V Puppis	B1	1·45	7·5	19·2	0·04
u Herculis	B3	2·05	4·6	7·3	0·09
β Persei	B8	2·87	3·1	4·6	0·16
β Aurigae	Ao	3·96	2·8	2·5	0·11
U Pegasi	F3	0·38	0·6	0·2	0·88
W Ursae Majoris	Go	0·33	0·7	0·7	1·9
Castor C	M1	0·81	0·8	0·6	1·4

TABLE IV. DIAMETERS OF STARS AS CALCULATED FROM TEMPERATURE AND ABSOLUTE MAGNITUDE

Name	Spectral type	Temperature in deg. K.	Diameter (Sun = 1)	Mass (Sun = 1)	Density (Sun = 1)
Giants					
Antares	M1	3,000	300	10	0·0000005
Aldebaran	K5	3,200	43	4	0·00005
Arcturus	Ko	4,000	24	4	0·0003
Capella A	Go	5,300	16	4	0·001
Main sequence					
β Centauri	B1	19,000	6	4	0·02
Vega	Ao	10,600	2·6	3	0·2
Sirius A	Ao	10,600	1·9	2·4	0·3
Altair	A5	8,200	1·6	2	0·5
Procyon	F3	6,300	2·3	1·1	0·1
α Centauri A	Go	5,750	1·3	1·1	0·5
The Sun	G2	5,785	1·0	1·0	1·0
70 Ophiuchi A	Ko	4,900	1·0	0·9	0·9
61 Cygni A	K7	3,900	0·7	0·5	1·4
Krueger 60 A	M4	3,300	0·3	0·3	9
White dwarfs					
Sirius B	F	7,500	0·034	0·96	25,000
o₂ Eridani B	Ao	11,000	0·019	0·44	64,000

TABLE V. TEMPERATURES OF STARS OF VARIOUS SPECTRAL TYPES

Spectral type	Temperature In deg. K. (Main sequence)	(Giants)
O5	50,000	
Bo	21,000	
B5	14,000	
Ao	10,600	
A5	8,200	
Fo	7,100	
F5	6,300	
Go	5,760	5,300
G5	5,400	4,500
Ko	4,900	4,000
K5	4,300	3,200
Mo	3,400	3,000
M2	2,870	2,800
M8	—	2,000

Star atlas, an aid for anyone interested in the stars as objects on the celestial sphere. A simple *S.a.* gives a particular projection of stars throughout the sky down to a certain magnitude, and also the main planetary nebulae*, star clusters*, galactic nebulae* and extragalactic nebulae*. The charts are usually provided

TABLE II. THE NEAREST STARS

Name	Right ascension (1950)	Declination (1950)	Apparent magnitude	Absolute parallax	Distance in light-years	Annual proper motion
α Centauri D	14 h. 36 min.	—60° 38′	0·3, 1·7, 11	0·760″	4·3	3·68″
Barnard's Star	17 h. 55 min.	+ 4° 33′	9·6	0·545″	6·0	10·30″
Wolf 359	10 h. 54 min.	+ 7° 20′	13·5	0·421″	7·7	4·84″
Luyten 726–8 D	1 h. 36 min.	—18° 13′	12·5, 13·0	0·410″	7·9	3·35″
Lalande 21185 D	11 h. 0 min.	+36° 18′	7·5	0·398″	8·2	4·78″
Sirius D	6 h. 43 min.	—16° 39′	—1·6, 7·1	0·375″	8·7	1·32″
Ross 154	18 h. 47 min.	—23° 53′	10·6	0·351″	9·3	0·67″
Ross 248	23 h. 39 min.	+43° 55′	12·2	0·316″	10·3	1·58″
ε Eridani	3 h. 31 min.	— 9° 38′	4·2	0·303″	10·8	0·97″
Ross 128	11 h. 45 min.	+ 1° 7′	11·1	0·298″	10·9	1·40″
61 Cygni D	21 h. 5 min.	+38° 30′	5·6, 6·3	0·293″	11·1	5·22″
Luyten 789–6	22 h. 36 min.	—15° 37′	12·2	0·292″	11·2	3·27″
Procyon D	7 h. 37 min.	+ 5° 21′	0·5, 10·8	0·288″	11·3	1·25″
ε Indi	22 h. 0 min.	—57° 0′	4·7	0·285″	11·4	4·67″
BD + 59° 1915 D	18 h. 42 min.	+59° 33′	8·9, 9·7	0·280″	11·6	2·29″
Groombridge 34 D	0 h. 16 min.	+43° 44′	8·1, 10·9	0·278″	11·7	2·91″
τ Ceti	1 h. 42 min.	—16° 12′	3·6	0·275″	11·8	1·92″
Lacaille 9352	23 h. 3 min.	—36° 9′	7·2	0·273″	11·9	6·87″

D = Double star

with a co-ordinate system based on declination and right ascension (*v.* Celestial sphere). Occasionally the brighter stars are joined up by a series of straight lines to emphasize their pattern in the sky (→ 1). Individual stars in each constellation are designated by the letters of the Greek alphabet, figures or Roman capitals, followed where necessary by the Latin name of the constellation in the genitive case: for example, α Geminorum is star α on the constellation Gemini. The use of Greek letters is derived from Bayer (1603). These letters are normally allocated to the stars in order of magnitude: α indicates the brightest star in the constellation, β the second brightest, and so on. When the Greek alphabet is exhausted, a system originated by Flamsteed (1729) is used, whereby the stars are numbered in sequence from west to east. Double stars are sometimes specially designated by the initial of the discoverer plus the number of the star in his catalogue: Σ 1873 is the star numbered 1873 in W. Struve's catalogue. Variable stars* again have the name of the constellation, preceded now by R, S and so on to Z, RR, RS, etc. to RZ, then SS, ST, etc. to SZ, and so on until ZZ is reached. Then we have AA to AZ, BB to BZ, etc., so that by the time QZ is reached for any one constellation (the letter J is not used), 334 variable stars have been named; subsequent stars are designated by V and a number, e.g. V 335, V 336, etc.

Star clusters, planetary nebulae, bright nebulae and external galaxies are indicated in various ways: *a.* by the letter M and the object's number in Messier's* catalogue (1781); the Great Nebula in Andromeda is M31; *b.* by the letters NGC and the object's number in Dreyer's *New General Catalogue* (1888): M31 is also NGC224; *c.* by the letters IC and the object's number in the *Index Catalogues* which are supplements to the NGC.

A good, simple *S.a.* is *Norton's Star Atlas and Reference Handbook*; more detailed is the *Skalnate Pleso Atlas* (Czech or American edition). Some very detailed photographic atlases exist, such as the *Harvard Sky* and the *Franklin-Adams Charts*. An extremely comprehensive photographic atlas, the *National Geographic Society— Palomar Observatory Sky Atlas*, has been issued over the past few years. This consists of negative copies of 1,758 photographs taken with the 48-inch Schmidt telescope on Mount Palomar (*v.* Pl. 81). Each photograph was taken twice, once in blue light and once in red (*v.* Astrophotography). Because of the geographical position of the telescope, only the celestial sphere north of −27° Dec. was photographed. The photographic magnitude of stars and other objects mapped goes down to 21·1 on the blue plates and down to 20·0 on the red. The work was begun in 1949 and the last photographs were taken in May, 1956.

Star catalogue, a list of stars with their positions (usually in declination and right ascension) and generally with their magnitudes and spectral classes. The oldest *S.c.* known is the *Almagest* of Claudius Ptolemaeus (A.D. 150), which lists the latitude and longitude of 1,025 stars. Other old catalogues are those of Ulugh Begh (1450) and Tycho Brahe (1580). Modern catalogues can be classified, according to their purpose, into:

Durchmusterungs. These are not very accurate, but they provide a survey of all stars down to a certain magnitude in a certain part of the sky, and list positions and magnitudes. In this type of catalogue astronomers can, for instance, find the stars they wish to use in order to identify an asteroid* or a faint comet*, or they may look up comparison stars in the neighbourhood of a variable star (*v.* Pl. 37) in order to determine the latter's change of magnitude.

Examples are: *Bonner Durchmusterung des nördlichen Himmels*, F.W.A. Argelander (1862, reprinted 1903), which describes 324,000 stars in the northern hemisphere from the pole to Dec. −2°; *Schönfeld Durchmusterung*, E. Schönfeld (1886), a continuation of the preceding for stars in the southern hemisphere to Dec. −23°; *Cordoba Durchmusterung*, J.M. Thome (1892), the continuation of the preceding for stars in the southern hemisphere with Dec. −23° to −61° (this work is being continued at Cordoba as far as the south celestial pole); *The Cape Photographic Durchmusterung*, D. Gill and J.C. Kapteyn, which describes 455,000 stars in the southern hemisphere between Dec. −18° and −90°.

The various Durchmusterungs list stars down to about the 10th magnitude. They are divided into zones with a width of 1° of declination and arranged according to right ascension.

Precision catalogues. These give very accurate positions for a relatively small number of stars. The stars they list are evenly distributed over the sky and are used as standard stars with which to determine accurately the positions of other stars or objects from the differences in declination and right ascension.

Examples are: *Astronomische Gesellschaft Katalog* (from 1809 on); *The Astrographic Catalogue*, started in 1887 and not yet completed: this work will contain the positions of 3–4 million stars (*v.* Star atlas).

General catalogues. Works in which the data from precision catalogues are collated, particularly with regard to changes in position as a result of proper motion (*v.* Pl. 35). Example: *Preliminary General Catalogue of 6,188 Stars for the Epoch 1900*, L. Boss.

Special catalogues for variable stars, double stars and other objects.

Examples: R.G. Aitken, *New General Catalogue of Double Stars within 120° of the North Pole*, 1932, which contains the measurements of 17,181 double stars up to 1927; S.W. Burnham, *A New General Catalogue of Double Stars within 121° of the North Pole*, 1906, containing the measurements of 13,665 double stars; J.C. Hagen, *Atlas et Catalogus Stellarum Variabilium*, 1899–1941, listing 488 variable stars, along with 24,000 comparison stars; *Katalog und Ephemeriden Veränderlicher Sterne*, quarterly from 1870 to 1926, then annually until 1941; B.V.Kukarkin and P.P.Parenago, *General Catalogue of Variable Stars*, 1948–52, in Russian and English.

In using the positions of the stars as given in the catalogues it has to be remembered that these are only correct for the period stated (e.g. epoch 1900). For the *Bonner Durchmusterung* the corresponding epoch is 1855. To obtain the present position of a star it is necessary to allow for the annual change in declination and right ascension due to precession. The positions can be brought up to date for the year of observation with the aid of certain standard formulae.

Star cluster and stellar association, collections of stars which are physically related to each other.

STAR CLUSTERS. These are divided into open, or galactic, clusters and globular clusters. Open clusters are found in the plane of the spiral arms of the Milky Way, and globular clusters in the spherical halo in which stellar Population type II* occurs. (*v.* Globular star cluster and Pl. 40, 41, 51, 53, 58, 59, 60). Since the halo and the plane of the spiral arms intersect, globular clusters may also be found in the latter. The open star clusters consist of the younger stars of Population type I. These clusters are numerous; about 500 are known in the small part of the Galaxy that we can observe, while far more can be recognized on photographs taken with the 48-inch Schmidt telescope on Mount Palomar. They are neither uniform in their structure nor in the types of their constituent stars.

The most significant classification is linked with the evolution of the cluster (v. Evolution of the stars). Comparison of the H.-R. diagram (→) for various galactic clusters shows that their ages differ. The age depends on the range of stars that are still in the main sequence. If the main sequence of a cluster still contains O- and B-class stars, which evolve very rapidly, it follows that the cluster is young. If a proportion of the hotter stars in the main sequence has evolved to the right of the H.-R. diagram, the cluster is older. It appears that the open clusters are all much younger than the globular clusters.

The distance of a S.c. can also be found from the H.-R. diagram. This diagram is prepared by plotting the stars of the cluster, using colour as one co-ordinate and the apparent magnitude as the other. By comparing this diagram with a diagram for stars whose distances, and hence absolute magnitudes, are known, the distance modulus*, i.e. apparent magnitude minus absolute magnitude, is obtained, from which the distance can be calculated, allowance being made for interstellar absorption*.

For the open clusters so far investigated, distances vary from about 150 to 15,000 light-years and diameters from 5 to 60 light-years. The density, even at the centre of open clusters, is not great, e.g. 83 stars per cubic parsec* at the centre of M11 and 2·8 stars per cubic parsec at the centre of the Pleiades (v. Pl. 40).

The stability of an open cluster depends on the strength of its gravitational field. This must exceed the attraction exerted on each star by the Galaxy as a whole. A cluster will be fairly stable if its density exceeds 0·1 times the mass of the Sun per cubic parsec. Yet in the long run all open clusters will lose their stars and their identity as clusters. At any rate their possible lifetime is only a small fraction of that of the Galaxy. This accords with the view that new galactic clusters are still being formed. An example of a very young galactic cluster is found in the vicinity of the Trapezium (θ Orionis) in the Orion nebula (v. Pl. 53). Three hundred stars have been counted inside 5 min. of arc in infra-red photographs.

This cluster is thought to comprise at least 400 members with a combined mass approximately equal to that of the Pleiades (over 350 solar masses). The motions of the individual stars in the cluster were measured accurately by comparing recent photographs with photographs taken 50 years ago with the same telescope. The conclusion drawn was that the cluster is expanding rapidly; and it was possible, by calculating backwards, to show that these stars were close to each other 300,000 years ago. It is now thought that they all originated at about that time. The fact that these stars are very young is confirmed by the Hertzsprung-Russell diagram* for the cluster (v. Evolution of the stars).

STELLAR ASSOCIATIONS (v. Pl. 61, 90) are very loosely bound groupings of stars. Because of their low concentration, these groupings as such must have a very short lifetime. It is possible that all stars may have originated as members of an association in local concentrations of interstellar matter* (v. also Evolution of the stars). The diameters of associations are of the order of 50 to 400 light-years. It appears that the centres of some associations are situated in galactic star clusters and that associations form haloes around these clusters. For example, it has been found that the double cluster in Perseus (NGC869 and NGC884) (v. Pl. 41) has a halo of this kind consisting of B- and A-class supergiants and red M-class supergiants.

The density of an association is very low. NGC6231, for instance, contains some 40 stars spread out over a space with a diameter of about 100 parsecs. This is equivalent to only one star per 100,000 cubic parsecs.

V. A. Ambartsumyan gives the following classification: a. O-associations, consisting of young giants (O- and B-class stars and P Cygni-type stars); b. T-associations, consisting mainly of young red dwarfs. All associations have been in existence a comparatively short time, are situated in the spiral arms (v. Pl. 90), and therefore share in the Galactic rotation. The parts of an association that are closest to the Galactic centre revolve faster than parts farther away, with the result that the association is being stretched out in the plane of the spiral arms—in the direction of Galactic rotation (v. Pl. 90). Many associations are still almost spherical in shape, and must therefore be very young. A. Blaauw (Leiden) found that the association grouped round the star ξ Persei is expanding at an average rate of 7½ m. p. sec. (12 km/sec.). Calculations based on this value, on the distance of the cluster (1,000 light-years) and on its diameter (50 light-years) show that the stars must have been close together 1·2 million years ago. The age of this association is therefore estimated by Blaauw to be about 1·2 million years. This same method gives an age of 70 million years for the Scorpius-Centaurus association, which accords with the fact that the group does not contain any very young stars (O-class stars) and is already markedly elongated in structure.

A well-known association is that in Orion; it consists of O- and B-class stars and variable T Tauri stars, which have probably not existed long (v. Variable stars). Study of this group strengthens the belief that stars tend to originate simultaneously in large groups or associations from nebular masses.

Stellar population, v. Population types.

Stereo comparator, an instrument embodying the principle of stereoscopic viewing and used to trace small differences between two photographic plates. Two photographs of the same part of the sky taken at different times are examined with a stereoscope (usually a stereoscopic microscope). Small differences of position or magnitude are immediately obvious, so that the image becomes three-dimensional. If the instrument is so designed that the two plates can be viewed in rapid succession, it is called a blink comparator* or blink microscope.

Stratosphere, a part of the Earth's atmosphere between heights of about 10 and 25 miles (v. Pl. 5).

Summer solstice, the position on the ecliptic occupied by the Sun on 21st or 22nd June. It is the most northerly point reached by the Sun. Dec. 23½ N., R.A. 6 h. (v. Celestial sphere).

Sun, the star nearest to the Earth. It is a main-sequence yellow dwarf (v. Hertzsprung-Russell diagram) of spectral class G2. As regards temperature, luminosity and diameter, it is not an outstanding celestial body. A large proportion of the Milky Way* consists of stars similar to the Sun. The Sun is the centre and energy source of the solar system. It is also the dominant member of this system with respect to size and mass. Its mass is over 330,000 times that of the Earth, and it is over a million times as large in volume as the Earth. The Moon's entire orbit around the Earth could be placed inside the Sun.

All the light and heat received by the planets and their satellites comes from the Sun. Although the Sun is quite insignificant in the Galaxy as a whole, it is for us the source of life (v. Pl. 27, 28, 29, 30, 31, 32, 60).

Examination of the remains of plants and animals in the Earth's crust shows that there has been life on Earth for at least a thousand million years. Remains of algae and sponges have been found in strata which were at the surface a thousand million years ago. The Sun has therefore been radiating enough light and warmth since that time. Since life, as we know it on Earth, is possible only within very narrow limits of temperature, the radiation of the Sun must always have been very uniform.

The Sun is the source of a great proportion of the energy available on Earth. Coal is solar energy which has been absorbed by plants, converted into chemical energy and which is released by combustion. Petroleum, too, is organic in origin and owes its power content to the Sun. The winds in the atmosphere are kept in existence by the heating of the Earth's surface; the evaporation of water from the oceans and the return of this water in the form of rain gives rise to brooks and rivers, the flow of which can be used by man to generate power. The animal kingdom depends for food on vegetable matter, so that the solar energy absorbed by plants serves in another form to make life possible for man and the animals.

The regularity with which the Sun traverses the sky has always given man a feeling of security, while a solar eclipse (v. Pl. 27, 28) was regarded as a sign of impending disaster. Yet the Sun invariably survived the attacks of the unknown powers of darkness, just as it rose again every morning from the death of night. No wonder, then, that it was identified with life and worshipped as the highest deity. In ancient Egypt the Sun-god was Ra who rolled the red-hot solar disk across the sky. Ra was the golden calf which is born every morning, becomes a bull and in the evening fertilizes the celestial cow-goddess who brings forth a new Sun next morning.

As early as the eighth century B.C. astronomers in Babylonia began listing solar eclipses and the saros* was discovered (v. Solar eclipse). Three centuries later Anaxagoras first measured the Earth's distance from the Sun and argued that the Sun must be an incandescent rock, probably as large as the entire Peloponnesus. In the third century B.C., Aristarchus thought that the Earth and planets moved around the Sun. He came to the conclusion that the Sun was 19 times farther away than the Moon and about 600,000 miles from the Earth, and that it was about the same size as the Earth. Hipparchus reckoned the distance from Earth to Sun to be $4^1/_2$ million miles and the Sun's diameter to be 7 times the Earth's. Not until 1672 did Cassini find a distance approximately the same as that now known, viz. 93 million miles, with a solar diameter of 865,000 miles.

The study of the Sun is of crucial importance to astronomers, because the Sun is the only star which can be observed in detail from close quarters. The second nearest star is 275,000 times farther from us (v. Pl. 35). The Sun is a hot gaseous sphere. Its interior is not accessible for direct observation and can only be studied theoretically. The visible surface or photosphere (→) has a granular texture of brighter and fainter patches, occasionally broken by some much larger dark patches, called sunspots. The gas above the photosphere is much more tenuous and transparent and is called the atmosphere. It is divided into: a. the chromosphere, a layer several thousands of miles thick and red in colour owing to hot gaseous hydrogen. Prominences erupt from the chromosphere to heights of thousands of miles, or project almost motionless above it; b. the outer atmosphere, or

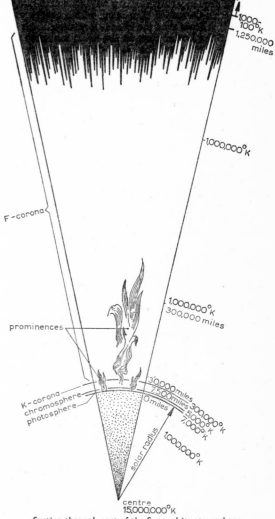

Section through part of the Sun and its atmosphere

corona, which is divided into the F-corona* and the K-corona*. Above it are other layers of transparent gas. This region is filled with extremely tenuous gas at very high temperatures. During total solar eclipses the corona is visible with the naked eye as a silvery cloud around the Sun. The shape of the corona, the number of sunspots and the activity of prominences vary in cycles of approximately 11 years. The entire gaseous layer from the photosphere upwards, which is accessible to direct observation, is known as the Sun's atmosphere. The total mass of the entire atmosphere is only 10^{-10} times that of the Sun.

THE PHOTOSPHERE. The surface of the Sun has a mottled appearance called 'granulation'. These granules are bubbles of hot gas which rise from lower layers, mingle with their surroundings and sink back. The individual granules are therefore not permanent but appear and disappear all the time. They are brighter than their surroundings, because they are hotter than the gases around them.

SUNSPOTS. As early as the first few centuries of our era, Chinese astronomers reported spots on the Sun. These must have been the very largest of spots, which are the only ones visible with the naked eye. Galileo was the first to see sunspots through a telescope, in 1610. He deduced from the movement of the spots across the solar disk that the Sun's period of rotation was about a month. The smaller spots (several thousand miles across) exist for only a few days, while the larger (up to several terrestrial diameters) sometimes survive for a number of months. One of the largest ever observed occurred in March, 1947.

A sunspot consists of a dark central portion called the 'umbra', separated from the photosphere by the 'penumbra', a brighter, often finely shaded, border. It only appears dark by contrast with its surroundings. The penumbra is usually surrounded by brighter patches called 'faculae' (v. Pl. 30, 31).

The motion of the sunspots over the solar disk enables the Sun's period of rotation and the position of its axis of rotation to be determined. The Sun's equator is found to be inclined at 7° to the ecliptic. The Sun does not rotate as a solid body, and different periods of rotation are found for different solar latitudes. From the motions of sunspots the synodic period* is found to be about 27 days, while the sidereal period* is about 25 days. As a rule no sunspots occur in latitudes higher than 40°. Rotational velocity in higher latitudes can be found spectroscopically (v. Spectrum and Doppler effect). The Sun rotates faster at the equator than at higher latitudes (v. Pl. 29).

Sunspots are usually found in pairs or groups. The fact that the umbra appears dark is merely due to its being cooler than the surrounding photosphere, viz. about 4,500° compared with 6,000°. The spots are associated with a magnetic field which is probably the surface manifestation of a more extensive internal field. The cause of spots is not understood.

In some years the spots are numerous, in others they are few; in fact, the Sun is occasionally without a single spot. The occurrence of sunspot maxima and minima is found to be cyclic. The mean interval between maxima is 11·1 years. The last maximum was in 1957.

The spots are located in narrow zones situated near latitudes 30° north and south of the equator at the start of a cycle. As sunspot activity increases, these zones widen in the direction of the equator. Thus, after a sunspot minimum, the first spots appear about a latitude of 30°, while towards the end of a cycle the last spots appear in the vicinity of latitudes 8° north and south. Simultaneously, the first spots of the new cycle re-appear about 30° from the equator. The cause of these cycles is unknown.

Spectroscopic examination of the light from sunspots shows that some of the spectral lines are split (v. Zeeman effect and Spectrum) which indicates the presence of powerful magnetic fields. Sunspots oc-

curring in pairs are opposite in polarity, or bi-polar. The direction of the field of the leader spot gives its name to the polarity of the group as a whole and is called north or south. The polarity of almost all such groups in the northern hemisphere is uniform, and opposite to that of groups in the southern hemisphere. If, during a particular sunspot cycle, the polarity in the northern hemisphere is south and that in the southern hemisphere north, then the polarities during the next cycle will be reversed, viz. north in the northern hemisphere and south in the southern.

In 1908, Hale found a general magnetic field for the Sun and stated that it varied in strength. The existence of such a field was doubted, but it was measured again by Babcock (value one gauss). Recently it has definitely been found to be variable.

The radiation we receive from the Sun in the form of light and heat comes from its deep interior, where it is generated by ($\rightarrow$) nuclear reactions*. The main process is probably the proton chain. This radiation leaves the Sun through the photosphere whence it is emitted into space (v. Solar energy and Pl. 31). Sunlight can be analysed with the aid of the spectroscope (v. Spectrum). The visible spectrum of the Sun is continuous, i.e. it contains light of every colour. It also, however, contains thousands of dark absorption lines where there is less light. These are the Fraunhofer lines*.

The missing light is mainly absorbed by the cooler, upper layers of the solar atmosphere on its way to the spectroscope. (Some lines, the 'telluric' (v. Pl. 32), are produced by absorption in the Earth's atmosphere.)

As certain absorption lines are characteristic of a particular element that has absorbed the corresponding light, the chemical composition of the Sun's atmosphere, where these lines originated, is known. Moreover, the intensity of a line depends on the number of atoms that have absorbed the light as well as on a number of other factors such as temperature and pressure. It has been found possible to deduce the relative abundances of the elements, (see table).

LIST OF ELEMENTS
OCCURRING IN THE SUN'S ATMOSPHERE
(Goldberg and Aller, *Atoms, Stars and Nebulae*)

Element	Percentage number of atoms	Mass (milligrams per column of one sq. cm section)
Hydrogen	81·760	1,200
Helium	18·170	1,000
Carbon	0·003,000	0·5
Nitrogen	0·010,000	2·0
Oxygen	0·030,000	10·0
Sodium	0·000,300	0·1
Magnesium	0·020,000	10·0
Aluminium	0·000,200	0·1
Silicon	0·006,000	3·0
Sulphur	0·003,000	1·0
Potassium	0·000,010	0·003
Calcium	0·000,300	0·2
Titanium	0·000,003	0·003
Vanadium	0·000,001	0·001
Chromium	0·000,006	0·005
Manganese	0·000,010	0·01
Iron	0·000,800	0·6
Cobalt	0·000,004	0·004
Nickel	0·000,200	0·2
Copper	0·000,002	0·002
Zinc	0·000,030	0·03

THE CHROMOSPHERE. This layer gives a line emission spectrum and so can be isolated for study by photographing the Sun in the light of one of these emission lines, using a spectroheliograph*.

Photographs of the chromosphere taken in the light of calcium (the K line) or hydrogen (the Hα line) reveal light and dark areas called flocculi. These are masses of gas hotter or cooler than their surroundings. Calcium flocculi are usually bright and form 'plages' which are continuations of photospheric faculae; hydrogen flocculi (hydrogen filaments) are more elongated in shape and darker or brighter than their surroundings. The chromosphere consists of myriads of pointed spurs, or spicules*, rising to a height of 4,000 to 10,000 miles. These last for an average of 4–5 minutes and present an ever-changing picture (v. Pl. 28, 29, 31).

The chromosphere is visible during a total eclipse*, when the dazzling light of the disk is blotted out by the Moon. It can then be seen as a bright, narrow ring. The spectrum of this light, the flash spectrum, can be photographed with a slitless spectrograph. The positions usually occupied by the darker absorption lines in the ordinary solar spectrum, which are due to the fact that there is a hotter light source beyond the cooler gases of the atmosphere, (v. Spectrum) are now occupied by the bright lines of the emission spectrum of these same gases. The flash spectrum is a series of small images of the narrow visible crescent of the chromosphere in different types of light.

Gigantic eruptions which occur in the chromosphere are visible as prominences on the Sun's limb. Through the spectrohelioscope they look like motionless clouds at the edge of the Sun, but it can be shown by cinematography that they are fiery explosions. Prominences may rise hundreds of thousands of miles from the Sun's surface into the corona. A prominence is a relatively thin gaseous cloud with, on the average, a length of 125,000 miles, a height of 25,000 miles and a thickness of 4,000 miles. Above the Sun's limb, they are connected to the chromosphere by one or more columns. According to their shape and movement they are divided into various classes. They are bluish-pink in colour, which is due to the Hα, Hβ and Hγ light of hydrogen.

One particular form of prominence is the flare prominence or surge, which looks like a pillar of light. Material is first ejected at high speed from the Sun and then falls back to the chromosphere, appearing to be sucked back. The prominences are most easily seen as luminous plumes and clouds at the Sun's limb, but they are also visible on the solar disk where they appear in absorption as thin streamers or dark filaments against the background of the Sun (v. Pl. 30, top right), but their height cannot be observed.

The chromosphere with its prominences at the limb, its dark filaments and its solar flares can also be clearly observed in the α line of hydrogen, the Sun being viewed and photographed through a monochromatic filter. Observation is therefore not confined to the short periods of solar eclipses (v. Pl. 30, top right).

THE CORONA. This is divided into the K- (or inner) corona and the F- (or outer) corona. During a total eclipse it is visible as a silvery cloud stretching far from the solar disk. It shows a delicate structure, including the streamers which radiate from the Sun's poles. The shape of the corona also depends on the state of solar activity. During sunspot maxima the corona extends almost equally far in all directions; during sunspot minima it extends farther in the direction of the equator than it does towards the axis of rotation. The corona consists of very tenuous gas with a temperature of 1,000,000°K., the atoms of which are very highly ionized (v. Ionization). The emission lines of such atoms have been found in the spectrum of the K- corona, and indicate the high temperatures. Matter there is extremely tenuous and part of the brightness is due to the scattering of sunlight by the large quantities of free electrons stripped from the atoms by the great temperature (high degree of ionization). The F- corona consists of dust as well as electrons. The proportion of dust increases in the direction of interstellar space.

THE RADIO IMAGE OF THE SUN. The visible part of the spectrum is only a small part of the total range of wavelengths on which energy is radiated. The emission of radio waves by the Sun was first measured in 1937. This radiation, with wavelengths ranging from several millimetres to several metres, is emitted by the chromosphere and the corona. The corona radiates wavelengths greater than 50 cm, the upper chromosphere wavelengths of several cm and the lower chromosphere wavelengths of several mm. As all radiation on wavelengths greater than 50 cm is derived from the corona, the latter can be studied individually by observing this radiation. Coronal radiation is mainly provided by the K- corona. Emission on radio wavelengths is also associated with the 11-year sunspot period, being most powerful during spot maxima, particularly round a wavelength of 10 cm (originating in the chromosphere) (v. also Radio astronomy).

Although emission on radio wavelengths from the 'quiet' Sun is fairly uniform, the same cannot be said for radiation associated with disturbances in the Sun's atmosphere. The occurrence of faculae and flares is often accompanied by increased intensity of radio-radiation. As soon as the number of sunspots starts to grow, i.e. as solar activity increases, emission becomes much more pronounced; sometimes there are veritable 'radio storms'. Sudden powerful bursts of radio emission are always local and of short duration (30 or 40 minutes). A solar flare is accompanied by a very intensive radio burst (flare burst) which may emit up to a million times more radio energy than the entire normal Sun. Radio emission can be picked up by a radio telescope*. Sources of small size are located on the Sun's disk with the aid of the radio interferometer (v. also Radio astronomy). The radio Sun appears somewhat larger than the visual Sun.

The last few years have brought a clearer understanding of the inter-relation between the various solar phenomena. It has been found that the Sun's activity is invariably concentrated in 'active regions'. These centres of activity are associated with a pre-existing magnetic field, extending from the lower layers of the Sun and appearing at its surface. This is a bi-polar field, with a field strength of several thousand gauss at the two centres. It probably originates in the upper 50,000 miles layer of the Sun, which is in convective movement. The process is thought to start when a weak magnetic field is set up in this turbulent gas. The motion in the solar gas may cause a group of lines of force to be twisted so that they come closer to each other locally and the field strength increases. A field of this kind may be brought to the Sun's surface by convection. The first visual sign of an area of activity is the appearance of a bright area of faculae in which the Sun emits more Hα light than in the surrounding region. The area of faculae becomes bi-polar. At first no spots can be seen in white light. Several days later small dark spots or 'pores' appear, which develop into the major spots. The two main spots in an area of faculae are the centres of fields of opposite polarity with a strength of at least 1,000 gauss.

A few days later, the mobile spot prominences, which are of short duration, may appear, and also the solar flares, accompanied by powerful radio bursts and the emission of high-speed particles. Optical means reveal the surges, which consist of gas with a velocity ranging from twenty to several hundred m. p. sec. and emit Hα light. In addition to radiation on radio wavelengths, (see below), the Sun can, after the occurrence of solar flares, emit X-rays with wavelengths from 15 to 20 Å approximately. These rays, which are absorbed by the Earth's atmosphere, have been observed with the aid of rockets.

Then quiescent prominences occur on the higher latitude side of the area of faculae. They are thought to be borne on the magnetic fields whose lines of force are more or less horizontal or even concave there. Were the material composing a prominence of this kind to start moving vertically, i.e. perpendicularly to the lines of force in the field, it would be promptly slowed down and stopped by inductance.

The density of gas in the corona above an area of activity is 2–5 times greater than in the surrounding region. It is possible for a corona condensation* to form there, with a density 10–20 times greater than that of the gas round about.

The life of a sunspot group is about 20 days, that of an area of faculae 100–200 days; the bi-polar magnetic field can survive even longer.

SOLAR DATA

radius (Earth = 1)	109·1
volume (Earth = 1)	1,300,000
mass (Earth = 1)	333,000
density (Earth = 1)	0·256
surface gravity (Earth = 1)	27·89
mean apparent diameter	31'59"
linear diameter	865,370 m.
equatorial period of rotation	25·35 days
mean distance from Earth	92,960,000 m.
parallax	8'80"
inclination of solar equator to ecliptic	7° 15'
inclination of ecliptic to Earth's equator	23° 27'
the solar radiation reaching the Earth is 2 thousand-millionths of the Sun's total radiation	
luminosity	500,000 times that of the full Moon
solar constant	2·0 cal./sq.cm/min.
visual magnitude	—26·86
photographic magnitude	—26·41
colour index	+0·45
absolute magnitude (bolometric)	4·62
effective temperature	5,785°K.
spectral class	dwarf G2
height of the chromosphere	0 to 4,000 m.
temperature of the chromosphere	up to 20,000°K.
temperature of the K corona	up to 1,000,000°K.
central temperature	14,500,000°K.
central density	90 gm/cc.
orbital velocity around centre of Galaxy	135 m. p. sec. (216 km/sec.)
period of revolution in that orbit	220 million y.

THE MOTION OF THE SUN IN SPACE. The Sun is one of the stars of the Milky Way*. It lies in the plane of the spiral arms and belongs to Population type 1*. It describes an orbit around the centre of the Galaxy, and in relation to neighbouring stars, appears to be moving towards a point (apex*) in the constellation of Hercules, at R.A. 18 h. 0 m. and Dec. 30°N., about 10° south-west of the star Vega in Lyra. The Sun is moving at a speed of about 12 m. p. sec. (20 km/sec.) relative to these stars. The point (antapex*) on the celestial sphere from which the Sun appears to be receding is in the constellation of Columba, south of Orion. In fact, the Sun is revolving about the centre of the Galaxy with a velocity of 135 m. p. sec. (216 km/sec.) and completes one revolution in 220 million years (v. Pl. 60).

THE EVOLUTION OF THE SUN. This depends on changes in the Sun's mass and chemical composition, the latter being the more important. The Sun is in a state of equilibrium, i.e. the quantity of energy radiated is equal to the energy produced inside it. As a result of the conversion of hydrogen to helium by nuclear reactions in its interior, the Sun's mean molecular weight tends to increase. Its temperature and its diameter will slowly increase, so that the quantity of energy radiated remains equal to the energy produced. In the far distant future the Sun may leave the main sequence (v. Hertzsprung-Russell diagram) and move towards the giants. The total time the Sun will spend in the main sequence is of the order of 5×10^9 years.

Sunspot, a cooler and therefore darker patch on the Sun's surface (v. Pl. 30), one of the phenomena associated with an active region (v. Sun).

Supergalaxy, a term for a super-group of galaxies proposed by G. de Vaucouleurs. The S. to which our Galaxy belongs, extends over 100 million light-years. The centre is near the Virgo cluster (v. Extragalactic nebulae), while the local group of galaxies (v. Pl. 69) is situated more towards the outer edge of this supersystem. The distance from our Galaxy to the centre of the S. is 32,000,000 light-years. If the equator of the S. were perpendicular to that of our Galaxy, this would explain why there are far fewer bright galaxies in the southern galactic hemisphere than in the northern. It has already been observed that the bright external galaxies are concentrated in a band across the sky. The local S. is markedly oblate. It is thought to be rotating and expanding, our Galaxy completing one revolution in a period of the order of a hundred thousand million years. The mass of this S. is estimated to be 10^{15} solar masses. The existence of three more S.s can be deduced from local concentrations of external galaxies in the sky.

Supergiant, v. Giant.

Superior planets have their orbits outside the Earth's, i.e. all except Mercury and Venus.

Supernova, v. Novae.

Surge, a disturbance in the Sun's chromosphere*, visible at the limb with, for example, the Lyot filter, as a bright column of light. During a flare, material is ejected at a high velocity from an active region of the Sun*. Upon attaining its maximum height it falls back to the Sun. This phenomenon is distinguished from a prominence by its short lifetime of a few minutes (v. Pl. 31).

Swan, v. Cygnus.

Swordfish, v. Dorado.

Symbols (astronomical) are used in data concerning celestial objects and astronomical events. Unfortunately, uniformity has not yet been generally attained, so that similar symbols are often used for different concepts and different symbols for the same concept. For the signs of the Zodiac, v. Zodiac, and for constellation abbreviations, v. Constellations.

α	right ascension	m	apparent magnitude
β	celestial latitude	m_v	apparent magnitude, visual
δ	declination	m_{pg}	apparent magnitude, photographic
θ	sidereal time	t	time of observation
λ	celestial longitude	t or H	hour angle
λ	wavelength	☉	Sun
μ	proper motion in seconds of arc per year	☿	Mercury (rod and serpents?)
μ	micron	♀	Venus (mirror with handle?)
π	parallax, in seconds of arc	♁	Earth
ϕ	geographical latitude	⊕	Earth
ω	angular distance, as seen from the Sun, between the ascending node and the perihelion	☾	Moon
		●	new Moon
Ω	longitude of the ascending node	☽	1st quarter
A	azimuth from south towards west	○	full Moon
Å	Ångström unit	☾	last quarter
A.U.	astronomical unit	♂	Mars (shield and spear)
C.I.	colour index	⑭	asteroids (number in circle)
C.M.	central meridian	♃	Jupiter (shaft of lightning)
D	diameter of objective	♄	Saturn (scythe)
E	colour excess	♅	Uranus
H	hour angle	♅	Uranus
J.D.	Julian day	♆	Neptune (trident)
M	absolute magnitude	♇	Pluto (P and L of Percival Lowell)
m	mass (Sun = 1)	☄	comet
P	period of an orbital motion	♈	vernal equinox—1st point of Aries
p	position angle from north towards east	☌	conjunction
R.A.	right ascension	□	quadrature
S	solar constant	☍	opposition
S.T.	sidereal time	☊	ascending node
T	time of perihelion transit	☋	descending node

T	temperature
T_e	effective temperature
T.U.	universal time (temps universel)
U.T.	universal time
d	distance in seconds of arc
e	eccentricity of an orbit
	inclination of an orbital plane to the ecliptic

Synodic period of a planet, the Moon, an asteroid or a comet is the time which that body takes to complete a single revolution, as seen from the centre of the Earth. For example, it is the interval between two successive oppositions of the object (*v.* Period). The *S.p.* of the Moon is the interval between two new Moons.

System of satellites, *v.* Jupiter.

T

Table Mountain, *v.* Mensa.

Tarantula nebula, example of an emission nebula (*v.* Interstellar matter and Pl. 64).

Taurus (the Bull) (*v.* Pl. 3, 4), a northern zodiacal constellation situated between 3 h. 20 min. and 5 h. 55 min. R.A. and 2°S. and 31°N. Dec. The constellation includes two open star clusters, the Pleiades (*v.* Pl. 40) and the Hyades, in which various individual stars are visible with the naked eye. The chart (→) also shows the radio source Taurus A, which coincides with the Crab nebula (M1) (*v.* Pl. 39). Various parts of the nebula are moving outwards from the centre. Chinese and Japanese annals record the appearance of a supernova in this part of the sky in A.D. 1054. M1 is thought to be the remnants of the star that exploded then.

Telescope, *v.* Telescopium.

Telescope, instrument used for visual and photographic observation of the sky. The purpose of a *T.* is: *a.* to gather more light and to enable fainter objects to be seen than is possible with the unaided eye; *b.* to determine directions (this is important in finding the positions of celestial bodies at a particular moment); *c.* to magnify the images viewed.

The light is gathered by the objective, which is a system of lenses in a refractor* and a mirror in a reflector*. The objective forms an image in the focal plane, and this image is usually either recorded on a photographic plate or viewed through an eyepiece* (*v.* Optics). Other instruments can be placed in the focal plane for various purposes, e.g. a photo-electric cell to measure the luminosity, the slit of a spectrograph* to analyse the light, or a thermo-couple to measure temperature. A star, which may be regarded as a point source of light, does not appear as a point-like image in the focal plane but as a small disk; this is due to diffraction of the light and to the Earth's atmosphere (*v.* Twinkling).

In a reflecting *T.* the support of the secondary mirror (*v.* Newtonian telescope and Hale telescope) causes a system of rays to appear around the brighter stars. Examples of these rays will be found in photographs taken with the giant reflectors on Mount Wilson* and Mount Palomar* (*v.* Pl. 57, 71, 72, 74).

Lenses and mirrors are subject to various defects (*v.* Optics and Pl. 40). In a refractor, if only one lens is used, the various colours focus on different planes, one behind the other, so that it is never possible to get all the colours together in a single sharp image. This defect can be remedied to a certain extent by combining two or more lenses of different types of glass (with different refractive indices), so that at least two colours of light are brought to a common focus. The colours chosen will depend on the purpose for which the *T.* is chiefly used; orange and green are chosen for visual observation, and violet and blue for photographic purposes.

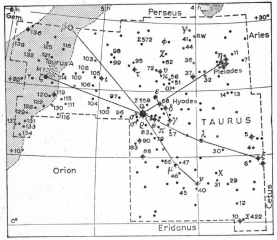

The constellation of Taurus

A mirror has no chromatic aberration. The objective of a telescope is not spherical but paraboloidal, and all rays parallel to the axis converge very accurately to a single focus. Various types of mirror system are referred to in (→ I) Hale telescope (*v.* also Newtonian telescope, Schmidt camera and Meniscus-mirror system).

The larger the diameter of a lens or mirror, the more light it gathers and the smaller the details that it makes visible of, say, the disk of a planet; in other words, the greater the 'resolving power' of the *T.* The resolving power therefore depends on the diameter of the objective. The greater the resolving power of a *T.*, the smaller the distance that may separate the components of a double star without preventing them from being seen as separate objects.

Diameter of objective in inches	Lower limit of measurable distance between the components of a double star in sec. of arc.
3	0·75–1·10
5	0·45–0·65
8	0·3 –0·4
11	0·2 –0·3

The invention of the refracting *T.* is often attributed to Hans Lippershey (1608), a Dutch spectacles-maker from Middleburg. Modern research seems to show that the inventor was not Lippershey but the Italian Giambattista della Porta of Naples. A certain Zacharias Jansen, also of Middleburg, is alleged to have copied a *T.* which came from Italy, and Lippershey to have sold a *T.* afterwards to the States-General for 300 guilders. Lippershey was, however, refused the patent. The first *T.* employed objectives consisting of a single lens. Galileo was the first to use the *T.* in astronomy (*v.* Pl. I).

To obviate defects occurring away from the axis (e.g. coma) the focal length was made large in relation to the diameter of the lens, as early as the seventeenth century. The disadvantage of this was that very weak images were obtained. The huge construction, 30 or 40 yards long, had to be moved by means of a block and tackle. In the case of very long telescopes the objective was placed on a long rod and the *T.* tube was omitted. Directing a *T.* of this kind at a particular point in the sky must have been a formidable task. Rhea, one of Saturn's moons, was discovered by Cassini in 1672 with a telescope 40 ft. long. Cassini also discovered Tethys and Dione in 1684 with *T.*s 100 and 136 ft. in length! In 1722 Bradley used a *T.* with a focal length of 212 ft. to measure the diameter of Venus.

The quality of the *T.* image in those days must have been very poor by our standards, and was certainly not better than that of a reasonably good modern *T.* with a 6-in. mirror and a focal distance of 3 ft., as used by an amateur. The greater, therefore, must be our respect for the excellent results obtained, by dint of infinite patience, by astronomers using such primitive equipment. Newton proved that a lens without chromatic aberration was an impossibility and he developed the reflecting *T.* (*v.* Newton telescope). His first *T.* had a mirror of only 1 in. diameter and a focal length of 6 in. The *T.* which he presented to the Royal Society of London in 1671 had a magnifying power of only 38, but the *T.* image was much sharper than that of existing telescopes.

The eighteenth century produced the first combination of a crown-glass lens and a flint-glass lens, designed to overcome colour separation with their different refractive indices. Great focal lengths had ceased to be necessary by then, and refractors again assumed manageable lengths. The quality of glass was still far from perfect, and the brightness and sharpness of the images obtained must have left much to be desired. By the second half of the eighteenth century the reflecting *T.* was the preferred form. In 1789, William Herschel made a 4-ft. mirror for his reflector. The largest reflecting *T.* in the nineteenth century was made in Ireland by the Earl of Rosse. It had a mirror which was 6 ft. in diameter with a focal length of 55 ft., and weighed nearly 15 tons. Block and tackle had to be used to move it. It was mounted so that it could be rotated from a horizontal to a nearly vertical position. The zenith was beyond this range, and only a narrow strip of sky on either side of the meridian* could be observed.

Mirrors at that time were made of polished metal (2 parts copper to 1 part zinc). Their reflectivity was not very great (50%) and they had to be repolished not only frequently but in such a way that they retained their perfectly paraboloidal shape. It was therefore not surprising that the refractor came back into favour. The largest refracting telescopes are those at the Lick Observatory (lens diameter 36 in., made in 1888) and the Yerkes Observatory (40 in., 1895).

No increase in light can be obtained by increasing a lens diameter beyond 40 in.; a larger lens has to be thicker to avoid collapsing under its own weight, and any light gained is more than offset by the greater absorption due to the thicker objective. A point is finally reached where any increase in diameter means a decrease of light! It was for this reason that astronomers reverted to the reflector in the twentieth century. Formerly, as we saw, when a metal reflector was polished, it had to be polished to the correct shape.

Nowadays, a thin reflecting coating of silver or aluminium is used; only this coating is renewed when necessary and the shape of the reflector remains unimpaired.

The largest reflecting *T.s* are the Hooker on Mount Wilson (100-inch, 1918), the Hale on Mount Palomar

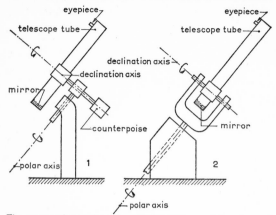

The equatorial mounting of a reflecting telescope (the polar axis is trained on the north celestial pole). 1. the standard mounting; 2. the fork mounting

(200-inch, 1948) (*v.* Pl. 1) and the new reflector at Lick Observatory (120-inch, 1956).

Basically, there are two possible ways of mounting a *T.*: the alt-azimuth (*v.* Pl. 2) and the equatorial or parallactic mounting (*v.* Pl. 1, 81). In the former, which is not much used, the *T.* can be rotated about a vertical and a horizontal axis. However, as the motion of stars on the celestial sphere is always circular and centred on the north celestial pole, the equatorial mounting is always used for larger *T.s*; this means that the *T.* rotates about an axis directed at the north celestial pole, i.e. the polar axis, so that this single rotation enables a star to be tracked in its diurnal rotation round the celestial sphere. Rotation round a second, or declination, axis at right-angles to the polar axis, allows stars of differing declinations to be brought into the field of the *T.*

Various versions of the equatorial mounting exist, e.g. the standard type, in which a counterpoise is necessary (→ 1), the fork type (→ 2) and the yoke type (→ Hale telescope and Pl. 1, 81). Alternatively, the *T.* itself may be mounted in a fixed position and the light brought to it from the desired direction by a moving mirror mounted parallel to the Earth's axis (the coelostat*).

Telescopium (the Telescope), an inconspicuous constellation in the southern hemisphere, situated between 18 h. 5 min. and 20 h. 25 min. R. A. and between —46° and —57° Dec. (→)

Tercidina, a small asteroid with a periodic variation of magnitude (period 8 h. 57 min.) (*v.* Eros).

Terminator, the great circle dividing the dark from the illuminated part of the Moon or a planet. During a 'lunar' day (29 terrestrial days) the lunar terminator completes one revolution of the sphere (*v.* Pl. 8, 10).

Tethys, one of Saturn's moons, discovered by Cassini in 1684. Mean distance from Saturn 183,200 miles, period of revolution 1 d. 21 h. 18 min., diameter 700 miles (?), magnitude at opposition 10·5.

Theodolite, an instrument for measuring angles very accurately. Much employed in surveying. In astrono-

my it can be used to determine the elevation and azimuth of celestial objects (*v.* Celestial sphere).

Three-body problem. If the masses, positions and velocities of a number of celestial bodies acting on each other in accordance with the laws of gravitation are known, their future movements can in theory be calculated. In the case of two such bodies, the problem offers no difficulty. When three are concerned, solutions of the problem have been found for various special cases. More general cases have to be tackled with electronic computers.

Tides are the high- and low-water levels that recur twice daily. They are caused by the gravitational pull of the Sun and the Moon, particularly by the Moon (→ 3, Moon) and to a much lesser degree by the Sun. The components of double stars and multiple stars cause tides on each other's surfaces in the same way.

Tiros is the name of a series of American meteorological satellites (*v.* Artificial satellite).

Titan, the largest satellite of Saturn. It is larger than our Moon. Discovered by Huygens in 1655. Mean distance from Saturn 760,000 miles, period of revolution 15 d. 22 h. 41 min., diameter 2,600 miles, magnitude at opposition 8·3. *T.* has an atmosphere in which the gases methane and ammonia have been proved to exist. *T.* can be clearly seen with a 2-inch telescope (→ 3, Solar system).

Titania, the largest moon of Uranus, discovered by Herschel in 1787. Mean distance from Uranus 272,000 miles, period 8 d. 16 h. 56 min., diameter 600 miles (?), magnitude at opposition 14. Clearly visible with an 8-inch telescope (→ 3, Solar system) (*v.* Pl. 22).

Toucan, *v.* Tucana.

Tower telescope, *v.* Solar tower.

Transit occurs when an inferior planet (Mercury or Venus) as seen from the Earth, moves across the Sun's disk, or a satellite moves across the disk of a planet (*v.* Mercury, Venus, Jupiter and Pl. 16). A star is said to transit at the moment when the diurnal motion takes it across an observer's meridian.

Triangle, *v.* Triangulum.

Triangle, Southern, *v.* Triangulum Australe.

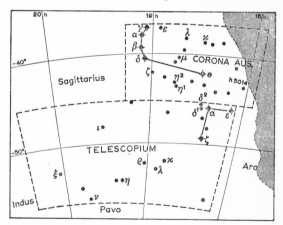

The constellations of Telescopium and Corona Australis

Triangulation, method of determining distance, whereby a distance which is not directly measurable is found from 3 directly measured elements of the triangle in which the required distance occurs. The method can be used to find stellar distances up to 100 light-years. This limit is imposed by the radius of the Earth's orbit. (*v.* Distance finding).

Triangulum (the Triangle), a constellation in the northern hemisphere, situated between 1 h. 30 min. and 2 h. 50 min. R.A. and between 25° and 37° N. Dec. (→)

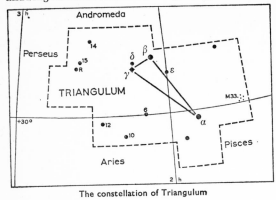

The constellation of Triangulum

Triangulum Australe (the Southern Triangle), a constellation in the southern hemisphere, extending from 14 h. 50 min. to 17 h. 10 min. R.A. and from —60° to —70° Dec. (→)

Triton, one of Neptune's two satellites, discovered by Lassell in 1846. Mean distance from Neptune 220,000 miles, period of revolution 5 d. 21 h. 3 min., diameter 2,800 miles (?), magnitude at opposition 13·6. *T.* has an atmosphere in which methane is probably present (→ 3, Solar system).

Trojans comprise 15 asteroids* each of which has a mean distance from the Sun almost equal to that of Jupiter. They move in two loose clusters in the orbit of Jupiter, one group 60° ahead of the planet and the other 60° behind. Each asteroid can oscillate round the central point of the cluster. The first was discovered by Wolf in 1904. (→)

Troposphere, the part of the Earth's atmosphere nearest to its surface. Height at the equator up to 11 miles, at the poles up to 5 miles. Phenomena determining our weather take place within the *T.* (*v.* Pl. 5).

Tucana (the Toucan), a constellation in the southern sky, situated between R.A. 22 h. 5 min. and 1 h. 25 min. and between Dec. —57° and —75°. The globular star cluster NGC 362 is visible with the naked eye as a small hazy star of the 6th magnitude. *T.* also includes the Small Magellanic Cloud (*v.* Magellanic Clouds), a small galaxy which forms a triple system with the Large Magellanic Cloud and the Milky Way (*v.* Pl. 63).

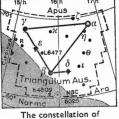

The constellation of Triangulum Australe

Twinkling or **Scintillation** is the apparent sparkling of stars. It is due to the turbulence of the Earth's atmosphere causing continual small changes in the refractive index of air. As a result, the brightness of the beam of light that enters the eye from a star is continually changing. In a small telescope, there is the same effect but the star image is also seen to have slight sideways displacements. In a large telescope, both these effects diminish, but the star image is seen to be much larger than the theoretical image for the telescope objective. The size of the image changes during the night and from night to night. When there are small and steady images, it is said that the 'seeing' is good. Large and fuzzy images correspond to bad seeing. In order

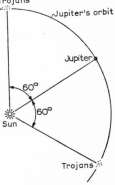

The Trojans and Jupiter in relation to the Sun

to see fine detail on, say, a planet, not only do we need a telescope of fairly large aperture but also a night of superlatively good seeing.

Twins, *v.* Gemini.

Types of extragalactic nebulae, *v.* Extragalactic nebulae and Pl. 75, 76.

U

Ultra-violet is the invisible radiation beyond the violet end of the spectrum. It extends to link up with soft X-radiation at a wavelength of about 100 Å.

Umbra, part of the shadow cast by a planet or satellite. As the diameter of the Sun is greater than that of the other members of the solar system, the shadow takes the form of a cone, the apex of which is directed away from the Sun and in which there is a complete absence of light. Surrounding this cone is another cone, with its apex between the Sun and the planet or satellite. This volume, the penumbra, receives only a part of the Sun's radiation. The penumbra is thus the region of partial shadow. During a lunar eclipse* the part of the Moon's surface in the Earth's umbra is totally eclipsed, and the part in the penumbra partly eclipsed (→ p. 219).

Umbra, the darkest, central part of a sunspot*. The lighter part, which surrounds the *U.,* is called the penumbra (*v.* Pl. 29, 30, 31).

Umbriel, one of the moons of Uranus, discovered by Lassell in 1851. Mean distance from Uranus 166,000 miles, period of revolution 4 d. 3 h. 28 min., diameter 250 miles (?), mean magnitude at opposition 15·8. Only observable with a large telescope.

Unicorn, *v.* Monoceros.

Universal time, (U.T. or T.U.) is Greenwich Mean Time and is counted from 0 to 24 hours, starting at midnight. *U.t.* is used by astronomers throughout the world, but has been superseded in astronomical almanacs by ephemeris time* since 1960.

Universe, in astronomy, signifies space with its entire content of matter and energy. Throughout the ages man has attempted to formulate an image of the *U.* which would conform with the phenomena observed. The ancient Greeks produced a model of the *U.* which provided a descriptive explanation of the motions of Sun, Moon, planets and stars in the firmament, as far as they were aware of them. It was suggested that the

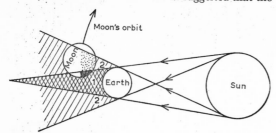

Moon's orbit

End of lunar eclipse. Part of the Moon's surface is still in the umbra (1) and the adjacent part is in the penumbra (2). For the sake of clarity the drawing is not to scale

U. consisted of a number of concentric spheres with the Earth in the centre. The rotations of these spheres combined to produce the daily and other motions observed in the heavens. The outermost sphere contained the fixed stars. Beyond this was the *Primum Mobile*, the source of the power which kept the whole complicated machinery in motion. This idea, with some modifications, was held in turn by Aristotle, Hipparchus and Ptolemy (*v.* Ptolemaic system), and survived until the Renaissance. Although some astronomers, notably Ptolemy, were inclined to regard the idea merely as a mathematical device for computing the positions of the heavenly bodies, many thinkers considered the arrangement of the spheres as the true pattern of the *U.* Not until the invention of the telescope was it possible for sufficient observational data to be obtained for the final overthrow of the Ptolemaic system in favour of the Copernican view of the solar system and the associated ideas of Digges and Bruno concerning the stellar system.

In recent years our knowledge of the *U.* has increased enormously: instead of regarding the *U.* merely as the space occupied by our own Galaxy (which, according to nineteenth-century ideas, possessed perhaps a diameter of 10,000 light-years), scientists now believe that it must contain thousands of millions of galaxies in the region accessible to observation by modern instruments, extending to a distance of perhaps 5,000 million light-years. Various attempts have been made to construct theoretical models of the *U.* capable of explaining the observational data.

It appears that the spectral lines of the light emitted by all the extragalactic systems are shifted towards the red, the displacement increasing with distance. This shift of spectrum towards the red is usually attributed to the Doppler effect* associated with recessional motion. On this interpretation, all external galaxies are receding from us with velocities which are proportional to their distances. At first sight this would seem to imply that the Milky Way occupies a special position in the *U.*, but this unlikely conclusion can be avoided in a way which is most simply explained with the aid of the following analogy. Let us compare (three-dimensional) space with the (two-dimensional) surface of a balloon. Upon this surface spots are painted to represent the galaxies, including our Milky Way. When the balloon is inflated, these spots not only recede from the particular

spot which denotes the Milky Way but also from each other. Indeed, they recede equally from any given point of the balloon's surface. In a similar way, the *U.* may be regarded as embedded in a space which is itself in the process of expansion. The rate of expansion can be calculated from the law relating red shift and distance. If we assume that the red shifts remain more or less constant, we can calculate approximately the time that has elapsed since all the galaxies were close together in space. The *U.*, at least in the form we know now, can then be said to have existed for that length of time.

The idea of an *expanding universe* was first advanced by G. Lemaître in 1927, although it was foreshadowed some years earlier in the pioneer researches of W. de Sitter (1917) and, more especially, in those of A. Friedmann (1922). Lemaître believes that all matter was originally contained in a highly unstable 'super-atom' (*v.* Pl. 94) which exploded violently and gave rise to the galaxies and all other constituents of the *U.* Lemaître's world-model is one of a wide range constructed in accordance with Einstein's General Relativity Theory*. Among these are models which pulsate, i.e. expansion is followed by contraction and then by expansion again. In 1932, E.A. Milne suggested a uniformly expanding model, constructed in accordance with the Special Relativity Theory, in which the galaxies are in uniform relative motion from a common origin.

Another theory, due to H. Bondi, T. Gold and F. Hoyle (1948), is based on the ideas of the continual creation of matter *ex nihilo*. According to this theory, the general state of the *U.* remains the same for all time and newly created matter fills the gaps that would otherwise be left as the galaxies recede from each other. To maintain the existing density of matter in the *U.*, only one new atom of hydrogen is required per litre of volume every few thousand million years. In this world model, often referred to as the 'steady-state model', both space and time are infinite.

All current world models assume a marked degree of spatial symmetry in the *U.* as a whole, and some, notably the steady state theory, also assume an equal degree of symmetry in time. Further observations, both by radio and optical telescopes, and possibly also some new theoretical developments are needed before we can decide which model best represents the *U.*

Unstable stars, *v.* Variable stars, Novae, Beta Lyrae stars, Double stars, Spectroscopic binaries, Pulsating stars.

Uranus, one of the major superior planets of the solar system, barely visible, with the unaided eye, as a 6th magnitude star-like object (*v.* Pl. 22). It is therefore not surprising that *U.* was not known until the eighteenth century.

This planet was discovered accidentally by W. Herschel in 1781 when he was examining a part of the sky in the neighbourhood of the ecliptic. It was then found that *U.* had been observed and its position measured on several occasions. It had always been taken for a star. The difference between its computed positions, based on the elements of its orbit, and its actual positions led, in 1846, to the discovery of Neptune* (which causes perturbations in its orbit). At opposition *U.* is clearly observable with a 6-inch telescope as a greenish disk with little surface detail. Occasionally, faint bands of the kind seen on Jupiter and Saturn are visible (*v.* Pl. 19, 21).

The planet is similar in composition to the other

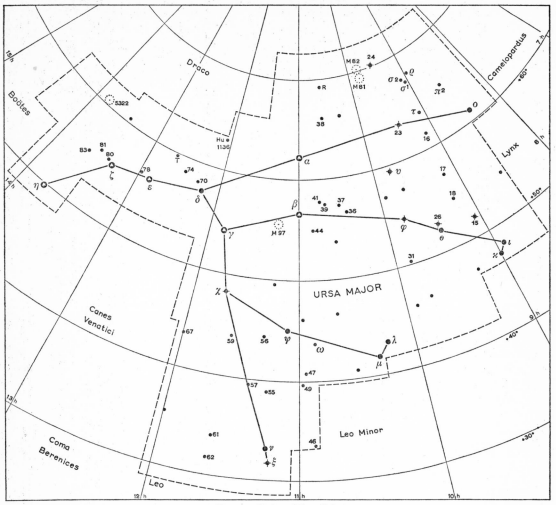

The constellation of Ursa Major

superior planets. We can see only the surface of the atmosphere, probably consisting of hydrogen and methane. The atmosphere is thought to surround a thick layer of ice containing a rocky core. The temperature of the visible surface is 90° K. Owing to its fast rotation, the sphere is flattened at the poles (v. also Pl. 21, top).

SATELLITE SYSTEM OF URANUS

	Discovery	Mean distance from Uranus in miles	Period of revolution	Diam. in miles	Magn. at opposition
Miranda	Kuiper 1948	81,000	1 d. 10 h.	?	19
Ariel	Lassell 1851	120,000	2 d. 12 h. 29 min.	300 ?	15·2
Umbriel	Lassell 1851	166,000	4 d. 3 h. 28 min.	250 ?	15·8
Titania	Herschel 1787	272,000	8 d. 16 h. 56 min.	600 ?	14·0
Oberon	Herschel 1787	364,000	13 d. 11 h. 7 min.	500 ?	14·2

The planet's axis lies almost in the same plane as its orbit around the Sun, so that its equator is perpendicular to the orbit. Seasons of the terrestrial kind therefore do not exist; first one pole, then the equator, then the

other pole are presented to the Sun in the course of one revolution and each pole has a summer (or day) and a winter (or night) lasting 42 years!

Mean distance from the Sun 1,800 million miles, period of revolution about 84 years, mean orbital velocity 4·2 m.p.sec. (6·8 km/sec.), mean diameter 32,000 miles, mass 14·58 × Earth's, volume 64 × Earth's, period of rotation about 10 h., magnitude at opposition 5·74, albedo 0·66.

As the moons lie in the equatorial plane (which is perpendicular to the orbit plane), the system, as seen from the Earth, is alternately circular and linear in shape every 21 years. When linear, it is edgewise towards the Earth.

Ursa Major (the Great Bear), an important constellation (→) in the northern sky. It is situated between 8 h. 5 min. and 14 h. 30 min. R.A. and between 28° N. and 73° N. Dec. The constellation is very conspicuous and can be used to locate several bright stars:
the line joining β and α points to the Pole star,
the line joining δ and α points to Capella,
the line joining δ and β points to Castor and Pollux,
the line joining δ and γ points to Regulus.

The bright stars in the constellation that can be used for this purpose are circumpolar for much of the northern hemisphere, and can therefore always be found in the sky (v. Celestial sphere).

Ursa Minor (the Little Bear) (→ Draco), a constellation in the northern hemisphere, mainly situated between 13 h. and 18 h. R.A. and between 66°N. and 90°N. Dec. The constellation includes the north celestial pole, which is near Polaris (α Ursae Minoris; the distance was 1° in 1950).

Van Allen radiation belts. The most important discovery made so far with the aid of artificial satellites is the previously unsuspected existence of two distinct and widely separated rings, or belts, of intense particle radiation surrounding the Earth. The most complete information is due to Van Allen and his team in the United States of America. The inner, and narrower, belt extends from about 600 to about 2,500 miles above the Earth's surface and may be composed of particles which result from cosmic disintegrations occurring near the top of the atmosphere and diffusing outwards. The outer belt, at a distance from the Earth's centre of between 3 and 4 times the Earth's radius, is much wider and extends north and south to the auroral zones. It is thought that the particles in it may originate in the Sun, from which they are blown off in intense solar flares (v. Cosmic rays).

Vanguard, the name for a series of American satellites (v. Artificial satellite).

Variable stars are stars which vary in brightness. Two *V.s.* were known to antiquity: Mira (o Ceti), 'the wonderful', and Algol (β Persei), 'the devil star'. Their variability was rediscovered in more modern times, that of Mira by Fabricius in 1596 and that of Algol in 1783 by Goodricke. More than 10,000 *V.s.* are now known. Three per cent of all stars visible with the naked eye are variable (v. Pl. 37, 38).

The chief characteristic of a *V.s.* is the light-curve (→ Double stars 4 and 5) obtained when the luminosity is observed at regular intervals (photographically or visually) and its value determined by comparison with non-variable stars.

V.s. are divided into: *a.* Eclipsing variables; the light variation is caused by two or more component stars revolving around each other and temporarily eclipsing each other (v. Double stars).

b. Pulsating stars; the light variation is due to the periodic expansion and contraction of the star. The following types are known: Cepheids*, long-period variables with a period of about 250 days, semi-periodic variables and irregular variables. (The light-curves of the last two reveal, respectively, some regularity and a complete absence of regularity.) The study of the light-curves and the sometimes complicated variations in the spectra of these stars led to the so-called pulsation theory (Eddington, 1919), according to which both the star and its atmosphere regularly expand and contract. The explanation of the pulsation is perhaps to be found in nuclear reactions.

c. Explosive stars, novae or new stars*. These become very bright in a short time and then quickly fade away. Part of the star's atmosphere is blown off by an immense explosion. Nuclear reactions are believed to be responsible. This group of stars is subdivided into novae, supernovae and nova-like stars. The latter show the same phenomenon but on a smaller scale.

Vega, the star α Lyrae, apparent magnitude 0·1, spectral class Ao.

Veil nebula. This may be the remains of a supernova explosion (v. Pl. 47).

Vela (the Sails), a constellation in the Milky Way, with numerous bright stars. It is situated between 8 h. and 11 h. 5 min. R.A. and between —37° and —57° Dec. (→)

VARIABLE STARS

	Period	Spectral class
Pulsating stars		
δ Scuti stars	3·5 h.	F
β Canis Majoris stars	3·6–6 h.	B
RR Lyrae stars	2–17 h.	A to F
Cepheids	2–39 d.	F, G, K
W Virginis stars	13–19 d.	G
RV Tauri stars	25–90 d.	K, M
SX Herculis stars	25–90 d.	G
Red semi-regular variables	42–430 d.	K, M, N
Long-period variables	100–700 d.	K, M, N, R, S
Irregular variables		
R Coronae Borealis stars	irregular	G
RR Tauri stars	irregular	G
P Cygni stars	irregular	B
T Tauri stars	irregular	G
Explosive stars		
Z Camelopardis stars	13–22 d. with irregular variations	G
U Geminorum stars	97–340 d.	G
Z Andromedae stars	900 d.	M
Novae		
Supernovae		

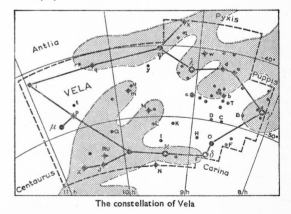

The constellation of Vela

Velocity of escape is the smallest velocity an object must possess in order to escape from the gravitation of a celestial body. It is the same as the velocity with which an object from space falls on to the celestial body.

Venus, one of the two inferior planets of the solar system, its solar distance being between that of Earth and that of Mercury (v. Pl. 16). Of all the planets *V.* comes closest to the Earth. Its high albedo and its occasionally relatively short distance from the Earth make it very conspicuous. Its orbit lies inside the

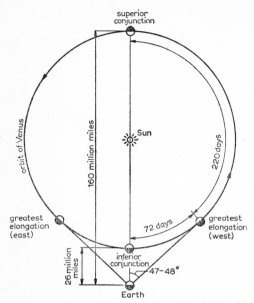

Fig. 1. Positions of Venus. The greatest distance from Earth to Venus (Venus in superior conjunction) is 160 million miles, the least (Venus in inferior conjunction) 26 million miles. Venus takes 72 days to move from inferior conjunction to greatest elongation, and 220 days to pass from greatest elongation to superior conjunction. The angular distance of Venus from the Sun as measured from Earth cannot exceed 47°–48°

Earth's and it is never more than 48° east or west of the Sun as seen from the Earth (greatest elongation) (→ 1, 2). If *V.* is west of the Sun, it sets before the Sun and rises before the Sun, and is then a 'morning star'. If it is east of the Sun, it sets after the Sun and is visible as an 'evening star'. *V.* is mentioned as a morning star (Eosphorus) and an evening star (Hesperus) in Homer, but it is doubtful whether Homer knew that they were two appearances of the same celestial body. In moving between its two greatest elongations, as seen from the Earth, *V.* normally does not pass across the solar disk but above or below it. It is in conjunction with the Sun when its right ascension is the same as the Sun's. It is at inferior conjunction when between the Earth and the Sun, and the dark side of the planet is presented to us. At superior conjunction, i.e. when beyond the Sun as seen from the Earth, its bright side faces the Earth. As *V.*'s distance from the Earth is smallest at inferior conjunction, the planet's disk attains its maximum (apparent) size then. At superior conjunction the planet is on the other side of the Sun from the Earth and its disk appears small. The interval between inferior and superior conjunctions is 292 days. Details of the planet's orbit for the current year can be found in the British *Astronomical Ephemeris* or in the American *Astronomical Ephemeris and Nautical Almanac.*

Like the Moon and Mercury, *V.* shows phases in the course of its orbit. When it is at inferior conjunction, the disk appears dark to us and comparable with the new Moon. At superior conjunction, the disk appears

fully illuminated. The phases at greatest elongations are roughly equivalent to the first and last quarter of the Moon. When the planet is 'new' during inferior conjunction, a very thin rim of light usually remains visible in the direction of the Sun. The Moon is brightest when full, but when *V.* is 'full', it is also farthest from the Earth, and is therefore not at its greatest brightness. It is brightest when its phase is comparable with that of the Moon 2 days before the first quarter: its greater apparent diameter then more than offsets the fact that a smaller proportion of the disk is illuminated, as seen by us. As an evening star, *V.* shows the same phases as the waxing Moon; as a morning star, the same phases as the waning Moon. Its phases were first observed by Galileo in 1610. If the orbits of *V.* and Earth lay in the same plane, *V.* would always pass across the Sun (transit) (→ Mercury and Pl. 16) or be occulted by the Sun in its apparent path through the sky.

Even with a large telescope, all that can be seen on the planet's surface are a few ill-defined spots. Photographs in red or infra-red light (v. Astrophotography) reveal no details on the disk, but dark spots are visible on ultra-violet photographs. This appears to show that the details are not on the planet's surface but are clouds in an atmosphere completely enveloping the planet. Its high albedo* is another proof that what we observe is not the actual surface but a covering of cloud. When its disk appears as a very narrow crescent, its cusps, unlike those of the Moon, extend a considerable way round the planet; this extension is the illuminated part of the atmosphere (v. Pl. 16).

Thus, although *V.* approaches closer to the Earth than any other planet, we know very little about con-

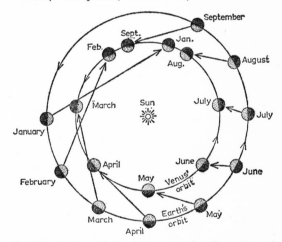

Fig. 2. The Earth, an inferior planet, and the Sun. The positions of Earth and Venus during several months are illustrated. During this time Earth covers ⅔ of its orbit, while Venus makes slightly more than one revolution. The direction of Venus in relation to the Sun, as seen from Earth, changes continuously. In June Venus is to the left of the Sun, in July it is to the right. In June and July the greater part of the dark side of Venus is presented to Earth, in January the greater part of the illuminated half. Like the Moon, Venus shows phases

ditions there. As no surface details are visible, it is difficult to determine its period* of rotation. Older estimates vary from 24 hours to 225 days! More recent spectroscopic research has at least shown that *V.* rotates more slowly than the Earth; G.P. Kuiper suggests a period of rotation of several weeks.

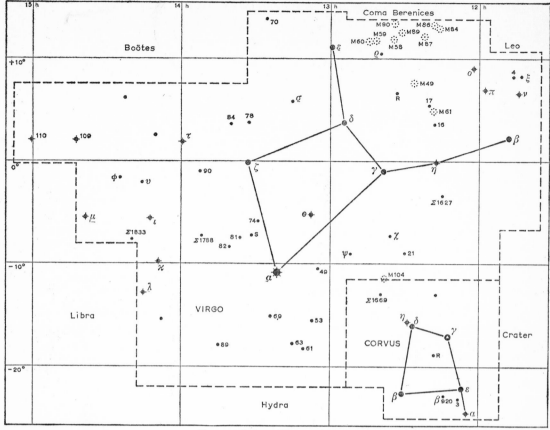

The constellations of Virgo and Corvus

Pronounced absorption bands of carbon dioxide have been found in the spectrum of sunlight reflected by *V*. (Adams and Dunham, 1932). The surface temperature is probably very high because the planet, by its closer proximity, absorbs more heat than the Earth, and is protected from loss of heat by its thick blanket of cloud. A surface temperature of 200–300° C. has been measured by radio observation. According to one theory (Donald H. Menzel and Fred L. Whipple, 1955), the surface is entirely covered by ocean. Carbon dioxide and carbon monoxide are products of volcanoes. As the land is covered by water, the carbon dioxide is not absorbed by the surface and converted to carbonates, but remains free in the atmosphere. This would explain the abundance of carbon dioxide in the atmosphere. Moreover, any oxygen originally present in the atmosphere is rendered very active chemically by the high temperature and can combine with the carbon monoxide to form carbon dioxide. This would account for the absence of oxygen despite the hypothetical water. Other astronomers think that the yellowish colour of the atmosphere may be due to the presence of dust clouds, which would suggest a solid surface. There is thus no unanimity about the nature of the surface of *V*. Spectra of Venus were obtained not long ago from a balloon at a height of 15 miles above the Earth; from these it has been deduced that the planet's atmosphere contains water vapour. The temperature of the outer atmosphere is about

—35°C. on the dark side and not much higher on the illuminated side. The mean distance of *V*. from the Sun is 67,200,000 miles, its sidereal period 224·7 days, inclination to the ecliptic 3°24′, diameter 7,700 miles or 0·973 × Earth's, period of rotation—according to latest estimate (Kuiper)—several weeks, albedo 0·76, greatest magnitude —4·4. *V*. has no satellites. According to Kuiper, the equator is tilted at an angle of 32° to the plane of the orbit. Radar echoes have now been used to determine the time that radiation takes for a journey to and from *V*.

TRANSITS OF VENUS FROM 1600 TO 2100

Date	Universal time		
	Start	Middle	End
7th Dec. 1631	3 h. 49 min.	5 h. 19 min.	6 h. 49 min.
4th Dec. 1639	14 h. 56 min.	18 h. 25 min.	21 h. 54 min.
6th June 1761	2 h. 01 min.	5 h. 19 min.	8 h. 36 min.
3rd–4th June 1769	19 h. 15 min.	22 h. 25 min.	1 h. 35 min.
9th Dec. 1874	1 h. 50 min.	4 h. 08 min.	6 h. 26 min.
6th Dec. 1882	13 h. 57 min.	17 h. 07 min.	20 h. 16 min.
8th June 2004	5 h. 15 min.	8 h. 21 min.	11 h. 28 min.
5th–6th June 2012	22 h. 12 min.	1 h. 33 min.	4 h. 53 min.

Vernal equinox, the point of intersection of the ecliptic and the celestial equator where the Sun crosses from the southern to the northern celestial hemisphere (*v*. Celestial sphere).

Vertical circle, the circle along which a plane passing through the zenith and perpendicular to the horizon intersects the celestial sphere. If a vertical circle is drawn through a star, the angular distance from the star to the intersection of the vertical circle and the horizon is the altitude of the star at a particular moment (*v.* Celestial sphere).

Vesta, one of the four largest asteroids*, discovered by Olbers in 1807. Although not actually the largest, *V.* is certainly the brightest of the asteroids, being sometimes visible with the naked eye (magnitude at opposition 6·5). Its diameter is 245 miles, its albedo 0·26.

Virgin, *v.* Virgo.

Virgo (the Virgin), constellation on the equator lying between R.A. 11 h. 35 min. and 15 h. 10 min. and between Dec. 15°N. and 22°S. It lies across the ecliptic and is thus one of the signs of the Zodiac. In the northern part of this constellation many extragalactic nebulae are to be found, including those with Messier numbers 49, 58, 59, 60, 61, 84, 86, 87, 89 and 90. There, too, is found the radio source Virgo A (R.A. 12 h. 28 min., Dec. 2°37′). This source is identified with the elliptical galaxy NGC 4486 which is a member of the Virgo group. In photographs one sees a straight ray which appears to come from the centre of the system. The light of the ray is bluer than that of the nebula itself. It is not known what really happens here (*v.* Pl. 84). (→ facing)

Virgo cluster, a group of more than 500 galaxies in the constellation Virgo. Its distance is estimated at 30 million light-years (*v.* Extragalactic nebulae and Supergalaxy).

Visual binary is a binary star whose components are sufficiently far apart to be observable with a telescope as individual stars (*v.* Double stars and Pl. 36).

Visual magnitude, the magnitude of a star as seen by the eye. As the eye is most sensitive to green and the ordinary photographic plate is most sensitive to blue, the visual and photographic magnitude* will not generally be the same (*v.* Colour index).

Volans (the Flying Fish), a constellation in the southern sky, situated between 6 h. 35 min. and 9 h. R.A. and between —64° and —75° Dec. (→ Carina).

Vulcan, a hypothetical planet which was supposed to lie within the orbit of Mercury. Deviations of Mercury's orbit from the predicted path led Leverrier to speculate on the existence of an 'infra-mercurial' planet, i.e. one closer to the Sun than Mercury (a similar hypothesis led to the discovery of Neptune and Pluto). In 1859 Lescarbault observed a dark spot moving across the Sun. Was it Vulcan? It is now believed to be certain that there is no planet inside Mercury's orbit. The perturbations observed in the latter, which take the form of a discrepancy in the predicted positions of its perihelion*, were later accounted for by Einstein. Newton's law of gravitation is not completely accurate, and deviations occur in the perihelion of all planets. In the solar system, this deviation is greatest in the case of Mercury (*v.* Relativity Theory).

Vulpecula (the Fox) (→ Sagitta), a constellation in the northern hemisphere, situated between 18 h. 55 min. and 21 h. 30 min. R.A. and between 19° and 29° N. Dec.

W - X - Y

Walled plains, the largest of the lunar craters. Examples are Clavius, Grimaldi and Schickard (*v.* Moon and Pl. 14).

Wavelength of light is the distance travelled by a light-wave in a complete cycle (→). Emission of energy by an atom* causes an electromagnetic wave phenomenon of a precise *W*. The frequencies (the number of cycles per sec.) of light oscillations are very high and the corresponding *W.s* are very small, since the product of frequency and *W*. is equal to velocity. For example, incandescent sodium atoms produce light with *W.s* of 5,896 Å and 5,890 Å, or 0·00005896 and 0·00005890 cm, in the

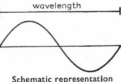

wavelength

Schematic representation of a wave

visible part of the spectrum. Difference in *W*. is seen as a difference in the colour of light (→ Spectrum).

Water-bearer, *v.* Aquarius.

Water-serpent, *v.* Hydra.

Water-snake, *v.* Hydrus.

Whale, *v.* Cetus.

Wilson, Mount, *v.* Mount Wilson.

Winter solstice, the position on the ecliptic occupied by the Sun on 21st or 22nd Dec. It is the Sun's most southerly position. Dec. —23½°, R.A. 18 h. (*v.* Celestial sphere).

Wolf, *v.* Lupus.

Wolf-Rayet stars, very hot stars with an average absolute magnitude of —3·4. Originally assigned to spectral class O, they now form a class on their own, spectral class W. The first star of this type was discovered in 1867 by Wolf and Rayet at the Paris Observatory. Their continuous spectrum shows bright, broad emission bands, frequently terminated on the violet side by dark absorption lines. This indicates that these stars (of which more than 100 are now known) are surrounded by rapidly expanding envelopes of gas. The width of the emission lines indicates velocities of the order of 1,850 m. p. sec. (3,000 km/sec.) (*v.* Doppler effect).

X-rays are short wavelength electromagnetic radiation. Their wavelengths range from ½–100 Å. All matter is more transparent to X-rays than to light.

In the deepest interior of stars, all radiation exists in the form of γ-rays which are electromagnetic radiation of even shorter wavelength than X-rays and carry more energy. As the γ-rays diffuse upwards, they tend to lose energy and to increase in wavelength and so are converted into X-rays. In diffusing still further upwards, bouncing from atom to atom as it were, the X-rays in turn lose energy and increase in wavelength, until finally they appear at the surface as visible light.

X-rays have been detected (by rockets) coming from the Sun's surface. They probably originate in solar flares or other high-temperature phenomena.

They have not yet been detected from any other celestial body.

Year, the time taken by the Earth to complete one revolution around the Sun from perihelion to perihelion (anomalistic year). Astronomers distinguish two other types of year, which are defined in terms of the Sun's apparent motion on the celestial sphere. A sidereal Υ. is the time taken by the Sun to return to a certain fixed position relative to the stars, or the time within which it completes one circuit of the ecliptic*. The tropical Υ. is the time that elapses between two successive solar transits of the vernal equinox. This is the meaning of the term Υ. as normally used. It consists of 365·24220 solar days. The length of a sidereal Υ. is 365·25636 solar days and that of an anomalistic year is 365·25964 days.

Zeeman effect is the process by which some spectral lines of an incandescent gas are split up into two or more close components if the gas is in a magnetic field. This splitting is observed in the spectra of sunspots and of some stars and it indicates the presence of a magnetic field. It is named after a Dutch physicist.

Zenith, the point where a perpendicular through the place of observation intersects the visible part of the stationary celestial sphere (*v.* Celestial sphere).

Zodiac, the band of the celestial sphere on either side of the Sun's apparent path. It is divided into 12 'signs' or 'houses' (*v.* Astrology), used at least since the time of the Babylonians. The Sun spends one month in each sign. Two thousand years ago the zodiacal constellations coincided with the signs of the same names, but they now lead the signs by one 'house' as a result of precession*. The constellations and the signs will again correspond about the year 26,000.

The names and symbols of the 'houses' are:

Aries	γ	Leo	Ω	Sagittarius	$\nearrow$
Taurus	$\otimes$	Virgo	$\mathfrak{m}$	Capricornus	ζ
Gemini	$\amalg$	Libra	$\underline{\Omega}$	Aquarius	$\approx$
Cancer	$\odot$	Scorpius	$\mathfrak{m}$	Pisces	$\mathcal{H}$

Zodiacal light, a wide cone of light rising from the horizon and extending along the ecliptic. In northern latitudes it is visible in the west after sunset in the spring, and in the east before sunrise in autumn. Theoretically, it is visible throughout the year but it is so faint (roughly as bright as the Milky Way, but more uniform) that it can be distinguished only when the ecliptic is steeply inclined to the horizon. It is generally thought to be due to sunlight reflected from a vast disk of cosmic dust extending from near the Sun to beyond the Earth's orbit.

The barely perceptible *gegenschein** or counterglow is similar in origin.

BIBLIOGRAPHY

Allen, C. W.: *Astrophysical Quantities*. London: Athlone Press, 1955.
Allen, Van: *Scientific Uses of Earth Satellites*. University of Michigan Press, 1956.
Aller, L. H.: *Gaseous Nebulae*. London: Chapman & Hall, 1956.
    Astrophysics – the Atmospheres of the Sun and Stars. New York: Ronald Press, 1953.
Ambartsumyan, V. A.: *Theoretical Astrophysics*. London: Pergamon Press, 1958.
Baker, R. H.: *Astronomy* (7th edition). London: Van Nostrand, 1959.
Binnendijk, Leendert: *Properties of Double Stars*. University of Pennsylvania Press, 1960.
Bok and Bok: *The Milky Way*. Cambridge (Mass., U.S.A.): Harvard University Press, 1957.
Bondi, H.: *Cosmology*. Cambridge University Press, 1960.
Dufay, Jean: *Galactic Nebulae and Interstellar Matter*. London: Hutchinson, 1957.
Hanbury Brown, R., and Lovell, A. C. B.: *The Exploration of Space by Radio*. London: Chapman
    & Hall, 1957.
Hoyle, Fred: *Frontiers of Astronomy*. London: Heinemann, 1955.
Hynek: *Astrophysics*. London: McGraw Hill, 1951.
King, H. C.: *The History of the Telescope*. London: Griffin, 1955.
King-Hele, D.: *Satellites and Scientific Research*. London: Routledge & Kegan Paul, 1960.
Kopal, Z.: *The Moon*. Chatham: Mackay, 1960.
Kuiper, G. P.: *Atmospheres of the Earth and Planets*. University of Chicago Press, 1952.
    The Sun. Chicago University Press, 1953.
Lovell, A. C. B.: *Meteor Astronomy*. Oxford: Clarendon Press, 1954.
Lyttleton, R. A.: *The Modern Universe*. London: Hodder & Stoughton, 1957.
Massey, H. S. W., and Boyd, R. L. F.: *The Upper Atmosphere*. London: Hutchinson, 1958.
Menzel, D. H.: *Our Sun*. Cambridge (Mass., U.S.A.): Harvard University Press, 1959.
Minnaert, M.: *Light and Colour in the Open Air*. London: Bell & Sons Ltd., 1959.
Moore, Patrick: *Guide to the Planets*. London: Eyre & Spottiswoode, 1955.
Norton, A. P., and Inglis, J. G.: *Star Atlas*. Edinburgh: Gall & Inglis, 1959.
Ovenden, M. W.: *Looking at the Stars*. London: Phoenix House, 1957.
Payne-Gaposchkin, Cecilia: *Introduction to Astronomy*. London: Eyre & Spottiswoode, 1956.
Peek, B. M.: *The Planet Jupiter*. London: Faber & Faber, 1958.
Shapley, Harlow: *The Inner Metagalaxy*. Oxford University Press, 1957.
Smart, W. M.: *Textbook of Spherical Astronomy*. Cambridge University Press, 1944.
    Some Famous Stars. London: Longmans, Green, 1950.
Struve, O., Lynds, B., and Pillans, H.: *Elementary Astronomy*. Oxford University Press, 1959.
Vaucouleurs, G. de: *Physics of the Planet Mars*. London: Faber & Faber.
Wilkins, H. P., and Moore, Patrick: *The Moon*. London: Faber & Faber, 1955.

    Periodicals:
Sky and Telescope: Sky Publishing Co., Cambridge, Mass., U.S.A. (Monthly).

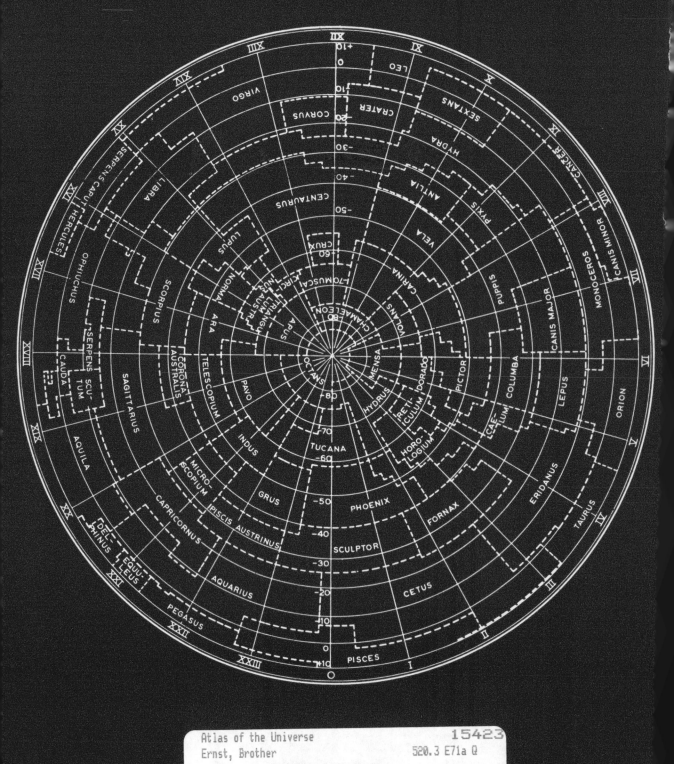